History, Psychology, and Science:

SELECTED PAPERS

Edwin G. Boring

History, Psychology, and

Science: SELECTED PAPERS

꧁꧁

BY Edwin G. Boring, HARVARD UNIVERSITY

꧁꧁꧁꧁꧁꧁꧁꧁꧁꧁꧁꧁꧁꧁꧁꧁꧁꧁꧁꧁꧁꧁꧁꧁꧁꧁꧁꧁꧁꧁꧁꧁ EDITED BY

ROBERT I. WATSON & DONALD T. CAMPBELL, Northwestern University

John Wiley and Sons, Inc.   NEW YORK AND LONDON

Library of Congress Catalog Card Number: 63-19878

Printed in the United States of America

Editors' Foreword

෴෴෴෴෴෴෴෴෴෴෴෴෴෴

HERE is a collection of essays coming from a specialty that may be called *the science of science*. Such a title seems overly ambitious but conveniently designates a vital field of endeavor, which Boring philosophers, but one in which they disclaim unique or special competence. has tilled and in which many more should labor. It is a field often left to In the analytic, empiricistic, and positivistic traditions, philosophers assign to science the determination of *synthetic* or empirical truth, and reserve for themselves questions of *analytic* truth. Typically, they regard a philosophical question as one which no possible scientific data would help solve. If empirical evidence could decide an issue, then it is a matter for science, not philosophy. Since the time of Hume, it has been recognized that the inductive achievements of science cannot be proven in any logical, deductive fashion. Not as well recognized is the fact that this limitation holds not only for specific inductions but also for any general principles of efficacious inductive procedure. While not all philosophers hold to this view, it would probably be accepted by a great majority of philosophers of science, epistemologists, and linguistic analysts.

Thus science of science—propositions as to how science develops, propositions as to effective strategies, criteria of proof, doctrine as to necessary controls in experiments—will involve assumptions as to the nature of the world and of man as a knower which are not deductively provable and will involve questions upon which empirical evidence is relevant. Philosophers of science are, and probably will continue to be, the major practitioners in this area. But they are such not as analysts but rather as generalists and students of man-the-knower. Their analytic tools are usefully applied in explicating the synthetic laws presumed in the inductive procedures of science, but the evaluation of the truth of these laws is a matter of science, albeit a metascience. There is a great need to augment the efforts of the philosophers with the efforts of other relevant specialties.

In focusing on the analytic-synthetic distinction, we are led to a usage of the term *science* broadened to include those fields of humanities which aspire to empirical truth, such as history and the nonquantitative aspects of sociology, anthropology, and psychology. The science-philosophy distinction has been made on the basis of aspiration rather than mode of, or degree of, achievement. The science of science thus described is, of course, not yet generally established. Yet it has several well-developed subfields. The history of science is the foremost of these, playing several important roles. First of all, it stands in its own right as a field for historians, to be studied for its own sake in a manner comparable to the study of the history of nations. Beyond this, the history of science gains a still more pervasive and central importance as the source of instances for testing generalizations coming from other subfields of the science of science, such as the sociology and psychology of science. The history of science is established at least to the extent of having its own journals and a few specially designated chairs.

Next in degree of establishment is the sociology of science, or the sociology of knowledge. Though not as yet provided with journals or departments of its own, it is a recognized field within sociology and is the major specialty of a number of persons. The province of the sociology of science extends broadly. Illustrative problems include: (*a*) the social determination of discovery and invention, as illustrated through the occurrence of multiple independent discoveries of the same thing; (*b*) the relation of ideology to scientific belief, both at the individual level and at the level of social class and society; (*c*) the effect of social systems in furthering or hindering science; (*d*) the impact of science upon society; (*e*) the social validation of scientific truth; and (*f*) the institution of science, considered as a social system *sui generis.*

As a subfield of the science of science, the psychology of science is less well established but is potentially of as great importance as are the two areas just discussed. It is interesting to note that philosophers have made a case for this field in the process of distinguishing between the philosopher's and the scientist's tasks in the study of induction. For example, in discussing a philosopher's effort to justify induction, Feigl says, "I fail to see the philosophical importance of any attempt in this direction. If it were the success of human adaptive learning and theorizing behavior that is to be accounted for I would be the first to admit that this is a genuinely meaningful question—but surely a question of science, not of philosophy. This question can indeed be answered. And the answer is clearly along the lines of the biology and psychology of knowledge. It is the same sort of question that can be raised on a more lowly level in regard to the learning and generalizing behavior of that pet of our psychologists, the white rat. Given the rat's equipment of learning capacities, how complicated a maze will it be able to master, in how many trials, under what conditions of previous training, etc.? While it is a long way from the orientation of rats in a maze to the intellectual adaptations (if I may be forgiven the irreverent comparison) of the Newtons, Maxwells, and Einsteins in their theoretical constructions of the physical universe, the nature of the problem is the same" (Feigl, 1956, 25–26). Elsewhere he has spoken of the pragmatic approach to scientific induction as in itself an empirical science, "being the psycho-bio-sociology of cognitive behavior" (Feigl, 1950). Bergmann, likewise discussing the difference between the philosopher's and the scientist's tasks, says "the logical analysis of science is one thing, the psychology of discovery is another thing. The former is a philosophical enterprise; the latter, if we only knew more about it, would be a branch of the science of psychology" (Bergmann, 1957, 51).

Thus in purifying their own problem area, these philosophers have pointed to the potential psychology of science. Even though such a psychology is not established in courses, journals, or professorships, many in fact have been practicing it. At its present development, the psychology of science seems to have these problem areas: (*a*) the psychology of cognitive achievement as applied to the achievements in science—the psychological explanation of scientific creativity, discovery, problem-solving, trial-and-error learning, etc.; (*b*) the psychology of cognitive bias applied to the biases and blind spots of scientists (Francis Bacon gave this area a good start in his list of the biases or "idols" he found among his fellow philosophers); (*c*) the motivational psychology of scientists—the role of curiosity, aggressiveness, self-esteem, vanity, power, and other needs in shaping the final scientific product; (*d*) personality and science—the tendency of certain personality types to be attracted to science, and within science, the tendency for personality differences between those who take various roles and positions; and (*e*) psychological epistemology—the role of psychological experience in establishing the inductive base for all sciences, the psychological description of the criteria of evidence and proof used by scientists, psychological aspects to the mind-body problem, and the innumerable other points where psychological problems border epistemological issues.

If the foregoing is a fair description of the science-of-science of today, then E.G.B. is a scientist of science, for he has been contributing to these three major areas—history of science, sociology of science, and psychology of science—for some forty years. Here lie his best papers. In bringing them together in one volume, we have been able to provide both a book of "collected papers" and one edited around a coherent central theme. If, as in the title of his recent book, he has been a "psychologist at large" (Boring, 1962), it has been in his moving at an early age from a narrow focus on particular problems to a focus upon the science of psychology as a whole, with the activity of scientists something to be studied in its own right. "Psychologist at large" may seem to connote scatteredness. Apparent scatteredness, however, is an inevitable concomitant of participating within an integrated field which is not yet institutionalized as such, either in scholarly journals or in academic career-lines. Thus these papers of Boring's come from widely scattered journals, and from journals devoted to other specialties and consequently unread by many to whom they are relevant.

For the purposes of this volume, we have divided Boring's contributions into five sections. The first of these is called *The* Zeitgeist *and the Psychology of Science.* Boring's recurrent theme of *Zeitgeist* may in many aspects be classified as sociology of science. But the theme of social and cultural determination of scientific development is interlaced with consideration of such psychological issues as great men, controversy, creativity, and the motivation of scientific endeavor.

The second section, *History of Psychology,* is a collection of papers supplementing Boring's major books in this area. Note also their double-appropriateness. They not only illustrate E.G.B. as an historian of science, but the histories are focused on topics of scientific method and epistemological relevance.

In the third section, *Scientific Method,* Boring's papers on operationism are gathered together, in which he both anticipated and applied to psychology that methodological precept. Also included are his papers on probability theory, which, while less in the main stream, are still well worth considering and may turn up in tomorrow's stream in that shifting area.

The fourth section, *The Mind-Body Problem,* finds E.G.B. dealing with a traditional epistemological problem, bringing to bear the psychology of conscious experience and the physiology of the central nervous system, plus a positivistic and physicalistic approach to metaphysical issues.

In the final section, he deals with the psychological and strategic problems of *Communicating Science,* particularly as these problems emerge in scientific writing and in book reviewing.

June 1963

R.I.W.
D.T.C.

Editors' Preface

㋡㋡㋡㋡㋡㋡㋡㋡㋡㋡㋡㋡㋡㋡㋡

HOW did this book come about? One of us (D.T.C.) has a deep-seated interest in psychological epistemology and the other (R.I.W.) in the history of psychology. In the course of conversations, we had occasion to deplore the nonavailability of a collection of Boring's papers. We considered E.G.B.'s works to stand in the first rank in both epistemology and historical psychology. Just for the fun of it, we drew up a list of some of his papers that we most admired. We showed this list to our mentor on publishing matters, Gordon Ierardi of John Wiley and Sons. He agreed that their publication would be a good idea, and set out for Cambridge to broach the suggestion to E.G.B. There was the understanding that the two of us would bow out at this point, if this seemed desirable, but with a promise of our willingness to carry on editing chores. Boring's reaction to the proposal was that "only modesty would have prevented me from suggesting it myself." He asked that we serve as editors. In theory this might have left him in Olympian aloofness from the whole enterprise, but neither we nor anyone who knows Dr. Boring would have expected him to disassociate himself from the project. True, he leaned over backward to make sure that we knew the decisions were our own, but his enthusiasm and good sense were reflected in many varied activities as "editorial consultant."

It was decided that material readily available in books should not be reprinted, if at all possible. This meant that selections from *The History of Experimental Psychology* (1950 Edition), *Sensation and Perception in the History of Experimental Psychology* (1942), and *The Physical Dimension of Consciousness* (1933) were not reprinted. The last mentioned book is not in print at the moment, but arrangements to have it reprinted are under way. *Psychologist at Large* (1961) is very much in print and contains certain crucial papers. Permission was received from its publisher, Basic Books, and E.G.B. to reprint again one paper. In the introductions to the five sections into which the articles are grouped, mention is made of the more outstanding relevant contributions not reprinted.

We acknowledge gratefully permission to reprint from the American Association for the Advancement of Science, the American Philosophical Society, the *American Journal of Psychology*, the American Psychological Association, Appleton-Century-Crofts, the History of Science Society, the *New Republic*, Phi Beta Kappa, the Seventeenth International Congress of Psychology, the University of Chicago Press, and Yale University Press. Specific citation of source and acknowledgment of permission are given on the first page of each paper.

R.I.W.
D.T.C.

Contents

𝕽𝕽𝕽𝕽𝕽𝕽𝕽𝕽𝕽𝕽

The *Zeitgeist* and the
Psychology of Science

𐃩𐃩𐃩𐃩𐃩𐃩𐃩𐃩𐃩𐃩𐃩𐃩𐃩𐃩𐃩𐃩𐃩𐃩𐃩𐃩𐃩𐃩𐃩𐃩𐃩𐃩𐃩𐃩𐃩𐃩𐃩

*I*N his approach to the science of science, Edwin Garrigues Boring places primary emphasis upon the intertwined Zeitgeist and Great Man theories. The papers, themselves, will bring out his thinking. At this point only a preliminary notion of the meaning of these theories need be given.

The Zeitgeist is expressed in the conventions of thought and implicit assumptions of the individuals sharing that Zeitgeist. For particular purposes its boundaries may be said to shift, allowing one to speak of the American Ortgeist, the psychological, scientific Fachgeist, a particular in-group Fachgeist, and the like. Thus the Zeitgeist of psychology in the United States operates under the circumstances arising from a competitive democratic ideology; at a level specific to psychology it is dominated by physicalistic, positivistic, operationalistic, objective, scientific traditions, and still more narrowly, it is manifested by various in-groups designated by eponymous terms such as the Titchenarians, the Hullians, the Skinnerians, and the Lewinians.

An adherent of the Great Man theory sees certain exceptional individuals as supplying the innovations that are turning points in the progress of a science. A Great Man appears in the person of someone of vision and brilliance who redirects the course of scientific advance or decisively deepens an already faintly traced path.

Boring considers the Zeitgeist and Great Man theories in terms of their relative influence, asking whether or not they serve as causes, symptoms, or agents, whether their influences produce progress or cause hindrance in psychology as they are expressed through time.

Over the years Boring's thinking has shown a progression from adherence to a view that would hope for the Great Man as originator, to a position (never completely ignored by him) that the great man is a convenient handle on the surface of a science. The great man may be used to grasp the nature of progress, his elite group per se being the instruments of their times, the Zeitgeist. The climax of Boring's mature view is in his address, "Eponym as Placebo," as Honorary President of the Seventeenth International Congress of Psychology at Washington, D.C., on August 20, 1963.

In this address Boring makes considerable use of the concept of eponym. In a preliminary fashion one may say that an eponym is a word derived from a name of a person and used to designate a scientific theory or period of intellectual history, for example, Darwinism, Watsonism. In a larger sense eponymy is the use of the name of a given individual to stand for, or designate, a phase of scientific history. Appeal to an individual makes the Zeitgeist more comprehensible.

The progression of Boring's thinking and its ramifications are given in his other papers. In the *First Edition* (1929) of A History of Experimental Psychology, he concluded the book with an "Interpretation" expressing disappointment that psychology, although application of the experimental method to it had been the greatest event in its history, had had no Great Man unto itself. In a paper published more than twenty years later, he offers a searching scrutiny of the relation to the Zeitgeist of "Great Men and Scientific Progress," in which he states that the Great Man theory, although self-evidently true, does not specify either the conditions or attributes of greatness, which, after considering the conditions of scientific progress, he then proceeds to discuss. A relevant issue, "The Problem of Originality in Science," is illustrated from the history of physiological psychology and shows that much of that originality depends on the availability of elements of that discovery. Boring stresses that discovery often consists not in making the necessary observations but in breaking away from the traditional way of interpreting them. Copernicus, Harvey, Einstein, and, to use an example from psychology, Wertheimer all made their contributions against the Zeitgeist.

Another article reprinted in Psychologist at Large (Boring, 1961a) shows that while the "Dual Role of the Zeitgeist in Scientific Creativity" can facilitate, it also can hinder scientific progress. Other papers not contained in this section further elaborate the Zeitgeist theme. For example, in "The Influence of Evolutionary Theory upon American Psychological Thought" (pp. 159–184), he shows how the American Zeitgeist (or Ortgeist as he calls it) altered the psychology imported from Germany.

The Zeitgeist theme can be classified as sociology of science. One of the chapters of that field is the social conditions of discovery; one of the laws, the social determination of innovation; and one of the evidences, the data on simultaneous invention. Boring's achievement of this position is reflexively an illustration of the Zeitgeist, for he did it independently. In his 1927 paper on "Originality" he is unaware of the 1917 anthropology of Kroeber or the 1922 sociology (published in a political science journal) of Ogburn, which he cites to the same point in his 1950 paper on "Great Men." His illustrations all come from psychology and physiology, having no overlap with those of Kroeber and Ogburn. They are a fresh induction, a cross-validation, of the theory from studies of psychology's history.

While the sociology of science and the psychology of science are clearly distinguishable, as we have argued in the foreword, they do interdigitate, and Boring has frequently dealt with both in the same paper. For this reason, it has been most convenient to present his contributions to both areas in this single section. In "Originality," and more extensively in "Great Men," E.G.B. deals with the psychology of creativity, ranging from moments of scientific discovery to laboratory research on puzzle solving. He treats the psychology of discovery as differentiated from the psychology of the discovered, placing emphasis upon specifying the conditions for such discovery. His psychology is not only cognitive but also motivational, stressing the role of aggressiveness and dedication.

Still more psychological are the remaining papers. "The Psychology of Controversy" is not a general psychological discussion, but rather is a discussion concerned with the specific psychology of scientists' controversy. However, the social perspective is still present in Boring's emphasis on the importance of the motivation of controversy in sustaining the institution of science (a theme elaborated by Merton, 1957) and in his recognition of role of controversy in establishing truth, analogous to its role in law. The motivational theme is carried further in "Dissent." In "Science and the Meaning of its History" (pp. 87–91), aside from factors important in the psychology of science already discussed, he considers how independence, prejudice, pride, and compulsion contribute to the work of the successful scientist—provided he knows what he is doing. In this paper, the history of science almost becomes coordinate with the psychology of science, as when he speaks of "the psychodynamics of the history of science" (p. 89).

If we had a complete psychology of science, one aspect of it would be a personology of science. This would ask such questions as "What kind of people go into what kinds of science?" It would move from a general psychology of science to an individual-differences psychology of science. Boring's "Human Nature vs. Sensation: William James and the Psychology of the Present" is a contribution to this field. He discerns two general personality types among psychologists, finding a number of correlated symptoms that distinguish them and a number of persons illustrating each. The reductionist-operationist, positivist nothing-but type is contrasted with its Jamesian antithesis.

One way of posing the psychology of science is to understand the activity of scientists as analogous to the cognizings of individuals through perception and learning. Boring's trial-and-error theme (e.g., in "Great Men") uses the latter analogy freely. Analogies to perception also occur. In "The Role of Theory in Experimental Psychology" (pp. 210–225), E.G.B. identifies a theory with perceptual object: "Here I am suggesting, with the contributions of Gestalt psychology in mind, that an object is a theory about an invariance in ever changing and chaotic experience" (p. 215).

Many papers not included in this section nor just cited continue the psychology of science theme. Several of these deal with cognitive bias as it is manifest in scientists, as in "Psychological Factors in Scientific Process," reprinted in Psychologist at Large (Boring, 1961a). This theme also recurs in "The Validation of Scientific Belief" (pp. 245–252) and in the section on inhibitions to scientific progress in Sensation and Perception in the History of Experimental Psychology (Boring, 1942, esp. 611–613).

Eponym as Placebo

冖冖冖冖冖冖冖冖冖冖冖冖冖　1963

IT is a good thing that psychologists—most psychologists although not all—are interested in the history of their science. It is, in a small way, a good thing to know a fact, although not such a very good thing, for there are too many facts for any one mind to have more than a few in stock, and a selected inventory is better than a store of rummage. The best fact is one that is set in a context, that is known in relation to other facts, that is perceived in part in the context of its past, that comes into understanding as an event which acquires significance because it belongs in a continuous dynamic sequence of the thought and discovery which constitutes an historical trend. The scholar is distinguished by this need to see new facts in relation to old events. He is not concerned with history in order to avoid repeating the past. All his life he will rethink old thoughts to his advantage, often picking them out of the current of the *Zeitgeist* in which he lives and which he breathes unconsciously. He is not concerned with history in order to predict the future. The past is not a crystal ball. It has more *whence* than *whither* to it. The seats on the train of progress all face backwards: you can see the past but only guess about the future. Yet a knowledge of history, although it can never be complete and fails miserably to foretell the future, has a huge capacity for adding significance to the understanding of the present. It gives the scholarly mind a context that enormously increases its capacity to perceive the meaning of the objects of its attention.

Thus it comes about that to understand history one needs to pay some attention to the history of history. I am speaking of history as man's account of what has happened in his world, not the events themselves which are also called history. Let us look first at the history of political history, and here I

An expansion of the address of the Honorary President of the Seventeenth International Congress of Psychology at Washington, D.C., on August 20, 1963. Reprinted with permission of the Congress.

5

begin by giving you Tolstoy's view of the matter as he argued vividly, a hundred years ago, for a deterministic view of history in his great novel, *War and Peace* (Tolstoy, 1869, passim, but especially Epilogue II).

When the Church dominated European thinking it was believed that the course of history and the fate of nations was determined by the Divine Will. God chose for a people a leader who ruled by Divine Right and who, as an agent of the Deity, led the people in whatever course the Divine purpose required. That view persisted for a long time, but eventually it failed of acceptance by historians because it created so many contradictions. Who really led the people, the monarchs, the generals, or perhaps the writers who had, at the time Tolstoy was considering, been speaking eloquently about liberty and equality? Were Napoleon's purposes and those of Czar Alexander both the Divine Will? The theory raised too many contradictions to prevail.

There arose then what Tolstoy called in 1869 "the new school of history," which ascribed the course of history to the Will and Power of Great Men. It was the Will of the genius, Napoleon, that dominated Europe in the early nineteenth century, and subsequently Alexander's Power that thwarted it. In support of this belief, Thomas Carlyle had written in 1840 his *On Heroes, Hero Worship and the Heroic in History*. "The history of what man has accomplished in this world," he said, "is at bottom the History of the Great Men who have worked here" (1840, lect. 1, part 1). Carlyle's paradigm for this thesis was the history of Frederick the Great (1865), and this view has been called the Great-Man theory of history. It is the view that William James (1880) supported against Herbert Spencer (1873, chs. 2 and 3) and others (Boring, 1950*b*), for James could never quite bring himself to depreciate human dignity by reducing man to a bundle of causations.

Now the Great-Man theory is still with us, both in the political history of nations and in the history of science. We think of the wills of Hitler and of Mussolini as having been prime causes of many important events in the history of the present century, and we still think of the great powers as being controlled by the decisions of their leaders, as indeed they may be. There is, however, a necessary next question: What controls the wills and decisions of the leaders and supports the genius of scientists? The history of science is studded with the names of Great Discoverers. We keep saying "after Newton," "the Darwinian age," "since Freud." It is true that such men had enormous influence, but where, we may ask, did they find their ideas? They were Great Originators, but surely originality has antecedents. Ideas are not really generated spontaneously.

Tolstoy thought that Great Men are agents of the forces of history that act upon them, that their decisions and the choices of lesser men are determined in part by personal idiosyncrasy, in part by chance, but enough by the cultural stream of opinion and belief for the great trends of history to be distinguishable, in spite of the hurly-burly of superficial human activity that so easily obscures the big underlying movements. History is the aggregate of an infinitude of tiny events which make up, as he put it, "the hive-life of mankind."

Such a theory is deterministic. It looks for causes as well as effects. It does not regard the decisions of Great Men as free, because freedom is a negative concept, an assertion of ignorance about the causes of choice, the causes which the deterministic view demands. In the history of science it is the concept of originality that has negative status, that provides a license for ignoring the causes of the Great Ideas, and thus for escaping from the deterministic strait jacket. It is true that the occurrence of revolutionary insights in the stream of scientific progress seems to break the continuity of the stream, but at the same time it demands that the continuity be recognized for its fractionation to be understood.

At any rate this much can be said by way of introduction. There have been altogether three theories of history. Historians have abandoned the first belief that political history follows a Divine plan. Instead they have accepted the second theory as a satisfactory paradigm by which to explain the course of events in the life of nations. This is the Great-Man theory, the belief that the direction of progress is determined by the Will and Power of leaders who make decisions. For a long time that view dominated the character of political history, while the history of science employed the concept of freedom in a different but comparable manner. It represented the knowledge of nature as moving ahead by spurts that have their beginnings in the originality and creativity of exceptionally able men—the Great Discoverers they might be called, the Newtons, Darwins, and Freuds, each of whom stands at the head of a scientific revolution. This eponymous kind of history in which revolutionary movements and periods are named after Great Discoverers, the eponyms whose names are borrowed to label new paradigms of scientific thinking, is still with us as the second phase in the history of history, but it can now be seen as making way for the third phase.

The third stage in the history of history is the phase of the deterministic paradigm, the attitude that tends to depersonalize the history of science and to emphasize the long continuing trends, the causes as much as the effects. Leo Postman's new volume on the history of psychology (1962) picks out eleven trends as examples of how psychology has progressed, and in many ways this attitude toward the history of science is coming nowadays into more general acceptance. Yet the slow course of its emergence serves well to emphasize the continuous nature of all historical development, for this trend toward the understanding of trends goes all the way back to Tolstoy and is thus at least a century old. The recent brilliant essay by T. S. Kuhn (1962b) has only within the past year undertaken to make this view acceptable by showing how continuity of development is not incompatible with scientific revolutions or with mutations in the model that guides scientific endeavor.

Herein lies one of the illuminating frustrations in understanding the history of history and of science. If it is true that the emergence of new patterns of thinking in history and in science is slow (Kuhn, 1962*a*; 1962*b*, 52–64), then this new pattern of thinking, viz., that new patterns of thinking emerge slowly, must itself emerge slowly. In such a case the difficulty of getting the new view accepted does not suggest that the view is wrong but instead acts as reinforcement because the view itself includes the presumption that it should not be accepted easily.

This address undertakes to examine the consequences for the history of psychology of the emerging new attitude in historical thinking. Certainly in such an enterprise one will not proceed by parading the contributions of Great Discoverers. One needs rather some kind of depth analysis which can reach into the stuff of the stream of history to reveal its Great Trends.

Determinism

In respect of determinism, if one is to say anything new about this age-worn problem now removed by nuclear physics from the realm of basic scientific morality, one must say something about both the nature of the scientist and the nature of science, in order to see when and why determinism is a good paradigm.

The scientist—at least as Bernice Eiduson has recently analyzed him (1962)—is a compulsive, hardworking, methodical person whose work is more important to him than anything else in his world, including his family from which very often he was isolated in childhood or adolescence; he is a man who is often unable to distinguish work from play and in any case brings his methodical work habits into his play, someone who is bright and open-minded, devoting his life to the discovery of new relationships and content to accept the obsolescence of the old when the newly arrived future requires the abandonment of the past. The scientist's egoism, of course, may distort this picture of flexibility. Many commentators have remarked at the difficulty with which scientists abandon a theory, once important but now outmoded, until its author dies, for the author's prestige may maintain the authority of the Great Man even in the face of contradictory evidence. In general, how-ever, the able scientist accepts change, for change is his constant goal, and he also knows how to suspend judgment. Judge Jerome Frank (1930, 166) has argued that this capacity of the scientist indicates his maturity. In 1930 he wrote:

> With maturity doubt and inquiry should no longer be unpleasant, but should rather become a source of interest and satisfaction. Maturity is wakeful and vital. The constant effort to achieve a stable equilibrium, resembling sleep, is regressive, infantile, and immature. The acceptance of everything as transitory,

the welcome of new doubts, the keen interest in probing into the usual, the zest of adventure in investigating the conventional—these are the life cherishing attitudes . . . of the so-called scientific mind . . . the emotionally adult or mature mind.

Can such a mind, we may ask, bear to be screened off from possible knowledge by the convention that Great Men, being originators, are not to be explained by discovering, when possible, the derivation of their novel contributions? If a belief in freedom is a license for ignorance, then the scientist must, because of the compulsions that make him what he is, set himself to penetrate the screen, "probing into the usual," as Judge Frank put it, for the very reason that the acceptance of freedom being usual, invites a probe. In short, determinism—even before the acceptance of the conservation of energy with Helmholtz in 1847, and before Laplace in 1773 (Laplace, 1808) —was the scientific paradigm, and it is still a good paradigm for the social and behavioral sciences, even though physical complementarity has diminished its status as truth.

This useful word *paradigm* is employed by T. S. Kuhn for describing what it is that science does. Wise men have long known that the business of science is the induction of generalities from observed particulars, and these generalities form the theories and laws which constitute the body of scientific fact. It used to be supposed that such "facts" had truth-value, that in expanding knowledge science was discovering more and more of the truth. Eventually, however, investigators came to realize that this kind of "truth" is transitory, that the laws change with new discovery even though the observed data from which they were induced may still be replicable. The result of the emergence of this piece of wisdom has been that we hear more nowadays of models and less of theories and laws. The theory used to be thought of as true even when it continued to persist for long periods in the face of discovered contradictions. The model, on the other hand, although it is internally consistent, lacks truth-value. The investigator undertakes to find out how closely his data fit the model and to adjust the model for closer fits. The model has no actual existence, but it may be as concrete as the model of a molecule or the mathematical formula for the learning curve. Kuhn prefers to use the word *paradigm*, a formal model like *amo, amas, amat*, which is part of the paradigm for the first Latin conjugation. The paradigm is, however, more complex than the model, less concrete, and, as Kuhn thinks of it, less fully conscious, being in large measure carried in the stream of the *Zeitgeist*, the current of credence, which is so often not recognized by he who shapes his thinking in respect of it. The business of science revolves about its paradigms, and, when an old paradigm is abandoned for a new, in a scientific revolution, an enormous number of new problems is generated in respect to the relation of old and new data to the new paradigm. This "acceptance of everything as transitory," these "life-cherishing attitudes," might seem to make science less secure than it has proved to be. The justification of such a view is, however, that it works, that it yields something which men like and call *progress* and *civilization*.

So determinism is a good paradigm for social science and psychology and the history of thought (Boring, 1957). There is no reason to believe that it should be abandoned in our present investigation, no reason to think that we should magnify the importance of History's Eponyms by attributing to them a special capacity for the spontaneous generation of ideas.

Continuity and the Psychosocial Matrix

One of the interesting characteristics of the history of science is the oc-currence of what Robert K. Merton (1961) calls *multiples*. A multiple is the independent discovery of the same fact or the independent announcement of essentially the same new theory by more than one person. The coincidence invites especial attention when it is nearly simultaneous, but there may be a lapse of years between the two members of a doublet when the earlier dis-covery or theory has had little or no publication or has faded out of thought, perhaps because it was premature and did not, when first announced, fit the temper of the time. The historian has long been noting the occurrence of anticipations, which are, of course, the beginnings of multiples. Merton, however, observes that multiples are the rule and may involve more replica-tions than one. For instance, he and Elinor Barber, having analyzed 264 cases of multiples, found that two-thirds of them were doublets, one-fifth of them were triplets, and the one-seventh remaining involved greater repetition. There were actually two cases of nine replications (Merton, 1961, 342).

The discovery or affirmation of multiples is, moreover, itself a multiple. It "is an hypothesis confirmed by its own history," says Merton. The classical paper on the largely unconscious replication of important thoughts and dis-coveries is by Ogburn and Thomas (1922), who listed 148 instances. This discovery has kept on being remade and may yet be made again, unless every-one is inveigled into reading Merton's dramatic résumé of the phenomenon. He counts twenty anticipators of Ogburn and Thomas in the century that preceded their paper, a list that includes the names of Macaulay, Comte, Sir David Brewster, François Arago, Sir Francis Galton, Friedrich Engels, Ein-stein, the anthropologist Kroeber, and the dean of the history of science, George Sarton. Nor did the belief in multiples begin with Macaulay a mere hundred years before Ogburn and Thomas. Inevitably the phenomenon be-comes obvious to every thoughtful historian or historically sophisticated scien-tist. Merton cites Benjamin Franklin as having commented on the matter.

Of course, adequate publication forestalls replication—to the degree that it has been adequate. So it comes about that scientists, recognizing that multiples are the rule and that the causes of discovery are embedded in the current of history, struggle for priority so that they may not have been anticipated in publication—for prestige goes to the first to be heard. Both authors in a doublet may have been equally independent, equally "original," yet there remains always the possible doubt that the later drew upon the earlier. If scientists believed consistently in the prevalence of multiple discovery, there might be less quarreling about priority, but the sure evidence for independence is indubitable ignorance. The evidence is mixed as to whether, in the scientific explosion of the present age and with the increase of multiple authorship and the diminution of individual responsibility for research, there is a decrease in the way the goal of priority acts as a prime motivator. Merton (1961, 483) and Gerald Holton (1962, 373–381) both note that controversy over priority is diminishing, but Frederick Reif (1961) comments on the increasing pace of competition in modern research and the symptoms of anxiety that it produces.

The Bell-Magendie Law of the Spinal Nerve-Roots (Boring, 1950a, 31–33, 45 ff.), as it has been named by the posterity of those two eminent physiologists, furnishes an excellent example of how a doublet comes into being by the inadequacy of the first publication. (Actually this instance was saved from being a triplet only because a third claimant, Alexander Walker, a student of Bell's, got the law stated backwards in his assertion of priority.) Bell described the sensory functions of the spinal cord's dorsal roots and the motor functions of the ventral roots in his lectures to his students and published the facts in 1811 in a small pamphlet of a dozen pages, a mere hundred of them privately printed and circulated. The brochure is titled *Idea of a New Anatomy of the Brain,* and its subtitle reads: "Submitted for the Observations of His Friends." That was in London. In Paris, Magendie, eleven years later, described similar but more detailed experiments that led to the same conclusion. Controversy about priority arose. There is no doubt that Bell was first and did not pick up his idea of this new anatomy from Magendie. Magendie's experiments were later and also better; they were not only more thorough but also more adequately controlled. Posterity never believed that Magendie had read Bell's pamphlet, but of course this judgment lands us at once into the problem of unconscious plagiarism. People do, indeed, read things, forget about them, and then later revive the idea, forgetting the source and believing it to be their very own (Boring, 1954). My colleague, S. Smith Stevens, once caught himself plagiarizing himself. He had what he thought was a brand new idea and he liked it. Starting to write it up, he searched for anticipations in the literature and failed to find any, until he discovered the very same piece of "originality" in his own files under his own authorship. He had become a doublet all by himself. This time there was, however, no public controversy over priority.

With all these rediscoverers making lists of those multiples that have especially astonished each of them, it would be redundant now to parade a representative battalion of replications here. Everybody knows how Newton and Leibnitz formed a doublet in respect of the invention of the calculus, with the possibility that Newton's teacher, Isaac Barrow, makes the instance into a triplet. Most people know how Adams and Leverrier, within a few days of each other in November 1845, "discovered" the planet Neptune by computing its probable location and orbit from a study of the perturbations of the planet Uranus, whose irregularities had been seeking an explanation for over fifty years. Adams was first with his data, but Leverrier's calculations were a little more accurate, and each was taking the last step in a discussion that had been going on among astronomers for a long time.

Some of the doublets belong to the history of psychology. Besides the Bell-Magendie pair there is the one for Bell and Johannes Müller on specific nerve energies. Bell made his point in this same little pamphlet of 1811. Müller formulated his theory in 1826 and turned it into a formal doctrine in 1838. Actually both were anticipated by Thomas Young's casual suggestion in 1801 that there must be three kinds of optic fibers, and there is a sense in which John Locke's doctrine of secondary qualities constitutes a vague foreshadowing of this fundamental conception (Boring, 1942, 68–74).

The James-Lange theory of emotion is one of psychology's most famous doublets. James wrote in 1884, Lange in 1885. There was no controversy. The idea was in the air. An odd doublet was formed by Ernst Mach's and Richard Avenarius' joint contribution of the positivistic background to introspectionism, especially to the systematic views of Külpe and Titchener. It was Mach who said that Avenarius' complicated doctrine was the same as his own, although actually Mach had more to say about the identity of physics and psychology, and Avenarius more about the difference. One could go on, noting anticipations, raising the question of whether Bishop Berkeley in 1709 was anticipating Titchener's context theory of meaning in 1909 (Boring, 1950a, 184–186, 225 ff., 415 ff.), whether Gestalt psychology's use of the concept of "psychophysical isomorphism" began with Lotze, Fechner, Mach, Hering, G. E. Müller, or Wertheimer (Boring, 1942, 87–90), but these instances suffice.

In this way it becomes obvious that the growth of science is continuous, that the present grows out of the past. The unpredictable future, when it has at last arrived, will be the consequence of trends which are with us in development now. The basic question is: Does the intermittent spontaneous intervention of genius break this smooth flow, or is the continuity really uninterrupted and are the breaks artifacts, introduced by scholarly analysis, so as to render the course of history comprehensible within the very considerable limitations of human thinking?

Often the strands in the development of thinking exhibit a trend that ends in a "nova"—a discovery of a new idea. The record of approaching discovery is clear ex post facto, as it was in the discovery of Neptune. At other times the historian may tease out the strands by dissection, as it were, as happened for the history of psychophysical isomorphism. Picking up anticipations shows what was being fed into the stream of the *Zeitgeist* that affects, consciously or unconsciously, the thinking of the man who creates the nova. When the nova is what Merton calls a singleton, when no adequate anticipations can be found, then the scholar has his choice between believing in spontaneous originality and inscrutable determinism. Most scientists will choose determinism, but it may sometimes be the inner determinism of a single thinking brain.

The inscrutable *Zeitgeist!* It was Goethe's term that he used in 1827 for the source of events that occur "neither by agreement nor by fiat, but self-determined under the multiplicity of climates of opinion." It would have been better had he said "Glaubestrom," and in English a good phrase is "current of belief" or even better "current of credence," for the *Zeitgeist* keeps changing in the broad stream of history and some novae, inhibited by the *Zeitgeist* when they come too early in history, are reinforced later. This current of credence told against Galileo's discovery that there are more than seven celestial bodies (Jupiter's moons) because common opinion was that the Creator would not create an imperfect universe by deviating from the perfect number seven. Helmholtz had trouble with the *Zeitgeist* when he measured the rate of the nervous impulse, because it was then believed that the soul is unitary and that voluntary action must be instantaneous or almost so. Presently, in both cases, the common credence adapted itself to new discovery, but the *Zeitgeist* by preserving the past works both ways: it delays progress and inhibits foolishness—and indeed there are times when we have to wait on posterity to tell one from the other (Boring, 1955).

There can be no sense in trying to define the stream of the *Zeitgeist* as unconscious or conscious. It is "the total body of knowledge and opinion available at any time to a person living within a given culture. There is, certainly, no rigorous way of distinguishing between what is explicit to a scientist and what is implicit in the forms and patterns of communication, between what is clear conclusion and what is uncritically accepted premise. Available knowledge is communicated whenever it becomes effective, and that is the *Zeitgeist* working" (Boring, 1955, 106).

After all, in spite of the resurgence of phenomenology and the rise of existentialism, consciousness seems to be becoming less and less important to psychology. So much that goes on in thought and behavior, if one speaks loosely, is "unconscious." The older psychologists protested Helmholtz' use of the concept of unconscious inference to explain perceptual events, but nowadays how could one get along in understanding perception without unconscious inferences and sets? Thinking very nearly turned unconscious under Külpe at Würzburg, nor did it take Freud to convince us that most thinking is unconscious. Nowadays the dynamics of Freud's conceptualism are well embedded in the current of credence that all psychologists use for orientation. These words that I speak now come readily to my mouth from the typed page and I perceive their meaning as do you, by listening to myself. The words were written by my typewriter to me, and I understood them best by reading them, and changed some because I did not like them, and kept the others with a sense of satisfaction. When I do not know what I think about a difficult problem, I turn to my typewriter and write out the answer. You'd be surprised at what good advice my typewriter seems to give me. If the matter is less important, I speak the answer and listen in.

And so we come back pretty much to Tolstoy's paradigm adapted to the history of science. The scientist is a thinking unit that acts in the psychosocial matrix within which all human history progresses. His motivations are not directed upon the great goals to which scientific progress is eventually seen to have moved on. They are smaller goals, sometimes economic, some concerned with prestige and pride, often—or perhaps nearly always, as Kuhn argues—of the order of puzzle-solving. The scientist just cannot bear to leave a seemingly soluble puzzle unsolved, and, if he solves what no one else has yet managed, he has his reward in pride—and in being released to tackle another puzzle.

Merton calls the study of the scientist in the psychosocial matrix the sociology of knowledge, but the term is too narrow. The domain is psychological as well as social. A great deal of scientific progress is made at times within the head of the single scientist, although even then he may be thinking about what other men have said or have written, perhaps centuries ago, or he may be effectively plagiarizing the *Zeitgeist* without knowing it, refusing to accept a conclusion because his habits of thought are dead set against it, or accepting a nova because it makes a new thought fit in with an old.

One must learn, I think, to see science going on causally in this psychosocial matrix. Every event in it is cause or effect and is usually both. Determinism reigns. The interactions are between man and man—social. Between man and the printed page—also social with a vicarious intermediary. Between the thinker and his memories—psychological. Between his habits of thought—psychological. What is the *Zeitgeist*, social or psychological? Certainly it is not truly a *Geist*. If you deal with the isolated individual, the interaction of thought, the way in which thinking is like a rat running a maze, forming hypotheses, abandoning them, trial and error, and resolution if success is achieved—all that goes into the psychology of creativity, quite beside the problem of whether there are individual differences in creative ability. These distinctions do not, however, matter. The scene of scientific action is the psychosocial matrix. What goes on there is the important business of the psychologist, the sociologist, the historian, as well as of many other wise men.

Great Events and Great Men

Ogburn and Thomas in 1922, with their list of multiples in hand, asked the question: "Are inventions inevitable?" Even earlier, in 1917, the anthropologist A. L. Kroeber had been listing multiples (Kroeber, 1917, 196–208). He proposed that the course of discovery is governed by a force superior to the individual, which he called the Superorganic, a concept that in those days resembled the group mind enough to fail to win wide acceptance. Tolstoy, as we have seen, anthropomorphized History with the capital *H* as the controller of history with the little *h*. Anyone who accepts determinism as a good paradigm for science and its history and who sees discovery as an event in the psychosocial matrix of historical cause and effect is bound to think of scientific novae as inevitable.

The atomic age has made this kind of thinking familiar to all of us, even though it has not done away with the belief in the originality of Great Men. The inevitability of the goal-directed process is summed up in the word *got*. The United States "got" the bomb first, ahead of Germany. Later the Soviets "got" it. The date by which they could get it was actually specified, but it turned out to be wrong. The general course of Soviet discovery proved predictable but the speed was greater than expected. Now France has the bomb and soon China will. It takes wealth to sustain the research that will ultimately produce the bomb when normal scientific communication is blocked by imposed secrecy. And it takes motivation too to maintain the research and the flow of wealth.

So sure were the scientists of the inevitability of discovery during World War II, given large quantities of wealth and motivation, that the creation of a new weapon, offensive or defensive, in one laboratory immediately forced other laboratories of the same government, even before the new weapon was perfected, to begin research on countervailance for it. It was taken for granted that discovery is inevitable for all nations that have sufficient wealth and motivation, but that speed is still enough subject to choice as to leave competition possible.

But are motivation and wealth enough? Not surely. Wealth does not always procure necessary materials and one of the materials needed is good brains. It is not only the lack of wealth and motivation that has prevented the great apes from building a civilization equal to man's.

There arises, therefore, the question as to what the deterministic theory of history does to the Great-Man theory. Are the two incompatible? It is easy to think that they are, that the greatness of a scientist depends upon his originality; yet how can originality be reduced to other prior origins which themselves have their necessary and sufficient causes? Sophisticated historians, among them Merton (1961, 483–485), claim, on the other hand, that there is here no insurmountable contradiction. The difficulty, I suggest, is resolved if one thinks of Great Events first, and then of Great Men as the consequences of the Great Events—not consequences in actual historical sequences but consequences in the analytical evaluation of scientific progress. The Great Events, what Kuhn calls the "scientific revolutions," are the reasons for the Great Men, the reasons why posterity singles out Eponyms to label and dignify the Great Events. Greatness is, moreover, both neurological and psychological. It is neurological insofar as it is a crucial event existing in history's causal chain that proceeds within the psychosocial matrix, since it consists of interactions within the thinking brain of one man on an occasion sufficient to produce a large or small revolution in scientific thinking. It is psychological insofar as it is a value formed to meet man's need to make history comfortable to understanding by personalizing it. The eponym can be a placebo, even though underneath the eponym there was real brain creating a noetic nova. We shall find no contradiction under the paradigm of determinism as long as we can distinguish the reality from the distortion that man adds to further his understanding.

Some years ago Francis Hackett (1948) complained that Freud's analysis of the springs of motivation had not helped the novelists to understand and portray their characters. The trouble is, said Hackett, that Freud's theory is deterministic, whereas the novelists need to have heroes and a hero is a person who, faced with a dilemma, chooses against odds. You cannot write a novel about robots and have one of them a hero. Even animal stories with a hero require anthropopsychic elaboration to ennoble one animal. Science and literature habitually use different paradigms that are carried only half-consciously in the current of credence, providing, as it does, a proper background for the exposition. Carlyle saw Frederick the Great as a hero. Tolstoy saw Napoleon as an Event, an Event that did not include an understanding of its own significance.

The Great Events of science are what Kuhn (1962b) calls revolutions, and we shall do well to accept his able exposition of this matter. A revolution occurs when a basic paradigm changes. One thinks of the Copernican revolution (the earth moves!), the Galilean revolution (the pendulum is not merely a falling body), the Newtonian (gravity is mutually universal), the Darwinian, Bohr's complementarity. The change to a new paradigm may be gradual in the sense that it takes a long time for it to win general acceptance, and there nearly always will have been explicit opposition at the start; nevertheless the change is not continuous. The old paradigm is not transformed through intermediate stages into the new. It shifts in all-or-none fashion like a perception—which is indeed just what it is. Kuhn uses the old duck-rabbit ambiguous figure (Jastrow, 1901, 29) as his illustration. The perception is always of a duck or of a rabbit; never is it a rabbuck sheathed with hairlike feathers.

Progress in science, Kuhn thinks, consists of these revolutions that occur by changes of paradigm, changes inevitably followed by a period of fitting new data to the new paradigm, and also by fitting old data to it, so that it can be said that a revolution changes the past as well as the future. It is the sciences that most clearly progress, so much so that Kuhn wonders whether the statement might not be inverted so as to define science as what progresses. Doubtless, art and the humanities, which do not stand still, must have some complementary kind of change or of development even, but progress is no *sine qua non* for them. Kuhn fails to perceive a goal for science. It is not helpful, he thinks, to say that its progress is toward truth, but certainly—say I— scientific progress is toward expansion and toward continued unity, and the paradigms that support this process are the most acceptable.

Of Newton, Alexander Pope wrote:

Nature and Nature's law lay hid in night;
God said, Let Newton be! and all was light.

That is the way men like to think about genius, but Newton himself seems to have come nearer to comprehending the Divine rule (Bell, 1937, 93):

If I have seen a little farther than others, it is because I have stood on the shoulders of giants.

Changing a paradigm usually takes more than a moment of insight, although Galileo's discovery of Jupiter's moons and thus of the fact that the Creator could use his omnipotence to create more than seven celestial bodies was a paradigmatic change that occurred in the mind of one man during a couple of days of observation. Nevertheless it took a long time to get the new paradigm into the current of credence.

The date 1859 was honored a century later as the birthday of the theory of evolution. Darwin had, however, been working on his theory for more than three decades before he published *The Origin of Species* under pressure from Wallace who had conceived the same theory and was prepared to make it into a multiple. It turned out that much of the centennial celebration consisted in uncovering the many anticipations of Darwin, and one geneticist even complained thus belatedly that Darwin had borrowed more than his due from his contemporary, Edward Blyth, without due acknowledgment (Eiseley, 1959).

Fechner thought it worth while to note that the basic idea of psychophysics came to him as he lay in bed on the morning of 22 October 1850 (Fechner, 1860, II, 554, Boring, 1961*a*, 4). Since Fechner, the founder of psychophysics, became thus in a sense the founder of modern experimental psychology, 22 October is often celebrated somewhat humorously as Fechner Day. For instance, when the seminar of Harvard's psychophysicist, S. S.

Stevens, fell on Fechner Day, his students provided a birthday cake for the idea that Cartesian dualism could be bridged by experimentally determining a functional relation between the psychic and the physical. Fixing of the date is, however, a placebo. Psychophysical measurements were being made before Fechner, who was himself primarily motivated in this matter by his battle against materialism with its own long history. People find pleasure in birthdays. To date the birth of a thought is to dignify it, and biographers pick up these anecdotes and embed them in history.

So it must be with many alleged moments of insight—Newton and the "apple," which was a story told Voltaire by a niece of Newton's; Descartes' triple dream on St. Martin's Eve, 10 November 1619, which is supposed to have brought analytical geometry into being; Max Wertheimer's changing his mind to get off the train at Frankfurt in August 1910 to buy a toy stroboscope for trying out something on seen movement in his hotel room (Newman, 1944, 431 ff.). That led him to the University and to the crusty Schumann who had just built an elaborate stroboscope that he wanted to have used; and that in turn led on to the "Experimentelle Studien über das Sehen von Bewegungen" of 1912, which led to Gestalt psychology, which changed quite an important paradigm in psychology from atomistic description to the study of Gestalten and field theory.

Still the major question remains unanswered. Are there geniuses or are there not? And does scientific progress depend on them if there are any? Here the answer is most certainly affirmative. Indeed there are geniuses who affect scientific progress decisively, especially when they are individually concerned with changes in important paradigms of science. A genius, of course, is an originator only in the sense that he puts the available natural resources of the mind together in a new noetic manufacture—or perhaps one should say cerebrofacture. The scientific genius is an artist in puzzle-solving, and the measure of this kind of competence is the degree by which the creation of a noetic nova takes place in the brain of a single person without help from the environment.

Of course the environment always does help. The schoolchild who rates high on measures of creativity is no wild oaf from the forest nurtured by wolves, but definitely a schooled child, a specially educated event in the psychosocial matrix of his time. The *Zeitgeist* has already affected him. If you wish to measure what is nowadays called his creativity, you test him in situations that are novel in particular but nevertheless not so independent of his knowledge and skills that these resources are not useful to him. Puzzle-solving is always done under rules. A game has clear limitations. Newton, for instance, delighted in solving mathematical problems. Leibnitz once challenged him with a mathematical puzzle which he thought would prove too difficult for him, but Newton solved it in the evening after he received it (Bell, 1937, 115 ff.). That was principally genius because it was individually cerebral. Newton for this time being was shut off from all social aid—except his past experience.

The pioneer work of D. W. MacKinnon and his associates (MacKinnon, 1960, 1962) and J. P. Guilford (1962) on creativity leaves no doubt that there are large individual differences in the creativity of adults and children, and in respect of these it is natural to follow Galton's reasoning (1869) by assuming that the creative abilities would fall into a unimodal distribution, of which the one extreme, representing maximal creativity, would show the existence of what might be called creative genius. That is where Newton and Leibnitz would belong and most of the other eponyms in the history of science.

Creativity is no simple trait, for it is turning out to depend on a variety of intellectual and motivational factors operating together, in one manner for one person but differently for another. Creativity is not intelligence (Taylor & Barron, 1963; Getzels & Jackson, 1962), but then intelligence itself is slipping out from under rigorous definition (Hunt, 1961). It is proving to depend more on nurture, less on nature, and thus it becomes more subject to change during the life of an individual than the concept of a constant IQ had led psychologists to expect. In another decade or so we shall know more about creativity without which scientific progress would not occur, and perhaps we shall even have some hopeful principles in respect to creating creativity.

Have we now answered our prime question? There are geniuses. Their noetic achievements have been the sufficient causes of great steps forward in scientific discovery, especially in respect of the revolutions in paradigms. Do these facts establish the Great-Man theory of scientific progress? Perhaps not. This is the point at which thinking readily goes astray. What is sufficient may not have been necessary.

Newton's genius contributed three outstanding novae to thought and understanding: the invention of the calculus, the demonstration that colored lights can be mixed to give simple white, and the formulation of the paradigm of universal gravitation. The last is the most important, but does anyone think that the facts of color-mixture would have remained undiscovered had Newton not formulated the laws in 1672? Would they have had to wait for another Great Man to come—Thomas Young (in 1807, say) or Helmholtz (perhaps in 1852)? If the more pedestrian Porterfield in 1759 had, under pressure from the stream of history, made the demonstration, would he necessarily have become a Great Man? Does every change in a fundamental paradigm in science create an eponym? Must every Great Event in science have an owner?

My thought is here that it would be more scientific in viewing the history of science to examine the facts, the Great Events and the Great Trends to which the events contribute, and to use the names of men as labels only when necessary for communication while shunning hero-worship. Such a change would alter a paradigm of the history of science. It would be a small Copernican revolution where man surrenders his vanity for the sake of better understanding. After all, a Great Man is only a piece of the psychosocial matrix, marked off from all the rest because this activity operated within a single brain with considerable, yet with minimal, social reinforcement. The history of science ought not to be hung on an enormous number of eponymic pegs. There are greater and lesser men in science just as there are greater and lesser ideas and instruments and methods and institutions. Was Newton in 1672 more important than the reflecting telescope which he designed? Is the difference simply because Newton was the originator of the telescope, whereas we remain largely ignorant of the origin of the idea in Newton's mind and, being ignorant, are free to engage in the mystique of hero-worship? Let us look at the artifacts that man's urge for personalization creates in the study of history, so as to form some estimate of the degree in which the greatness of the Great Man is a placebo.

Eponymy

Whence comes greatness? From nature, nurture, and posterity. Let us leave the parts played by the seldom separated factors of nature and nurture to the personologists who are studying creativity, for they are not likely to forget them, and let us discuss now the contribution to fame that posterity makes in assessing the past achievement of those persons whom it makes into eponyms. An eponym is a man who is said to give his name to a period or a time or a movement or a school or, of course, an important new paradigm. Never does he really offer his name; rather posterity wrests it from him and applies it to that period or event in which it sees his image more plainly than it sees others!

There are, it would seem, not less than three psychological principles that enter into the establishment of eponymies. Let us examine each.

(1) The first is the range of attention. For more than seventy years now it has been known that almost as many simple words as disconnected consonants can be correctly reported after a brief tachistoscopic exposure of them. Further experiments show that actually perceptual scope is not extended for the words but that the word is apt to be correctly reported when only part of it is sensed. With 100 milliseconds' exposure, "phycholoby" gets read as "psychology." As a matter of biological efficiency, perception telescopes its material, letting a part stand for a whole. The eponymization of history works in a similar manner. Great Men have to be rare because the range of human apperception requires that the distinguishing features of an

elaborate complex shall be as few as can be. For the same reason the business of science is to generalize. It must simplify nature in order to comprehend it. So the perception of history works on the principle of focus and margin. Focusing on the most prominent features, it exaggerates them and fixes them, diminishing the visibility of the margin.

It seems probable that the same sort of distortion occurs with professional prestige in shorter intervals of time. Prestige tends to be autocatalytic. Above a certain threshold, it builds itself up with positive feedback, but there must be this threshold, for not everyone on a stage can be outstanding. In general, honors go to the honored and importance maintains itself. Below the threshold, the less honored get overlooked as they make up the obscure margin of the historical scene. Derek Price (1961, 45–53) has just noted a similar phenomenon for books. The great classical books of Copernicus, Bacon, Galileo, Newton, and their kind were laboriously written over long periods and were necessarily founded upon the knowledge of their day, including the lesser books that had preceded them. But it was the book that won applause and fame that established itself and forced into oblivion the lesser earlier books that had made the great book possible. Price remarks of the *Novum Organum:* "Although Bacon was taken as the emblem on the shield of the Royal Society, he was, in truth, only the most publicized preacher of a method that had been growing for decades before him."

It is not at all clear that this eponymous distortion is unexceptionably bad. It brings the historical subject matter within the range of comprehension and memory. Scientists face other predicaments, like the motivational predicaments when the egoism that sustains the research drive conflicts with objectivity, or the analytical predicament when the analysis that description requires interferes with the Gestalt character of the whole. The practical solution for all these predicaments seems to be to allow them, to use them, but to recognize them and every now and then to take measures to offset them. The excellent egoistic drive need not be fatal to objectivity, nor need the apperceptive necessity of keeping the biographical focus narrow prevent the historian from seeking out the lesser figures in an attempt to give them their due.

(2) A second source of support for eponymy lies in man's gregarious nature. Mankind wants its heroes, as both Carlyle in his defense of hero worship and Francis Hackett in his discussion of the novel have made clear. The history of science is spattered with the aggressive demands of great and lesser men for recognition and acceptance as leaders, but one hears less about the equally urgent need for followership, because the ranks of disciples are not limited by anyone's range of apperception. One has only to read such vivid accounts as R. R. Holt's (1963) of the methods of forcible indoctrination by the Chinese in altering the personalities of deviationists to realize

how much man's thinking is controlled by social acceptance, all the way from the effects of the covert current of credence to the overt social pressure of propaganda. Derek Price (1961, 47) has written:

> The Scientific Revolution did not arise suddenly and out of nowhere through some mysterious generation of a set of unprecedented geniuses at that time and at no other. It is a product of certain demonstrable forces and ancestry, and in seeking a strategic line through this history we must first exorcise from our mythology all great men. Any attempt to do this immediately raises the hackles of all good scientists, and it is rather instructive to stop for a moment and recognize the seat of those emotions connected with anything that seems to be a denigration or belittling of the heroes of science . . . The psychology of the reaction is most interesting. Science seems tied to its heroes more closely than is any other branch of learning. It is the one study that contains the entirety of its successful past embedded in its current state; Boyle's Law is alive today as the Battle of Waterloo is not.

We have already observed how the common belief, that genius is capable of spontaneous originality and thus works by inspiration, leads to the fixing of the dates when the noetic afflatus struck. Genius often compliments itself by dating its own sudden inspirations. Fechner fixed on Tuesday morning, 22 October 1850. Freud's historic moment was Wednesday evening, 24 July 1895, when at the table in the northeast corner of the terrace of the Bellevue Restaurant in Vienna he realized that the essence of a dream is the fulfillment of a hidden wish. Later he quipped that a marble tablet ought to be erected at this spot: "Here the secret of dreams was revealed to Dr. Sigm. Freud on July 24, 1895" (Jones, 1953, 354).

An interesting example of the way in which a continuous development may have its identity fixed and its status enhanced by giving it a birthday is the selection of the date 1879 for the beginning or even the "founding" by Wilhelm Wundt at Leipzig of the world's first psychological laboratory. What are the facts? We have them from Wundt's own pen as he wrote in 1909.

Sporadic psychological experimentation had been going on in physiological and physical laboratories and in private quarters for a long time. Stumpf is said to have claimed that he had a psychological laboratory in the early days, but that he carried it about in a cigar box under his arm. The box contained tuning forks. In 1875, when Wundt went to Leipzig from Zürich, the Ministerium "with the concurrence of the Academic Senate" placed at his disposal a small unused auditorium in an old refectory building. It provided for demonstrations of facts described in Wundt's lectures and for Wundt's own experimentation. In the same year Harvard University gave William James two small rooms for similar use. At both institutions experimentation was begun in 1875 in space made specially available, but neither institution claimed that a laboratory had been "founded" then.

In 1879, as Wundt later recapitulated the history (Wundt, 1909; Harper,

1950), students and young docents began to use this space under Wundt's direction for their own independent research, research which presently resulted in publication in Wundt's newly founded *Philosophische Studien* (1883) and which served these investigators as dissertations for the doctor's degree. At the start these students were not even registered for a course at the University. At some later time, it must have been, Wundt and his collaborators perceived that the beginnings of a formal Institute were apparent in these early independent investigations and they began calling the rooms made available to Wundt the Psychologisches Institut. That impromptu laboratory was subsequently given more space on several occasions. It first received money for apparatus in 1883. It moved to another building and moved again. Only in 1894 was it belatedly recognized by the University as its Psychologisches Institut. By that time, however, the *Philosophische Studien* was already in its tenth volume and had published more than fourscore experimental articles, most of them based on research in this not-yet-officially-founded Psychologisches Institut. Wundt, of course, was the entrepreneur for the new experimental psychology. He established the many firsts that gave the new field status—the title ("physiological psychology"), the systematic handbook updated through six editions in thirty-seven years (*Grundzüge der physiologischen Psychologie*), a laboratory (Institut für experimentelle Psychologie der Universität Leipzig), and a journal for publishing experimental research (*Philosophische Studien*). Thus the laboratory dates from 1875, whereas the research began in 1879. Wundt's choice of 1879 as the important date when the space assigned to him began actually to contribute to scientific progress was made for a good purpose, even if it was not a "founding" as it has so often been said to have been (Boring, 1950a, pp. 323 ff.).

(3) Besides the desire to participate in followership—a very common human need, which Henry Murray called the need for deference ("n Def")—there is a way in which the desire to assume leadership ("n Dom") supports eponymy. Ambitious men need goals, and the awards and honors available for them activate them. Unfortunately the autocatalysis of prestige operates here, so that honors build up for a few and are suppressed for the many, and, because of this distortion by positive feedback, people are not in agreement whether awards are or are not good things (Boring, 1959). Still there can be no doubt that eponymy creates goals and enhances motivation. Scientists want success. There is more fun in writing a signed article for a journal than an unsigned one for an encyclopedia. For the one there may be feedback, for the other even a faint echo is unlikely. The heroes of science stimulate its neophytes. Once I knew one of psychology's great, an erudite man who had won his many well-deserved honors early. In maturity he was still ambitious but the available awards left for him were no longer significant—except one only, which he was not likely to receive and never did receive. I felt sad for

him. It should have been possible to find some new kind of laurel to maintain for him the excitement of productivity.

With the scientific explosion of the present day, the importance of the
individual investigator is diminished. The problem created by this car-
cinomatoid multiplication of research papers at the present time and in the
immediate future has been treated in detail by Price (1961, 92–124) and
Holton (1962), but they do not suggest what may be happening to motivation. Holton reproduces the title of a short announcement in the *Physical
Review Letters* by twenty-one authors in four laboratories in New York, North
Carolina, Tennessee, Maryland, and Italy (p. 374). These men were preserving priority for a joint discovery. Were they proud of their achievement?
If they were proud must each have been proud? What is 1/21 of one pride
like? Holton thinks they were not aggressive or potentially jealous, although
we have noted that the physicist Reif (1961) held a different opinion. If Holton and Merton are right in thinking that bitter aggressive competition is
diminishing in science, then times have changed greatly in the three hundred
years since Galileo disdained to answer Kepler's letter and in the eighty years
since Wundt refused to meet with Stumpf lest they should eventually find
themselves in controversy—as indeed they did.

Indeed it may be that Holton and Merton are telling us that personal
vanity and aggression, the usual consequence of frustrated vanity, are now on
the decline in science, that Reif is expressing a personal and exceptional
opinion, that Price will live to see science as untied from its heroes as any
other branch of knowledge. Thus they may be announcing the decline of
eponymy, and the resolution at last of the motivational predicament in
which egoism threatens objectivity. Perhaps it is possible now to get along
with the diminished greatness that comes from fitting personal pride to
reality. Certainly it is not impossible for two men to experience pride, nor for
twenty-one men. When a hundred million men feel it, it is called patriotism.
The Soviet Union is said nowadays to be managing to depersonalize the
individual in its educational system and to substitute aggressive competition
between "peer groups" as the first step in the socialization of collectives
(Bronfenbrenner, 1962). Surely the history of science would appear more
scientific if it could but get rid of the cult of personality.

In brief, then, eponymy distorts the view of history. It magnifies those
persons who are found above the threshold and diminishes those below it.
Eponymic distortion arises out of man's limited range of perception (for the
great are by definition few), out of his need for leaders with whom he may
identify himself, and out of his desire to perceive high goals upon which he
may train his ambition. The damage to objectivity that such distortions create
can be lessened by recognizing the fact of the distortion, but it is doubtful
that human nature, in the interesting but arduous task of scientific investigation, could be completely pacified and yet remain productive.

History of Psychology

A final question, which must be answered briefly, is: What would the history of psychology be like if all the names of Great Men were extirpated from it? Put thus, the question is unanswerable. What would the history be like if all the books and articles which make up the history of science had been published anonyomously? There would be a history to write, but the historian would have to find other labels. He writes now behind a screen of names. Every item is something someone did or thought or said.

I have wondered, nevertheless, if a pretty good general history of psychology could not be written with minimal eponymous distortion if it were composed as the histories of half a dozen trends; thus:

(1) Experimentalism: the ancients, the Academies, later experimentalism, psychophysics, physiological psychology, the laboratories, the relation to philosophy and phenomenology, later methods, apparatus and techniques, relation to physics, biology, and statistics. Fill that in with two hundred other details and you have a good section for a history book. I have used no names, but the names would come flocking in as soon as one got down to talking.

The other trends of equal importance might be (2) positivism, (3) measurement, (4) motivation, (5) the unconscious, and (6) schools and systems. In respect of schools and systems eponymy would, of course, reign. It would be fun to try such a volume, but the Copernican revolution toward modesty, in which the history of science loses its interest in man, the investigator, and confines itself to an account of discovery, must be a very long way off. Nevertheless, when that day comes, as I think it must, we shall look back—surely we shall or rather our posterity will—on the personalized history of science of the twentieth century with an indulgent smile and think: How egocentric and immature they all were in those days!

Interpretation

꽤꽤꽤꽤꽤꽤꽤꽤 1929

I T is now proper for us to ask ourselves the question: To what extent has the new psychology justified itself? There is a criticism of modern psychology, often spoken and sometimes written, that the new science has not quite succeeded, that it has been, as compared with its ambitions, relatively sterile, that it set out to study mind by the experimental method, and that it has gained a mass of knowledge about sensation (which the physiologists might have gained), a little else, and nothing of great moment about the rational mind, the personality, and human nature. This criticism, when expressed by philosophers, may be suspected of reflecting the disappointment of philosophers at the turn which the new psychology took, or even of their reaction to the negativism of psychologists toward philosophy. However, it is not at all impossible that psychologists themselves might express some dissatisfaction with the advance of psychology, were they relieved from the necessity of defending themselves. Has psychology been relatively ineffective in attacking its problems?—we may ask, now that the perspective of seventy years is before us.

The reader can formulate his own answer to this question, but he is entitled to the author's opinion. Here it is.

The author believes that the application of the experimental method to the problem of mind is the great outstanding event in the history of the study of mind, an event to which no other is comparable. He believes that the person who doubts that the results have justified the importance that has been attached to the invention of experimental psychology must be either ignorant or influenced by a disappointment that the progress of experimental psychology has not aided in the solution of his own particular problems. On the other hand, the author confesses to a certain disappointment of his own that experimental psychology has not accomplished more

Reprinted with permission from A *History of Experimental Psychology*, 1929, 658–661.

than it has in its seventy years of life. It started with such high hopes that all that was needed was the willingness to experiment, patiently, honestly, and industriously, and it has found that mere faith in experimentalism is insufficient for great and rapid progress, unless that faith is accompanied by some flash of insight as to method. There have been perhaps many little flashes, in addition to the tremendous amount of careful, painstaking research, but there has never been in the history of experimental psychology a dazzling light. Psychology has progressed and developed in a manner similar to the course of any science under ordinary circumstances; but there has not, except for the initial inspiration in the thought of experimentalizing mind, been any great idea or discovery that has revitalized the science—for a science it is—opening up new fields, releasing new energy and removing hidden doubts. Why?

Perhaps the answer lies in the fact that there has not yet been time, but—if we are to follow the author's opinion further—there are at least two explicit reasons.

The first reason is fairly obvious. There have been no great psychologists. Psychology has never had a great man to itself. Wundt was not a great man of the order of Helmholtz or Darwin. He 'founded' experimental psychology, but in that he was more the instrument of the times than an originator. The rest of his influence was due to his persistence and to the sheer mass of his production, and perhaps also to the fact that he was senior and that no other psychologist was ever any greater than he. The influence of Helmholtz was considerable, and the influence of Darwin in America and England was profound, but both of these men affected psychology only from the outside, as it were. There are signs that psychologists are ready for a great man or a great event, for they seize eagerly upon every new movement that aspires to greatness; but the great event has not yet occurred.

The second reason which the author would assign for the less than maximal advance of experimental psychology is an internal conflict within psychology itself, a conflict that is the natural outgrowth of its history. Psychology has never succeeded in taking philosophy to itself nor in leaving it alone. Such a diagnosis is not founded upon the necessary relation of science to philosophy, for this conflict is not to be found in the natural sciences. In psychology it lies very near the surface. Often the men who cry out most loudly against philosophy in psychology are the men who regard psychology as a system and who write of epistemological matters. All the movements in psychology that have led to self-conscious schools—Wundt's physiological psychology, introspectionism in America, functional psychology, *Gestalt* psychology, behaviorism, but not animal psychology nor the mental tests—have been philosophical movements, conducted, for the most part by men who would eschew philosophy and rely solely upon the experimental method. The degree to which the text of this book has entered upon quasi-philosophical and systematic matters while purporting to be an account of the history of experimental psychology, is a measure of the admixture of philosophy to experimentation within psychology. Ever since their foundation, the journals of psychology in all countries have been weighted down with "theoretical" papers that are really the expositions of psychologists, untrained to philosophy but writing on philosophical matters. Incompetent work can be ignored, but a division of the mind within psychology is not healthy. Inevitably it must hinder work in the individual and thus the most rapid progress in the science. There is too much to psychology now for psychologists to master their own material and philosophy too. Psychology ought to fare better when it can completely surrender its philosophical heritage, in fact as well as in voiced principle, and proceed, unimpeded by a divided soul, about its business.

Great Men and
Scientific Progress

𝕣𝕣𝕣𝕣𝕣𝕣𝕣𝕣𝕣𝕣𝕣𝕣𝕣 1950

Introduction

THE Great-Man theory of history is as old as history, as old as the kings who caused the records of their deeds to be cut in stone in order to let posterity know how it was that they had also carved out human destiny, as old as man's belief that he himself is a free agent who chooses his acts to shape his own life and the lives of those others whom his deeds affect. That makes this theory very old indeed, but its age does not render it obsolete. We still look to great men for the partial explanation of history, to Napoleon or Hitler, and we marvel that the little corporal or the paperhanger could so have changed the course of our civilization. In the smaller spheres of human affairs we acknowledge or seek out leaders, and the psychologist is told that the great need of the world now is for more leaders and better leadership. Certainly there are leaders and great men who play important roles in human affairs, and these persons are—practically by definition—those who greatly affect the lives of others. The Great-Man theory cannot be wrong. It expresses too obvious a truth about society.

Although the Great-Man theory cannot be wrong, since it is clear that men die having differed from one another in social effectiveness and therefore in greatness, there has been, nevertheless, for almost a century now, a growing suspicion that the theory asserts very little, since it specifies neither the attributes nor the conditions of greatness. What has been happening is that, as the new scientific age came on, philosophically minded persons began more and more to look for external causes of human action, abandoning free will as a positive explanation. Descartes (1641) had made it plausible to regard animals as automata but he had left man's rational soul free to choose what man should do. The French materialists and mechanists—writers like

Reprinted with permission from *Proceedings of The American Philosophical Society*, 1950, **94**, 339–351.

La Mettrie (1748) and Cabanis (1802)—extended the machine-theory to include man. In the nineteenth century, especially after Darwin's theory had made its great impress upon thinking, philosophers began to look, not merely for the attributes of greatness in order that they might understand its nature, but even more for the causes of greatness so that they might say when and why it occurs and perhaps take a hand in the production of genius. That is what Galton wanted to do.

Thus it comes about that there is a *personalistic* view of the operation of genius and a *naturalistic* one. The two are sometimes thought to contradict each other, but they are not really incompatible. The personalistic view is circumscribed. It exhibits man as a free originator, the genius as existing in his own right and solving problems more quickly or more correctly than the man in the street. The naturalistic view is broader and is capable of including the personalistic view. It shows genius, not only as the antecedent of new thought, but also as the consequence of its antecedent conditions. Thus the personalistic view preserves the dignity of man, for it leaves him a free agent accomplishing great deeds by the voluntary exercise of his capacities; whereas the naturalistic alternative robs man of this dignity by taking away his mystery and showing up his achievements and capacities as consequences of the conditions which create them. Science is always the great debunker because it reduces choice to necessity.

Status of the Problem

Now let us see how this discussion has run, for not everyone has been so clear about it. Many have thought that there is an issue here, that the philosopher must choose between personalism and naturalism in assessing the role of genius in scientific progress.

The old view, as we have said, is the personalistic one. It was pointed up by Thomas Carlyle in his famous lectures of 1840 *On Heroes, Hero Worship and the Heroic in History.* "The history of what man has accomplished in this world," he wrote, "is at bottom the History of the Great Men who have worked here" (1840, lect. 1, par. 1). Carlyle's paradigm for this hypothesis was his *History of Frederick the Great* (1865). Carlyle believed sincerely in the effectiveness of great men, and so he might, even though their greatness consists in their having been the agents of the inevitable.

Naturalism includes cultural determination, and we may note that the year 1859 is the date, not only for Charles Darwin's launching of his theory of evolution, but also for Karl Marx's *Zur Kritik der politischen Oekonomie,* the classical argument for the cultural determination of social history. More germane to our interest, however, is Count Tolstoy's depreciation of Napoleon a decade later in his great historical novel, *War and Peace* (1869), and his repeated return, late in that volume, to the theme of the adventitious cultural determination of history with the great men cast in the role of history's stooges. "A king is history's slave," he wrote. "History, that is, the unconscious, general, hive-life of mankind, uses every moment of the life of kings as a tool for its own purposes" (bk. 9, sect. 1). "The higher a man stands on the social ladder, the more people he is connected with and the more power he has over others, the more evident is the predestination and the inevitability of his every action" (*ibid.*). So History, Tolstoy thought, is controlled by History and not by the Great Men. What is History? History is the aggregate of an infinite of tiny events which make up, in Tolstoy's phrase, "the hive-life of mankind." The campaign of Napoleon in Russia in 1812 is to be understood as caused by a totality of little events, such as a whim of Napoleon on a certain day, the pique of Alexander on another day, the advice of a colonel who wished, not to advance History's Great Purpose, but to get for himself a promotion, and the fearless charge of the young cavalry commander who, unaware of danger, could not resist leading his men, without orders, in a gallop across the level plain. History, Tolstoy argued, reveals no Great Purpose in action. It is whatever the coincidence of many little events have made it and its Great Men are its distinguishing features. Just so you recognize a rhinoceros by its horn, a convenient label which the beast could nevertheless do without. Much more vital to the rhinoceros is his medulla oblongata, but that, since it does not show, is mentioned only by the biologist.

It was just at this same time that Francis Galton, influenced by the new theory of evolution, published his study of *Hereditary Genius* (1869). Galton believed that genius is biologically inherited and later he founded his gospel of eugenics upon this basic principle. His theory of genius was thus naturalistic although opposed to cultural determination. Galton held that genius will out, no matter what cultural inhibitors work against it, and that fame and reputation are therefore proper indices of the degree of genius. Galton was wrong, for culture plays an important role in determining achievement, but he helped to make usual the naturalistic interpretation of genius.

It was Herbert Spencer, the philosopher of evolution, who, while accepting Galton's notion of the inheritance of ability, maintained that social factors must also be taken into account. His basic postulate about society (and thus about History) was "that the character of the aggregate is determined by the character of the units" (1873, chap. 3, par. 1); yet he knew that the units also depend on the whole. It is not true, Spencer held, that genius will bloom no matter how poorly nourished. Beethoven, born of cannibal parents on a cannibal isle, would have achieved less than he actually did. At best his achievement would have been but relative to the current state of cannibal music. "Even were we to grant the absurd supposition that the genius of the great man does not depend on the antecedents furnished by the society he

is born in," said Spencer, "there would still be the quite sufficient facts that
he is powerless in the absence of material and mental accumulations which
his society inherits from the past, and that he is powerless in the absence of
the co-existing population, character, intelligence, and social arrangements"
(1873, chap. 2, par. 13). Spencer was arguing for the multiple causation of
achievements and events. Even if some one genius could have been a necessary cause for some particular historical event, he could hardly have been a
sufficient cause. He himself would be, moreover, the consequence of his own
antecedents, among which his ancestry would be but one of many items.
An Eroica Symphony written for drums by a Fiji Beethoven would have
differed greatly from the work which we know. It is thus clear that Tolstoy
and Spencer were making the same argument.

This naturalistic interpretation of history was part of the nineteenth-
century Zeitgeist. Personalism was on the way out then, although that fact
was not clear until later. To Darwin's, Galton's, and Spencer's voices were
added others. W. S. Jevons in his *Principles of Science* included a chapter on
the character of the experimentalist, a chapter in which he attempted to
reduce the discoverer to his attributes (1874, chap. 26). Grant Allen (1878)
supported Spencer. William James (1880) attacked Spencer and Grant Allen,
who replied (1881). The historian, John Fiske (1881), also replied to James.
Then James replied to them (1890).

William James was essentially a personalist. He never wholly accepted
naturalism or experimentalism in his psychology. In the late 1870's he used
Spencer as a text in Harvard courses because it gave his lectures point to
have someone with whom he could disagree. Thus James dissented from
Spencer's interpretation of genius, himself defending what Spencer had
called "the Great-Man theory." Spencer had complained that the Great-Man
theory was vague because it said nothing about the antecedents of genius nor
did it in any way account for the occurrence of genius. James hurled this
charge back. To hold that genius is the consequence of an enormous number
of undetermined and indeterminable antecedents, he said, is vaguer than to
recognize genius for what it is. James was coming to the rescue of the dignity
of man. He wanted to save man from too much naturalism, and a natural-
isticist, like a modern psychologist, cannot, of course, understand that.

In the present century we have had many studies of great men and of scientific eminence. Two outstanding books are Ostwald's *Grosse Männer* (1912),
which deals in detail with the lives of six great scientists and considers the
conditions of their productivity, and Lenard's *Grosse Naturforscher* (1929),
which gives accounts of the lives of sixty-five scientists. These books border
on personalism. They seek the conditions of genius, but they suggest that
the achievement of genius is much more than the means by which the Zeitgeist realizes itself. More recently both Sidney Hook (1943) and Eric Bentley
(1947) have re-created some of William James' nostalgia for a man of genius,

formed in the image of his Maker and not manufactured by mere circum-
stance.

On the whole, naturalism has been gaining ground. An important paper
was Kroeber's "The Superorganic" (1917, 196–208) which, in one place,
argued for the cultural determination of great achievement, argued by citing
instances of simultaneous independent discoveries. If half a dozen persons
invented telescopes in 1608 independently of each other, if Napier and Briggs
both invented logarithms in 1614 anticipated by the little known Bürgi in
1611, if Newton and Leibnitz discovered the calculus independently in the
1670's anticipated by Isaac Barrow, if D'Alibard identified lightning with
static electricity in 1752, just a month before Benjamin Franklin made his
famous experiment, if both Priestley and Scheele discovered oxygen in 1774,
may it not properly be argued that these discoveries depended, not primarily
upon the attributes of the great men who made the discoveries, but rather
upon the circumstances of the times, on the Zeitgeist, on Kroeber's "Superorganic"? The personalistic argument has been that the greatness of the man
determines the greatness of the discovery. The naturalistic argument inverts
the causal order; it is the greatness of the discovery which determines the
greatness of the discoverer. In either case *Great Men make Great Discoveries.*
Yet it may be that the Zeitgeist determines the Great Discovery and that he
who makes the discovery, the Zeitgeist's agent, is Great merely because the
times employed him. This theory reduces greatness from a cause to a symptom.

Kroeber's problem was tackled a little later by Ogburn and Thomas (1922).
They published a list of one hundred forty-eight instances of two or more
independent similar scientific discoveries or inventions, each pair or set of
which were nearly synchronous. Their items were not always well documented
and some appear to have been in error, but the total effect of the list is convincing. Discovery comes when the times are ready for it. Conant (1947) has
noted that it can hardly come before, or that, if made early—as was the case
with Mendel in 1870—there is apt to be no further advance so long as the
inertia of the Zeitgeist hinders progress in that direction.

There has been of late a lot of talk about the psychology of the scientist
and it is, of course, along naturalistic lines. Sometimes the problem of scientific originality is discussed and the frequency with which great discoveries
are anticipated is noted (Boring, 1927). Idhe (1948) has reiterated the argument of Ogburn and Thomas. Sarton (1937, 174–180), Conant (1947), and
Bernard Cohen (1948) have all been discussing how scientific thought progresses, whether continuously or by spurts, how it is facilitated or retarded
according as it is or is not in phase with the times, how a wrong theory can
be replaced only by a better substitute and is not driven out by contradictory
facts. This last is the *horror vacui* in scientific thought which Conant has
stressed. And then, of course, the sociologists are full of talk about cultural

determinations, which Toynbee (1933) has applied dramatically to the courses of civilizations. There is also Robert Warren's Penrose Lecture (1948) which suggests that the scientific age of the last four centuries may at last be closing and that a new New Learning, a fresh Renaissance, may be ready to emerge. These discussions bear on the main issue but do not advance it far. Our problem is more intimate, for we seek to know what happens in the mind of the Great Man at the moment when he is being the agent of Science in the emergence of a Great Discovery or a Great Achievement.

But first we must consider how discoveries and inventions are related to each other and so to the times in which they occur.

Advance of Knowledge

The advance of scientific knowledge is a complex social affair. It involves knowledge previously accumulated, modes of thought which become easy when current, individual research sustained by motives of which the investigator himself is apt to be unaware. All this action and interaction becomes clear if we lay down here a number of propositions, clarifying them by citing historical instances. Here then is a table of nine conditions for scientific progress or its failure.

A *discovery, an invention, an advance in knowledge is or may be.* . . .
1. *Dependent upon previous discovery.*
2. *Dependent upon the availability of new methods or instruments.*
3. *A specification of what was previously indefinite or unsubstantiated.*
4. *Synchronous with similar discovery, yet independent of it.*
5. *Derived from unconscious communication.*
6. *Distorted by prestige or promotion.*
7. *Derived principally by insight.*
8. *Derived from an accidental occurrence.*
9. *Prevented from realization by the Zeitgeist.*

These are catch-phrases. Now we can expand each of them into more formal propositions.

1. *A discovery is seen to all concerned to be an outgrowth of previous discovery.* This is the rule for a growing science and it is the relationship about which the histories of science principally concern themselves. Science is serial. The next idea or discovery has to come before the next idea but one or before the next discovery but one. Given the invention of a boat and of a steam engine, it requires only an insight into a new relationship to invent a steamboat. Wundt made the new physiological psychology about 1862 out of British empiricism and experimental sense-physiology, but he had to have the ingredients before he could compose the blend, and each component had

had its long history of development before it was ready for combination. It is these developments that Conant traces in his *On Understanding Science* (1947). There he shows the emergence and development of the concepts of the weight of the air and the spring of the air from Galileo in 1638 to Robert Boyle in 1666, and how Galvani's discovery in 1791 that a frog's leg will form the electrolyte of a battery if connected with two different metals led to the invention of the Voltaic pile in 1800 and the availability of direct currents thereafter. We need not labor this point. It is what everyone knows.

2. *Advance in knowledge is rapid when new methods or new instruments become available.* The building of telescopes in 1608 led to Galileo's constructing his in 1609 and his discovery of four of Jupiter's moons. That discovery upset theologically tempered science by showing that the Creator had exceeded the sacred number seven in his making of the celestial bodies, and later it provided the means for the measurement of the velocity of light. The improvement of the simple microscope in the latter part of the seventeenth century led to the discovery of bacteria and microorganisms, and the improvement of the compound microscope in the 1830's led to discovery of cell structure and the development of histology. Volta's invention of the battery, the invention of electromagnets and of the galvanometer, all in the early nineteenth century, made possible the study and measurement of the nerve impulse by du Bois-Reymond in the middle of the century and the invention of many other electrical instruments, like the chronograph and the chronoscope. The astronomers could measure absolute reaction times when they had these electrical devices. Similarly in the present century the development of the electronic tube has revolutionized, not only psychoacoustics, but also all sorts of laboratory work in physics, physiology, and psychology. This point too is obvious.

3. *Often a discovery or an advance consists in specifying what was formerly vague or in verifying what formerly rested on insufficient evidence.* This category cannot be rigorously applied to the particular case because it excludes those cases where the discoverer was unaware that he had been anticipated, the cases of the next two groups. That Newton's invention of the calculus was independent of Leibnitz's everyone agrees, but what about the contribution of Newton's teacher, Isaac Barrow? Johannes Müller's doctrine of specific nerve energies of 1838 was anticipated in various ways by John Locke in 1690, Thomas Young in 1801, and Charles Bell in 1811. It is quite certain that Müller did not know about Bell, but what about the others? Perhaps this is a case of the Zeitgeist's carrying along through a century and a half. There are, however, some clear cases. Helmholtz in 1852 definitely did know Thomas Young's color theory of 1801, and Helmholtz made Young's theory important by developing it and giving it experimental stability. The Gestalt psychologists came ultimately to recognize their debt to von Ehrenfels' discussion of *Gestaltqualität* in 1890, though they never acknowledged William

James' similar line of thought which also belongs to 1890. Köhler's doctrine of isomorphism between brain pattern and perceptual pattern has had a long history, and Köhler, when he first formulated his views, was aware of what G. E. Müller has said in 1896. In both of these cases the later formulation was clearer and more specific than the earlier ones and led to experimental programs and tests, but the progress of thought was nevertheless essentially continuous. There were no huge leaps.

4. *Two or more discoveries of the same fact are entirely, as far as can be determined, independent. They may be and often are synchronous.* These are the cases which constitute the chief evidence for the operation of the Zeitgeist, the "Superorganic." If Newton had not discovered and promoted the calculus, Leibnitz would have, or conversely, so runs this argument. If Bürgi failed to give logarithms to mathematics, there were both Napier and Briggs ready to do the Zeitgeist's bidding. The British speak of Boyle's Law, the French of Mariotte's. Legendre described the principle of least squares in 1806, Gauss in 1809, and both probably used the principle before they described it. Charles Bell in 1811 and Magendie in 1822 on the law of the spinal nerve roots: that was a famous controversy. Alfred Russell Wallace and Charles Darwin on the principle of natural selection: that was a famous gentlemen's agreement about the independence of their separate similar thinkings. Adams and Leverrier, each calculating the existence of the planet Neptune in 1845: it was a natural calculation to make just then. Gray and Bell each inventing the telephone in 1876 and fighting afterward over the patent rights. James in 1884 and Lange in 1887, each with the same physiological theory of emotion. Mach in 1886 and Avenarius in 1888, each with what they agreed was the same epistemological theory of the relation of mind to matter. Nearly all the others of Ogburn and Thomas' illustrations (1922) can go in here. You cannot get away from the fact that the times have something to do with discovery, something more than the fact that discovery must wait upon the necessarily antecedent discoveries.

5. *Apparently independent discoveries may nevertheless depend on some degree of unconscious communication.* The human mind being as it is, these cases must occur, but it is hard to prove them. Was Newton influenced in the calculus by Isaac Barrow? Why did Titchener, when he formulated the context theory of meaning in 1909, feel that he was making so original a contribution when the basic relation had been noted by Bishop Berkeley in 1709? Titchener knew his British associationists and he was being just exactly two centuries late; yet he never seemed to realize this fact.

Unconscious plagiarism also belongs in this class. Was Alexander Walker one such? When Bell and Magendie were disputing priorities about the law of the spinal nerve roots, Walker claimed priority over both, saying that he had lectured on the law in 1809, two years before Bell published, thirteen before Magendie. It happens that Walker got the specification of the spinal roots reversed and his claim is now treated only with amusement, but what was going on in his mind? Had he heard Bell lecture? Could he have been faking or was this a case of unconscious as well as faulty assimilation?

6. *Prestige, authority and good promotion may distort the historical record so that of two discoverers the more famous or more aggressive man gets the greater credit.* Prestige is autocatalytic. Greatness tends to build itself up. Fame is outfitted with positive feed-back. But promotion helps. Magendie was a better promoter than Bell and for a while he eclipsed Bell in their argument. Johannes Müller was a better promoter than Bell, and the doctrine of specific nerve energies was known as Müller's until long after the death of both men, in fact until a champion for Bell belatedly appeared. After all, the doctrine with that name was Müller's, for Bell gave it no name and did not elaborate it as a doctrine. He thought the principle was obvious. It was Müller who built the obvious up into a pronouncement. Broca had an aphasic patient die on his hands in 1862. At once he examined the brain, found deterioration in the left frontal convolutions, reported the matter and presented the brain in alcohol to the Société d'Anthropologie. So dramatically was the announcement made that Broca's speech center was turned into a scientific fact. Broca's anticipators, Bouillaud and Dax, never had a chance to get their names attached to this fact. Bouillaud, as a matter of fact, was out of phase with the Zeitgeist, for he made his discovery in 1825, when exact localization in the brain had been made unpopular by Gall's phrenology and by Flourens' excellent experiments which showed common functioning of large regions of the brain.

We can go on. The new experimental psychology was founded by Wilhelm Wundt with all the arts of founding a science—the writing of the new epistemological formula, the publication of the authoritative handbook of the new science and the keeping of it up-to-date through six editions through twenty-seven years, the establishment of the world's first formal research laboratory, the publishing of the world's first journal of experimental psychology, propaganda, controversy, argument, research, Ph.D. students scattered abroad in Europe and America—there you have the technique of founding a science. But Wundt did not create the science. Fechner and Helmholtz had as much claim to that, and astute observers say that the new psychology was born of the Zeitgeist. Wundt was a vigorous agent of what the times were about, a prophet, as it were; but prophets expound the truth, they do not make it.

7. *Exceptional insight may lead to an original discovery which has not been anticipated by others and which is relatively independent of the times.* Presumably no discovery is ever entirely independent of the times but there are degrees of independence and originality. Newton's theory of color was one such instance, his discovery that white light is a mixture of colored lights. We feel that that discovery was not all ready to be made by someone else

if Newton had failed, because Newton's senior colleagues in the Royal Society, when they read Newton's letter on the subject in 1672, ridiculed the absurdity that white can be a mixture of colors. Yet suppose that Newton had reacted to the ridicule, had abandoned his plan to write an *Opticks* to remain satisfied with the *Principia*. Do we think that no one would have found out about white light's being a mixture of homogeneous lights? That seems quite impossible. The discovery could in that case have waited a century, but late in the eighteenth century the times would surely have created some necessity for this discovery and it would have been made. Would the Zeitgeist have waited for Thomas Young, or is that question prompted by the faith that personal genius is half the reason for discovery and the Zeitgeist only the other half?

Perhaps the best example of insight is Fermat, an excellent example because the insights of his genius have not fully been equalled since. The story about Fermat is that he noted on the margins of his copy of Diophantus his comments about solutions of certain theorems. Not always did he give the solution but mathematicians since 1637 have been able to prove all his assertions right except one. That is Fermat's "last theorem," that $x^n + y^n = a^n$ can be true for whole numbers only when n is not greater than 2, as in $3^2 + 4^2 = 5^2$. Fermat wrote in the margin that he knew a splendid proof but had no space there to write it down, and mathematicians believe him because he has been proved right in every other case. In that insight of Fermat's there is something which was not an inevitable product of the Zeitgeist, because it did not happen again and the passage of the centuries did not force a discoverer to come on the stage of science and perform his act. The naturalistic theory has its place for Great Men, for not all brains are alike.

8. *An accident may lead to a discovery.* This is Conant's case of the "happy accident." Presumably the accident may play the same role as insight, and, as we shall see presently, insight works by trial and error. There may be no case so dramatic as Fermat's, a case where an accident led to an original discovery which might otherwise have remained unknown for centuries, but there are lesser instances. Galvani discovered the electrical properties of frogs' legs because, when the legs were set up in certain ways, thunder storms made them twitch. Oersted is said to have discovered the magnetic field of the electric current during a lecture demonstration. Becquerel in 1896 left a uranium compound on a covered photographic plate and found later that it had affected the plate. That was the discovery of radioactivity. There are many other instances. A new fact is a new relationship, and these relationships can first be formed in the mind by insight or in nature by chance. In the latter case there has to be an insightful mind to note the relationship and to make use of its significance.

9. *A discovery or an advance in knowledge may be prevented from accept-*

ance or delayed in acceptance when it runs counter to conventional thought.
This is the inertia of the Zeitgeist, the way in which it slows or prevents
progress. Almost never, says Conant, will contradictory facts drive out an old
theory. It takes a new theory to displace an old. That is because convention
supports the old theory in the face of contradiction. When Kepler correctly
described the physics of the eye, noting that the crystalline body must be a
lens and that it would form an inverted image of the external world on the
sensitive retina at the back of the eye, he was puzzled as to how we see rightside up when the retinal image is upside down. He was still thinking of the
mind as a perceiving little man within the head, one who looks at the images
and impressions which the nerves bring to it. Kepler wrote in 1604. By 1691
Molyneux had the right answer, that *up* and *down* are relative and that the
brain does not look at the retina but perceives only the relationship. Berkeley
had the right answer in 1709. Johannes Müller had it in 1826, Helmholtz in
1866. Each of these men had to solve the problem over again and try to convince his audience for no better reason than that conventional theory about
the mind has always been personalistic and that only with difficulty can a
man come to think of his perceptions as neural responses and not as contact
with an actual object. For centuries now the Zeitgeist has favored the personalistic conception of mind.

Let that end our macroscopic survey of the ways in which the discovery
by one man is dependent upon the discoveries and thought of others. Now
let us enquire what goes on at the microscopic level, in the intimacy of the
consciousness of the Great Man.

Attributes of Greatness

It becomes plain that we have now rescued the Great Man from the toils
of the Zeitgeist without abandoning naturalism. The Great Man is a natural
object, a brain, if you please. And the events in that brain are natural events,
which depend upon the properties of the brain and the conditions, physical
and social, which instigate its particular actions. Not all brains are alike. Apes
have brains but no good science. Nor are all human brains alike. There are
Great Men, but they operate with different degrees of native ability under
the limitations and the facilitations of the situations in which they find themselves. The Zeitgeist at any time facilitates such mental activities as are consistent with its conventional habits and attitudes, and it hinders what is contrary to conventional thought or is otherwise out of phase with the times.

In a sense it is true that originality in the Great Man varies with the degree
to which his thought is independent of the Zeitgeist, but such originality is
only part of what makes the Great Man great. If he is too far out of phase
with the Zeitgeist, the world may not listen to his message and he may die in

obscurity. Perhaps he can overcome the resistance of the Zeitgeist by well chosen promotion which will gain acceptance for his revolutionary ideas, but then he needs, not only originality, but also energy, aggression, practical wisdom, and the will to compete. Or else he needs a sponsor, who may indeed be a posthumous sponsor, to promote his theories and point out their significance. So originality may merit Fame, and Fame go actually only to Recognized Originality. Galton ran into that difficulty in 1869 when he sought to use Reputation as a measure of Genius. Originality may measure genius, but the Great Man requires recognition in order to be great.

It thus appears that there are certain extrinsic attributes of greatness and we may mention three.

(1) The great discovery cannot occur until the necessary *antecedent discoveries* have been made. Discovery is serial and no amount of originality will enable a man to base an advance in knowledge on previous ignorance when what he needs is previous knowledge.

(2) Being *in phase with the Zeitgeist* helps the attainment of greatness, even if it lessens the degree of genius required. Presumably the Zeitgeist effectively prevents some discoveries, some revolutionary thoughts, but it must be regarded more as an accelerator and a brake than as furnishing necessary or sufficient conditions for discovery.

(3) And then varying degrees of *promotion* are required in order to gain acceptance for new facts or attention to them. If the promotion is posthumous—like De Vries' promotion of Mendel's discoveries—the greatness may also be posthumous. When greatness occurs *in vivo*, unpromoted by either the Zeitgeist or an enthusiastic colleague, then it is apt to be due to self-promotion, and we find ourselves adding *aggressiveness* to the list of the attributes of the Great Man. It is not necessary to cite here the names of scientists who have believed in their own correctness and who have said what they believed about themselves. We have already noted how Wundt brought all the means of promotion to bear on the establishment of the new experimental psychology. His vigor in controversy, his unrepressed conviction of his own correctness, were not, in spite of their force, self-validating.

When we turn our attention to the more important intrinsic attributes of greatness, it becomes obvious that the specifications of genius must be made in respect of *insight* and *motivation*. We need first, however, to consider the nature of insight and how it enters into original thinking.

Insight

The ape, unable to reach the banana through the bars of his cage with either of the short sticks in his possession, finds by accident that the two sticks fit together like a fishing rod to make one long stick, pauses, looks toward the

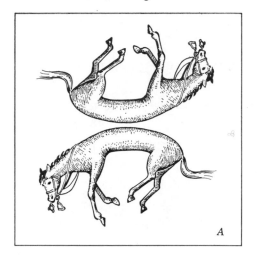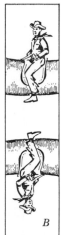

Fig. 1. Horse-and-rider puzzle. Problem: to place the riders astride the horses right side up. [From M. Scheerer, K. Goldstein, and E. G. Boring (1941).]

banana, back at the newly acquired long stick, rushes over and rakes the banana in. That is *insight*. Insight is the perception of a novel relationship. It can occur in thought with respect to absent objects, and then visualization is useful but not always essential. Let us examine three instances.

In Fig. 1 we have two separate pictures, A and B, each mounted on cardboard. The problem is to arrange these two pieces with respect to each other so that the two riders will be astride the two horses. Trial generally leads to errors. The riders are upside down and they do not fit in properly. The solution generally comes by chance manipulation or by the solver's being shown what to do, but once he sees the trick, once insight occurs, he has learned the problem permanently.

The problem is solved by turning the strip B through 90 degrees with respect to picture A so as to give the solution shown in Fig. 2. In Fig. 2 the forelegs of one horse in Fig. 1 are combined with the hind legs of the other horse. It is easy to see how predisposition prevents the solution of this simple problem. When you wish to have a horse, you do not pick up the essential parts from two different animals—not often.

The horse and rider problem is usually solved by the trial and error of manipulation, but the solution of the ring problem is usually a case of ideational trial and error. You work by vicarious trial and error (in Tolman's phrase), by hypothesis and the thought experiment. Figure 3 shows the device for the ring problem. The block P will not pass through either of the rings, R and S, nor will either ring pass through the hole Q. The problem is to get both rings on one loop. Able minds have puzzled for hours over this solution.

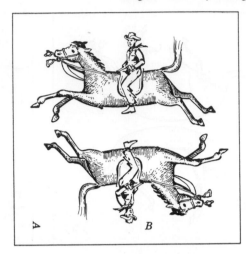

Fig. 2. Horse-and-rider puzzle. Solution of problem in Fig. 1.

The correct solution is rational. The solver sees that to get the ring S on the loop ABC, S must be passed along the cord to H, through the hole Q at G, around the loop FE, back through the hole to D and C, a series of events which puts both S and R on the loop ABC. This reasoning is correct except for the difficulty that the ring S will not pass through the hole Q. At that point the solver is frustrated, but there can come to him the needed insight. Usually it comes suddenly.

The solver sees that the ring is to pass through the hole only in order to be passed around the loop on the other side of the hole and then to be brought back to the side where it was at first. The ring will not, however, go through the hole. Nevertheless, since the ring would go through the hole only in order to go around the loop and then to come back again, there is the possibility—this is the moment of insight—of pulling the loop through the hole, letting the ring go around it, and then pulling the loop back where it belongs. That works. The cord may seem to get tangled in the process, but eventually everything straightens out and the rings are found side by side on the same loop.

This insight comes near to the sort of creative process which the able scientist uses. The insight in Figs. 1 and 2 resembles, on the other hand, discovery by "happy accident."

As a rule the investigator does not make his discovery with a single insight, but with a series of hypotheses which are trial-insights and which may, any one of them, be seen to be in error, sometimes as soon as it is formed, sometimes only after its consequences have been investigated. The process of dis-

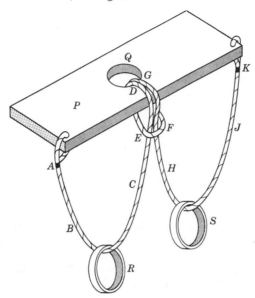

Fig. 3. Ring puzzle. Problem: to place both rings together on the same loop. [After Max Wertheimer, ca. 1941, presumably unpublished.]

covery thus comes to resemble the process of trial and error by which the rat discovers his food in the maze, except that there is in science more vicarious trial and error (thought experimenting) and less physical exploration of the blind alleys. The rat starts out at random or follows a hunch, tries an alley, abandons it when he finds it blind, tries another, keeps on by trial and error until he finds food. The investigator forms an hypothesis, a tentative insight, tries it out in thought or experiment, abandons it when he perceives it wrong, goes on to another if the first has produced progress, and finally reaches some success which is his goal or else surrenders frustrated. The analogy to this process we get in the block problem.

Figure 4 shows five blocks, A, B, C, D and E, piled on top of one another, always a smaller on top of a larger, and it shows three possible places where the blocks may be placed, I, II, and III. The blocks must be moved one at a time, placed only in one of these three positions, and never a larger block on top of a smaller. The pile of blocks is initially in position I, and the problem is to move them to position III in the minimal number of moves, and ultimately to determine the law of least action. Here is the way the insights generally go when they lead to success.

(a) The solver decides first to learn how to work with fewer than five blocks. If he uses only one block A, insight into the solution is instant. You move A from I to III. It takes one move. The problem is solved.

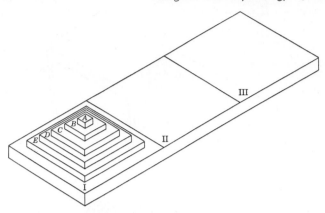

Fig. 4. Block problem. To move the pile of blocks from I to III, one block at a time, without placing a larger block on top of a smaller or placing any block in a position other than I, II, or III; and to make the number of moves a minimum; and to determine the rule of moving and the formula for the minimal number of moves with any number of blocks. [After J. C. Peterson, cited by W. S. Hunter (1928).]

(*b*) With two blocks, A and B, it takes three moves. Insight shows at once what to do. You move A from I to II, B from I to III, then A from II and III on top of B.

(*c*) With three and four blocks immediate insight usually breaks down, but the solver gets by induction from his trials, errors and success this rule: If *n*, the number of blocks is odd, the top block must be moved first to the

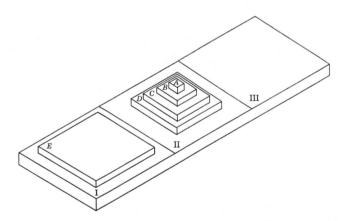

Fig. 5. Block problem. Partial solution. The problem has been solved for four blocks A to D which have been moved from I to II. It is still necessary to move the block E from I to III, and then to repeat the four-block solution in moving the blocks A to D from I to III on top of E. Thus N for 5 blocks = (N for 4 blocks) + 1 + (N for 4 blocks), and $N_n = 2N_{n-1} + 1$.

goal position (III), whereas, if n is even, then the top block must be moved first to the other position (II). This is a correct but unsatisfactory hypothesis. It is not clear why it is true.

(d) The next insight consists in seeing the relation of the problem for n blocks to the problem for $n - 1$ blocks. Figure 5 shows a stage of the solution of the problem of Fig. 4. To move the five blocks from I to III, as required in Fig. 4, you must first move the top four blocks from I to II. Then you can move E to III, and then the four blocks from II to III. If N_n is the minimal moves for n blocks, then N_5 is N_4, plus the move of E from I to III, plus another N_4; which is to say,

$$N_5 = N_4 + 1 + N_4 = 2N_4 + 1$$

or, more generally,

$$N_n = 2N_{n-1} + 1 \quad \dots \dots \dots \dots \dots \dots \dots \dots \dots \dots \dots (1)$$

(e) The solver is now equipped to solve the problem for any n, but he still lacks the general formula for N_n. If he is mathematically minded he derives it from (1) above. More often he writes down N for many small n's and induces the rule. Thus he finds from (1) or by applying the rules and counting actual moves:

$$
\begin{array}{ccccccccc}
n = 1 & 2 & 3 & 4 & 5 & 6 & 7 & & n \\
N = 1 & 3 & 7 & 15 & 31 & 63 & 127 & & (2^n - 1)
\end{array}
$$

which gives

$$N_n = 2^n - 1 \quad \dots \dots \dots \dots \dots \dots \dots \dots \dots \dots \dots \dots (2)$$

The problem has been solved by a series of insights. It was not solved by manipulative trial and error.

The history of science contains many instances of crucial insights, each of which brought about a great advance in knowledge and was had by a Great Man, often at a specified time. Many of the instances appear to belong to the folklore of science and not to be authenticated, but even the legends illustrate the point. Whether he did or not, it is perfectly possible that Archimedes could have conceived the hydrostatic principle in his bath with such assurance that he leaped out and rushed off crying, "Eureka!" without stopping to make an experimental test or two. That would have been easier under the rationalistic Zeitgeist of Greece than under modern empiricism, but we must not forget that theoretical physicists today accomplish wonders without a laboratory (Bell, 1937, 29). Descartes' second dream on the night of November 10, 1610, is supposed to have given him the insight into applying algebra to geometry, and thus the basic conception of analytic geometry —although just what form the insight took we do not know (Bell, 39 f.). It is undoubtedly true that Galileo's first insight into the law of the pendulum occurred as he watched the swinging lamps in the Cathedral at Pisa, noting that the time of the swing depended more on the length of the suspension than on the amplitude of the swing (Wolf, 1935, 43 f.). Voltaire's story of Newton and the apple is held to be apocryphal, but there must have been some moment when Newton first saw that the moon could be held in its orbit because its constant fall toward the earth was balanced off against its constant centrifugal departure from the earth (Bell, 105 f.; Wolf, 149 f.). William Hamilton's prediction of the principle of conical refraction was not the result of an instant of insight but the consequence of mathematical reasoning, as was Clerk Maxwell's prediction of the nature of electromagnetic waves. These well authenticated instances represent theoretical physics at its best. The empiricists verified the predictions later, but the genius lay in the prediction (Bell, 350 f.). Comparable to Descartes' dream and better specified was Fechner's reverie in bed on the morning of October 22, 1850, when he thought he saw how to resolve the conflict between materialism and spiritualism by measuring the magnitude of an immaterial sensation in terms of a material stimulus. From that insight was born psychophysics and a large portion of early experimental psychology (Fechner, 1860, 2, 553 f.). A recent instance is related about an insight of Max Wertheimer, an idea which began the whole movement of Gestalt psychology. Wertheimer was in the train going from Vienna to the Rhineland in the summer of 1910 when an idea came to him with such force that he got off the train at Frankfurt, bought a toy stroboscope, and went to his hotel room to experiment on seen movement. He stayed on at Frankfurt for two years, completing those now famous experiments on perceived movement and the phi-phenomenon which generated a whole new school of German experimental psychology (Newman, 1944, 431 f.).

While it would be interesting to know just what happens in the mind of the Great Man when he has the crucial insight, it is not certain that precise information would greatly increase our knowledge of the attributes of greatness. Some of these insights are legendary and have been dramatized in the telling and retelling. It is also true that a man who has had an insight seldom knows just what occurred and may be so moved by enthusiasm for his sudden revelation that his descriptive objectivity is impaired. Descartes' dream and Fechner's early morning reverie were both great emotional experiences to their possessors, were indeed revelations of the order of conversions, and both these great men may have attached more importance to the moment of alleged insight than the facts, if they could but be known, would warrant. Enthusiasm, as we have already remarked, is not self-validating. Take the simple controlled insight of seeing how the ring puzzle (Fig. 3) is solved. Who is there, that has had that insight, and can say *how* it occurred? At one moment you are frustrated. Then, if you are a visualizer, there is a breathless instant in which you see the loop being pulled through the hole and you wonder if that might not carry the solution, and then, suddenly, you see that it *is* the solution, that the ring can pass around the loop if the loop is brought through the hole to the ring. But to know all that is not to say *how* insight occurs, much less to say *why*. There is still an adventitious leap from nothing to something, an unconscious leap whose continuity and causes remain hidden in the nervous system.

Attributes of Genius

We have mentioned (1) previous knowledge, (2) the Zeitgeist, and (3) promotion as extrinsic factors contributing to greatness. We may now continue the list with the intrinsic attributes of greatness and thus also of genius.

(4) Certainly *erudition* is a property of those brains which have many correct and successful insights. Any bit of information may turn out to be unexpectedly relevant and nothing short of erudition provides enough material for the unpredictable requirements of genius. When Clerk Maxwell was explaining how Faraday got the electric current to flow continuously through a circuit when he moved a wire of the circuit through the magnetic field, how Faraday managed that effect by reversing the terminals of the outside circuit whenever he had to reverse the movement of the wire to shift it back through the field, Maxwell remarked that the invention was like Cyrus' when he had wished to get his army across the Euphrates. Cyrus sent his engineers upstream to alter the course of the Euphrates so that it would flow behind the army. If only Faraday, the discoverer, had had that insight instead of Maxwell, the biographer, we would have seen how an advance in physics can depend on historical knowledge.

Expertness is limited erudition, and often one kind of expertness will transfer to a problem in another field. The man who knows about rope tricks is all ready to solve the ring puzzle (Fig. 3). The boy who saw at once that 39 times 41 is 1599 had the insight that 39×41 is $(40 - 1)(40 + 1)$, which is $40^2 - 1^2 = 1600 - 1$; but he had to know algebra or he could not have had the insight. He could also have realized, with the same insight, that $(10m + n)(10m - n)$ is $100m^2 - n^2$, that $94 \times 86 = 8100 - 16 = 8084$.

It is said that a genius needs a *good memory* and there are, of course, individual differences in memory. Erudition, however, must include good memory. He who learns and forgets is not erudite.

(5) There is no good word with which to label interest in novel relations. We might perhaps call it *xenophilia*, love of the strange, the unexpected, the unconventional. Named or unnamed, that set or attitude must constitute a variable of the personality. The genius is constantly on the alert for what is new. The conventional irks him; the novel attracts him. He is the supreme punster because he is always bringing the previously unrelated together and

trying out the effect of combining them. Treating geometry with algebra was an Olympic pun, a mating of the previously unrelated to create, actually, analytical geometry, that indispensable servant of science and mathematics. Perhaps this attitude of being receptive to oddly novel relationships can be learned in youth or perhaps it has to be established adventitiously in infancy. We do not know. Certainly some persons delight in bringing the unusual together and others do not. Certainly the insights of genius, as of the puzzle solver, are favored by the xenophilic attitude.

It has been said that *availability of memory traces* is an attribute of genius, but that trait is either good memory or a large repertoire of knowledge or this special receptivity to novel relations. It is scarcely something new.

(6) V*isualization* is a special instrument of thought. People vary in respect of it and the capacity can be improved by training. It is useful in detailed memory, in insight into spatial or mechanical relationships, and thus into all logical relationships that can be represented by spatial design. It is not a *sine qua non* of many intellectual operations, but it is a natural tool, and the genius, who cannot visualize when he needs to, must have some other qualities to make up for his lack.

There are also the *motivational factors* which enter into genius.

(7) *Alertness* is one. Genius may not be an "infinite capacity for taking pains," but neither is it lazy nor lethargic. Nor is it reverberatory. It moves on restlessly to new situations.

(8) Nor does genius—or so it seems to me, for there is no scientific evidence for this point—gather wool. Most consciousness—as the writers about the stream-of-consciousness have shown—is full of wool gathering, the silly eddies of thought which retard the main current, the futile sallies up a blind alley once and then back and up the same alley once again. It is not true that the genius thinks faster per second than the ordinary man, or even per minute. Nervous impulses work for everybody at the same rate. But the genius seems to do more effective thinking per year and often per hour. How does he manage that? By good steering. By sticking to the goal. By not stopping to rest. By avoiding the irrelevant when it becomes known for what it is. By perceiving mistakes clearly and then not repeating them. In other words, inefficient thinking may proceed at the same rate as efficient thinking and yet take longer to reach the same goal. When Sherlock Holmes had observed that the killer could not have left the room, he did not waste time in doubting his own sound observations. He accepted his own conclusion that the killer was still in the room, improbable as that seemed, and sure enough, with the help of Conan Doyle, Holmes was right, for he was a genius.

Do we need a name for this steady directedness of purpose which keeps the genius still on the track while forging ahead? It is more than persistence. It consists in entertaining and assessing the novel, forging ahead, but keeping one purpose to the fore. Would *incidence* do for a name? This kind of thinking aims straight, though it can be deflected with reason.

Certainly this list of attributes must be far from complete. The question of what makes thought creative has had considerable attention, yet not nearly enough. We are now in the United States "training," as we say, thousands of young scientists. We teach them facts. We practice them in the use of methods. We endeavor, in ways not too clearly understood, to inculcate certain attitudes in them. And then, having done our best, we wonder why so seldom the spark of originality is found—for we never expect to uncover the flame of genius. Perhaps this *plus*, which is neither prevented nor assured by training, is not got by training at all but can only be captured by selection on its adventitious occurrence. Or perhaps, on the other hand, it could be created in young men if only its nature were better understood. We need to know better than we do now what makes Great Men great. It is not all the Zeitgeist. Some brains are better than others. Why? Does the difference lie in training? Do we know how to make the better brains or where to find them? Perpetually we tinker with curricula for making poor brains good, and yet we do not know just what it is that we should like to achieve, what the attributes of much-wanted Genius are.

Whatever the final description, I suggest that *insight* and *motivation* are satisfactory class names for two sets of parameters which are the dimensions along which civilization will be enlarged or lost. Carlyle was partly right. The History of Civilization is the history of the operation of Genius. We have, have had, and must have Great Men, even though no one of them could have arrived without the benefit of his Zeitgeist.

The Problem of Originality in Science

🝫🝫🝫🝫🝫🝫🝫🝫🝫🝫🝫🝫🝫🝫🝫🝫🝫🝫🝫🝫🝫🝫🝫🝫🝫🝫🝫🝫🝫🝫🝫🝫🝫🝫🝫🝫🝫 1927

O F all scientists the psychologist ought to be the one who is best prepared to take a knowing account of the personal equation as it enters into psychology and thus to understand the history of his science, for the history of science is primarily a history of thought, and the modes of human thought are something that a psychologist ought to understand. Yet psychologists, both in polemical argument and in historical evaluation, are apt to be quite uncritical of personal and mental factors that are essential to an understanding of the situation.

This unpsychological nature of psychological criticism shows clearly in the perpetual attempt to assign credit for discoveries or for new and original theories and systematic conceptions. Was Fechner or Wundt or someone else the 'father' or 'founder' of experimental psychology? Or was Fechner the 'father' and Wundt the 'founder'? Did Wundt found the first psychological laboratory at Leipzig in 1879 or was the cigar-box of tuning-forks under Stumpf's arm an earlier laboratory? Did Stanley Hall found the first laboratory in America at Johns Hopkins in 1883 or was James' room at Harvard in the seventies with the frog-rotator, the charts, and a few other things the first? It is with this matter of *originality* that I wish to deal, and I have chosen my examples from the history of physiological psychology.[1]

Now for all that has been said about creative imagination I take it that psychologists are pretty well agreed that thought is seldom strikingly discontinuous and that novelty in thought arises normally in a deliberate process of development and, even when it seems to be abrupt (as in wit), is largely a function of the past psychological history of the individual. If this picture is true of the individual, it must also be true of the genealogical group which contains him. Scientific thought is the thoughts of scientists, where one man takes both from others and from his own past, selects, and perhaps by novel

Reprinted with permission from *The American Journal of Psychology*, 1927, **39,** 70–90.

combination creates. "The stream of consciousness is sensibly continuous" in the history of thought as well as in the thinking of an individual. Certainly the historian is impressed by the fact that almost never does an idea seem entirely new. If it is a great idea that has helped to make a name or a date great, he looks for its previous occurrences. Generally he finds them. Not always can he be sure that the early instances actually fathered the great emergence, but often, when he is not sure of the fact of inheritance, he is also not sure of its absence. The bases of one's own present thought are often indeterminate; how much more difficult to form a judgment of the thought of another ten or a hundred years ago! Thus the historian may come to suspect every case of apparent originality. If he realizes, however, the tedious process by which thought develops, and by which novelty, after flitting about for years in indirect vision, is finally fixed for a brief space in the fovea of science (new thoughts do not occur; they hardly emerge even; they evolve), then he becomes aware of the grounds for his suspicion.

With this view of scientific evolution, what becomes of the 'fathers' and 'founders' in science? It is my intention to remind the reader by a few psychologists' instances, that the 'fathers' are necessarily also 'sons' and that the 'founders' are very apt to be 'promoters.'

The Specific Energies of Nerves. Right or wrong this doctrine has played a very important rôle in the history of physiological psychology. Helmholtz is said to have attached to it the importance within physiology that is given to the law of gravitation within physics. It lies at the bottom of Helmholtz' theories of vision and hearing and of Hering's theory of vision; it set the problem and method for the discovery of sensory spots on the skin in the eighties; it is the only generally accepted theory of sensory quality that we have ever had; and in general it supports and implies the projection theory of the nervous system and the theory of brain centers that have been orthodox gospel at the end of the last century and the beginning of the present. There is no doubt about its importance. How much of this credit should we give to Johannes Müller?

Sir Charles Bell is the other posthumous claimant for the origination of this theory. Bell (1811) privately printed "for the observation of his friends" one hundred copies of a little pamphlet of less than six thousand words, entitled "Idea of a New Anatomy of the Brain." It was circulated privately and was little known until reprinted in 1869 (and again in 1911). It contains the original statement of Bell's law (or Magendie's, for this is another controversy for priority) of the sensory and motor functions of the spinal nerve roots; but it also contains a discussion of sensory nerves which anticipates almost every statement that is essential to Müller's doctrine of the specific energy of nerves.

Müller published first (1826*a*, 44–45; 1826*b*, 6–9) in connection with his studies on the physiology of vision, but the view hardly gained the status of a 'doctrine' until his elaborate exposition and the formulation of the ten laws in the *Handbuch* (1838). Here Müller's exposition occupies more than six times as much space as Bell's.

In mere point of time Bell was first. However, the theory has always been referred to Müller and, in contradistinction to its extension by Helmholtz, it has sometimes been called the Müllerian doctrine. Müller does not refer to Bell in this connection, although he knew Bell's work. Whose theory is it? It is plain, I think, that the answer cannot be categorical. Bell was first in time, but he may not have been the psychological ancestor. Müller is so honest in giving priority to Marshall Hall in the case of the reflex, in spite of his own independent work, that I do not believe that he knowingly got the doctrine from Bell (Carmichael, 1926*b*, 198–203). In fact, it is only when one knows Müller that one can easily see the full significance of Bell's remarks. What Müller certainly did was to formulate the theory, to 'promote' it, to give it a complete statement and a systematic setting, to insist upon it, and to lend it the authority of his own immediate personal influence and the equally great influence of his *Handbuch*. He is certainly responsible for the 'doctrine' as a doctrine, and to call it the Müllerian theory is not so greatly to falsify history. Bell's account of these same facts was too casual, too obscure, seemingly of too little importance to its author, for Bell to insist upon the importance of the view as did Müller.

Nevertheless there still remains the question as to whether the view was psychologically original in Müller's thought, even though it had been less positively stated earlier. This is a difficult question to answer from the documents; still I think some light will be thrown upon it if we shift the ground and enquire: Was the theory original with Bell?

To the modern reader, who does not have to combat the common sense of physiology of the early nineteenth century, Müller's ten laws and exposition seem verbose and repetitious. The laws seem to reduce to seven fundamental principles, and the case for Bell's priority can be founded on the fact that for Müller's extended treatment of each principle a concise statement to the same effect (sometimes only a sentence) can be found in Bell. Let us consider these principles separately.

(*a*) The first and fundamental principle is that we are directly aware, not of objects, but of our nerves themselves; that is to say, the nerves are intermediates between perceived objects and the mind and thus impose their own characteristics upon the mind. There is, however, nothing new in the idea that the nerves are intermediaries between the external world and the brain; that had been said by Herophilus and Erasistratus (ca. 250 B.C.) and had been common doctrine since Galen (ca. 200 A.D.). That the nerves thus impose their own nature on the mind is a necessary consequence of the materialistic view of immediate causes and of the brain as the organ of the mind. Epistemologically this principle in Müller has been characterized as "a fruit of the anthropocentric standpoint, as the newer philosophy from Descartes down to Kant and Fichte has developed it," and also as the mere "physiological counterpart of a Kantian category." If we would transfer Müller's priority to Bell, it is irrelevant to remark that Bell was probably but little influenced by Kant, though Kant died in 1804. We do not have to go to the Continent. This principle is plain in Locke's doctrine of the secondary qualities (1690) and in the psychophysiology of Hartley (1749). It is essentially the physiological mechanism for English Empiricism. Bell may not have been interested in British philosophy but it would be strange if he could remain innocent of its influence two centuries after Locke. Philosophy becomes common sense slowly, but, when it persists within philosophy itself, inevitably.

(*b*) The second principle is that there are at least five kinds of nerves and that each imposes its specific energy or quality upon the mind. Is this principle after all so very much more than Aristotle's doctrine of the five sense-qualities, added to the modern view of the nerves? Vision has for its sense-quality color, hearing has sound, and so on; such is Aristotle's doctrine. It would seem almost that Bell and Müller had returned to Aristotle and to the obvious fact that one sees with the eyes, hears with the ears, and feels with the skin; and that the return was difficult only because of the well-intrenched but less obvious doctrine of the nerves as indifferent, passive conductors.

(*c*) The third point of the doctrine asserts that the same stimulus affecting different nerves gives rise to different qualities appropriate to the particular nerves, and conversely that different stimuli affecting the same nerve give rise only to the peculiar quality for that nerve. It is hardly more than the formulation of the evidence for the first two principles. Müller himself believed in the antiquity of this notion and cited Plato, Aristotle, and Spinoza in support. Both Bell and Müller drew instances from common sense (e.g., the colors seen on pressing the eye-ball) and from recent physiological experiment. Volta, the inventor in 1800 of the Voltaic pile and thus in a sense of the electric current, had described experiments showing how electricity could arouse the different sense-qualities. The evidence was meager and scattered, but it was there. Both Bell and Müller merely brought it together.

(*d*) Müller insisted, fourthly, upon the equivalence of external and internal stimuli. This is a point that has definite significance only as long as it is not taken for granted that the brain is the immediate organ of the mind. As soon as this latter view is admitted, it becomes obvious that internal stimuli, like external, are mediate to the mind and thus in the same relation to it as external stimuli. Bell took the point for granted and did not deal with it specifically. Both men write at a time when common sense was changing and the notion of the peculiarly mental function of the brain might or might not be considered obvious. But neither of them of course originated the view. It is very old; it was fundamental in Hartley, for instance; and early in the nineteenth century it was being established in common sense by Gall and Spurzheim and phrenology. That Müller, more than a decade after Flourens had assigned different mental functions to different parts of the brain, should feel it so necessary to insist upon the basic relationship is a little surprising.

(e) Müller found it necessary to explain in his laws how external objects can be perceived correctly, in spite of the fact that the mind is immediately aware only of the state of the nerves. Bell too gave a similar explanation. The discussion runs along the lines of what we now-a-days call adequate and inadequate stimulation. The general problem, however, is as old as the problem in idealistic philosophy, and was not original as problem or solution with either.

(f) Then both men raised the question of the exact locus of the specificity of the nerves. Bell assigned it definitely to the brain. Müller agreed that it must be either in the termination of the nerve in the brain or at least in its central part. Both appealed to the evidence from cut nerves. I do not know that this specific point had been definitely anticipated. It follows naturally, however, from the preceding argument, and it is implied in the numerous suggestions of physiological philosophers, from Descartes on, who have looked to different parts of the brain for different mental functions; in other words, it is of a piece with the theory of sensory centers in the brain.

(g) Finally, for the sake of completeness, we must note that Müller in his last law dealt with the selective power of the mind upon the perception of sensory impressions. Even in Bell we can find a single sentence to parallel the tenth law of Müller. The point hardly belongs among the laws of specific nerve energies, but at any rate it was not new, but as old as the problem of attention among the philosopher-psychologists.

What I have tried to show is that Bell's originality lies not in the enunciation of any new principles, but in the selection and collocation of certain old ones which gather force when brought thus into relation. How much of this Bell thought out explicitly and how much he absorbed unconsciously from philosophy-become-common-sense we shall never know, nor does it much matter. I have no desire to detract from his originality. My thesis is rather that originality is just this sort of affair, a matter of selection, of collocating, of emphasizing relationships, and of clarifying exposition. Such, I take it, is the psychology of originality in the individual and thus in science at large.

Müller then was less original than Bell only in that this same body of thought was more firmly established fifteen and twenty-five years later when he wrote, and thus more likely to transcend the limen of consciousness in Müller. It is just possible that Bell also had contributed to the body of thought from which Müller more or less unwittingly drew. To Bell's contribution, as we have seen, Müller added explicitness, documentation, systematization, authority, and publicity, that is to say, he made the view into a 'doctrine' which could have a name and quite naturally therefore came to be named for Müller.

Yet whose doctrine is it? Bell thought of it first, but Müller thought of it later and got it introduced into the body of science. I do not care how the reader decides. I have gone thus into my first example at length because it is the type of all. I believe that almost every new idea in science has been as little new as the doctrine of the specific energy of nerves in Bell—or Müller.

Helmholtz' Extension of the Doctrine of Specific Energies of Nerves. In the extension of the doctrine of the specific energy of nerves we find a situation similar to that in the origination of the theory. The original 'Müllerian' theory dealt with the differentiation of the five senses. Its amplification to apply to qualitative differences within the single sense-department is usually spoken of as "Helmholtz' extension." Helmholtz, as is well known, used the amplified theory as the basis for his theories of vision (1866, 192–208; 290–293, 839 f.) and of hearing (1863, i, Abs., vi). In vision, since all the colors can be obtained physically from three, he assumed, following Thomas Young, that there must be three specific visual energies. There is no such simple physical rule for the tones; in hearing therefore he assumed that every just noticeable tonal difference must have its specific energy, several thousand in all. It is probably this amplification and use of Müller's principle that has done most to fix the general doctrine in physiological psychology.

This extension of the theory was fairly obvious. Was it original with Helmholtz? No, for it had been specifically proposed by Natanson (1844) and A. W. Volkmann (1844) when Müller's exposition in the *Handbuch* was still only six years old. Natanson had laid down the general principle that for every organ of the nervous system there can be but a single function and that there must therefore be as many organs as functions, that is to say in the case of sensation, as many kinds of nerves as sensory qualities. This principle has in it the possibilities of greatness; it was not destined, however, to play such a rôle. Natanson applied his theory to touch, taste, smell, and color. In the case of color he assumed, like Helmholtz, the necessary three specific energies. He lacked Helmholtz' courage in assuming several thousand energies for hearing; since there is no known way in which all frequencies can be gotten from a few, he left the problem of hearing open. In every other respect he and Volkmann anticipated Helmholtz, and Volkmann at least wrote in a source with which Helmholtz must have been familiar.

The extension of the original theory, I have said, was obvious, although neither Bell nor Müller made it. It was so obvious that it occurred to Thomas Young in 1807 before there was any theory to extend. Young suggested that "each sensitive point of the retina" must contain "a limited number of particles" that vibrate in resonance with the frequencies of "the three principal colours, red, yellow, and blue." It is possible, he thought, that "each sensitive filament of the nerve may consist of three portions, one for each principal colour." [2] Now no one would claim that Thomas Young proposed the amplified theory of the specific energy of nerves in his explanation of color vision, and yet it is plain that Natanson's principle and Helmholtz' theoretical practice of finding a nervous structure for every elemental quality was a natural and obvious way of thinking to Thomas Young in 1807.

It appears then that, in so far as the historical process of origination goes, Natanson and Volkmann bear the same relation to Helmholtz in the extension of the doctrine of the specific energy of nerves that Bell bore to Müller in the doctrine itself, and that Thomas Young plays the part of some of the anticipators of Bell. The principal differences are incidental: the extension of the theory is not considered a great event; neither Natanson nor even Volkmann was, like Bell, a great man and neither, like him, had posthumous supporters who rise in defense; Helmholtz showed no desire to consider his amplification of the theory important or to claim originality for it. In both cases, however, the development of thought was gradual and not abrupt, and the fact that there has been no argument in this second case merely raises the question as to whether there should be in the first.

The Bell-Magendie Law. The controversy between Bell and Magendie concerning priority in the discovery of the law of the spinal nerve roots is famous.[3] Bell's original report of the facts is in the obscure monograph of 1811 already cited. Magendie published in 1822. The situation was somewhat complicated at the time by the fact that there was also a third claimant, Alexander Walker, who published even before Bell in 1809, but we know least of him and historians seem content to regard him simply as a plagiarist, whether conscious or unconscious one does not know. At any rate Bell announced his discovery in his lectures in 1807 and Walker had attended the lectures. Moreover, Walker got the facts reversed from what Bell and Magendie found and later work has confirmed! In general the discovery has been regarded as an independent discovery by both of the principal claimants: the finding is called the Bell-Magendie law. Those who are sticklers for priority call it Bell's law. Bell could not, of course, have gotten any hint from Magendie. One of Bell's students, Shaw, put the discovery in 1821 in a book which Magendie eventually read. Could he have been influenced by it or by earlier knowledge? No doubt the argument from priority for originality gains its force because it is never possible to be quite certain that a rediscovery is quite as original as the first discovery; there may at least have been obscure psychological factors operating.

For myself I am content to leave Magendie co-equal with Bell in this matter. He was certainly not a cheap plagiarist, though none of us can always be sure of all his sources. What seems to me most important is the fact that the dates we are considering mark the beginning of a remarkably fertile period of research in the physiology of the nervous system in both England and France. It is difficult to say what started growth except that the time was ripe; science in general and physiology in particular had come to the stage where research could be effective. Some say that it was this discovery of Bell's that began the whole process; but it seems to me that, if Bell had not made the discovery, someone else, if not Magendie, would. The distinction between movement and sensation was obvious, even if the nerves were thought to be the common conductors of both kinds of impulses. The cord and its nerve roots were more accessible in operative technique than the brain. It was a great discovery to find that there were two kinds of nerves respectively in the two kinds of spinal roots, but nevertheless it came out of the times and belonged to the times. If it had not been made in England, it would have to have been made in France at about that time, and Magendie first, and Flourens second, were the logical persons to make it. It seems to me most likely that the question of originality in Magendie is simply the question as to whether he had heard indirectly about Bell's belief and, perhaps forgetting the detail, had had his mind especially directed to the experiment. On such slender threads does the formal question of originality depend.

Localization of Function in the Brain. The history of scientific opinion as to the localization of function in the brain is a history of an intimately continuous development and one that is especially instructive because it seems at present to be returning upon itself. It begins of course with the establishment of the brain as the principal organ of the mind. We have noted above that the Alexandrians (Herophilus and Erasistratus, ca. 250 B.C.) and Galen (ca. 200 A.D.) held this view. Most people suppose that Descartes held it, although, as a matter of fact, he held specifically that the soul finds its seat in the entire body as a whole and that the pineal gland is simply the point at which it and the body interact. Nevertheless, on the Cartesian view, the brain becomes the primary organ of the mind for it is here that the soul, directing the course of the animal spirits, determines movement and is in turn affected by perception. The Cartesian brain is potentially a mass of mental 'centers.'

With the empiricism of the eighteenth century there grew up the view of the brain as the seat of mind with impressions conveyed to it and motion conveyed from it by the nerves. Hartley (1749) is most explicit, and one gets with him the impression of different associable vibratiuncles (and therefore ideas) as localized in different parts of the brain. It seems to have been phrenology in the early nineteenth century that fixed upon common sense the notion that the brain is the sole organ of the mind. The physiologists were in advance of common sense, though in general opposed to phrenology. Bell certainly took the relationship between the brain and the mind for granted, but Bichat (1801), while placing the seat of most mental functions in the brain, had assigned the emotions to the internal organs. Phrenology, for all the opposition it aroused among the scientists, helped to fix scientific opinion on this point.

However, no sooner was the matter of the seat of the mind practically settled, than investigators immediately began to raise the question of the specific seats of its particular functions. Rolando in 1809 sought, on experimental evidence, to attribute particular functions to the cerebrum, the cerebellum, and the medulla. Flourens' experiments (1824; 1825) on this problem are classic, and one tends to date the experimental work on localization from him, though once again one finds an incomplete anticipation of an important discovery; this time it is Rolando's priority over Flourens. The latter, using the method of extirpation, assigned separate functions to the cerebrum, the cerebellum, the corpora quadrigemina, the medulla, and the cord, insisting, however, at the same time upon the unity of the entire nervous system and the persistent interrelation of the parts. Every one of these parts had, it is true, its *action propre*, but it has also an *action commune*. Within each part, however, Flourens found no specific localization; extirpation of a part of the cerebrum, for example, did not cause the loss of a general function nor the loss of the ability to reacquire a particular function. In fact Flourens' general view of the cerebrum is surprisingly like the 'equipotentiality' of Lashley and the *Gestalt* of Köhler today.

In spite of Flourens, thought tended in the middle of the nineteenth century toward a more specific localization. Phrenology may have made some impression while being disproved. The doctrine of the specific energies of nerves favored localization, because it seemed that the specificity resided in the central termination. The improvement of the microscope and the discovery that the brain was a network of fibers connecting cells—an anatomical picture that resembled the associationistic psychology—favored it. The French psychopathologists made the view seem more plausible by their examination of the brain in a search for the cause of mental disease. There were many incidental facts or theories that told for localization. Finally Broca (1861) discovered the speech center at the base of the third frontal convolution of the left cerebral hemisphere. This event can be taken as the first discovery and proof of exact localization, but it is noteworthy that it is simply an incident in a continuous development.

Fritsch and Hitzig (1870) mapped by the electrical method the motor centers and there followed immediately a period of great activity in England, France, and Germany, in which the modern theory of cerebral motor and sensory centers was developed. Quite recently, however, the work of Franz (1912) and then of Lashley (1920, 1921a, 1921b, 1922, 1924) has led to great doubt about the existence of precise centers and thus to a hesitating return to a position that in its broad generality resembles Flourens' (Soury, 1899; Richet, 1897, II, 547–670).

Now who discovered exact localization of function in the brain? Descartes? Some empiricist, like Hartley? No, we are accustomed to say, they had no direct evidence; they were guessing. Bell? He was not sufficiently explicit. Gall? He was explicit enough, but wrong. Flourens? Perhaps, but he was not sufficiently specific. The physiologists who thought in this manner between 1840 and 1860? They were not explicit enough or emphatic enough, or else they lacked the evidence. Broca then? Yes, by a lucky chance, a readiness to see the significance of his good fortune, and a method which others were using without his luck. His discovery of course is wrong, but I take it that a discovery does not have to be true to be great. Though wrong it led to further discovery. Fritsch and Hitzig? Yes also, for their finding had even greater systematic meaning and stimulated fully as much research. It too perhaps is wrong.

What then about Franz and Lashley and some other contemporaries? Lashley owes a debt to Franz at least and has given us a great deal of new detail. But is his general finding something that marks an epoch? I have not space to attempt to draw the parallel between Flourens and Lashley but I think the fact that it can be drawn shows us something about originality in general. If there had been no intermediaries and if Lashley had come out with his general finding ninety years earlier, we should not have called him original and have dated the period from Flourens. As it is his work marks a reaction from the psychophysiology of 1870–1900 and is therefore more 'original.' Certainly one measure of originality is the degree with which a man can persist in the face of contrary opinion. The continuity of thought makes progress possible, but it works always against originality. There is no need to regret this conflict: Gall was original and should be respected for it, but only the gross underlying principle of phrenology contributed to progress. In general his originality impeded progress.

The Speech Center. We may pause here to note that even Broca's discovery was not uncontested on the grounds of priority. Bouillaud (1825) advanced the view on clinical evidence that the center for articulate speech lies in the anterior portion of the cerebral lobes. He thought that he was thus supporting Gall and confuting Flourens. In 1836 Dax presented a similar view. In 1865, after Broca's discovery and after forty years of interest in other matters, Bouillaud in an elaborate paper challenged Broca's priority.

Who then discovered the speech center? I think it is plain that most of us will want to discount Bouillaud. There is no doubt about his priority, but priority is not after all what we are primarily interested in. It is not so much the first appearance of an idea that concerns us as its first appearance in such a way that it can and does develop into progress. (This same remark could have been made with less force of Bell and Müller and the specific energy of nerves.)

Reflex Movement. The importance attached to the reflex in modern psychology tends to direct attention to the history and discovery of reflex movement or action. Here, I believe, it is customary to cite Marshall Hall as the discoverer, although no behaviorist has attempted to 'canonize' him. Perhaps attention goes most naturally to Hall, because Johannes Müller, who claimed to have discovered reflex movement independently, nevertheless yielded priority to Hall.

Apparently the facts of some reflexes, without the name or theory, have long been known. Galen, for example, described what we now call the pupillary reflex. The word, and its attendant theory, seem to come from Astruc (1736) in the sense of 'reflection' or 'reflected' movement. The theory was that, "as with light, angles of incidence and reflection are equal, so that a sensation produced by a concussion of the animal spirits against the fibrous columns [of the spinal cord] is reflected and causes motion in those nerve tubes which happen to be placed exactly in the line of reflection" (Hodge, 1890). Whytt (1768) published important observations on this kind of movement in decerebrate animals (Carmichael, 1927*b*). Such observations, however, could not have the importance that would have been attached to them if the distinction between motor and sensory nerves and some idea of their connection had been known. Thus Marshall Hall's discovery of reflex movement in decapitated newts and snakes in 1832 immediately assimilated to itself a significance that Whytt's work could not have. Moreover, we see once again that the significant discovery may come easily as soon as the preparation is such as to make it significant. I mean here that it was the Bell-Magendie law more than anything else that gave physiological significance to the bare facts of 'reflected' movement. The Bell-Magendie law was not known internationally until the twenties. Within a decade both Hall and Müller 'discovered' reflected movement. Hall reported his study in 1832 and published in 1833. Müller discussed reflected movement generally in 1833 and fully, claiming independence but yielding priority to Hall, in 1834 (1834, bk. III, sect. iii, chap. iii; bk. IV, sect. ii, chap. i, 4). It seems plain to me that this is another instance of originality depending upon scientific preparation (Eckhard, 1881; Hall, 1890; Hodge, 1890).

Hypnotism and Braidism. We are usually told that the discoverer of hypnosis was James Braid. The facts that Braid coined the word "hypnotism" and that others called the phenomenon "Braidism" seem to support this view. Nevertheless it seems to me that there could hardly be any scientific subject-matter where it is more unfair to single out a discoverer. In spite of the violent controversy that this subject at least twice engendered, one may dare seventy-five years later to attempt to state the facts.[4]

The phenomenon itself has probably been known since antiquity in the sense that it has occurred in religious ecstasy and has perhaps been intentionally induced in savage ceremonials. Animal magnetism, as a peculiar natural force related to mineral magnetism, has been believed in by some educated people from at least the sixteenth century to the present day.

Mesmer, a Viennese physician, expounded a view of animal magnetism as explaining the influence of the stars upon human weal in 1766, and used magnets for curing disease. Later he met a Swiss priest who effected cures by a similar method but without the magnets. Mesmer abandoned the magnets. Had he not been capable of open-minded tolerance and of the scientific capacity to learn, he would have kept the magnets and have ignored the priest. Vienna was suspicious of Mesmer, so he removed to Paris, and developed there the famous *baquet* and all the tom-foolery and mystery that surrounded it. The soft music, the purple robe, Mesmer's manner and personality, the mysterious *baquet* itself, were all well designed to induce hypnosis, and its attendant phenomena must have been what Mesmer got. But the significance of these things could only have been half-conscious; Mesmer never knew why they worked nor had a theory of their operation better than the plausible theory of animal magnetism. No wonder when, at the height of Mesmer's tremendous popularity, the French government offered a reward to Mesmer for the disclosure of his secret, Mesmer "refused" to disclose it. He had no secret to disclose. The commissions who had been appointed to investigate the phenomena knew presumably as much about them as he. However, the methods resembled the hocus-pocus of charlatanry; Mesmer 'would' not divulge the 'secret;' he was denounced as an impostor, and, all his popularity gone, he withdrew from Paris to die presently in Switzerland. Ever since this time "mesmerism," as it soon came to be called, has been held in poor repute among most educated persons, and yet Mesmer discovered certain fundamentals about the method of inducing hypnosis. Is it because the name "hypnosis" had not been invented that he did not "discover" hypnosis, or is it rather for personal reasons that scientists will not recognize him now as then? Mesmer was carried away by his discovery and never relinquished a belief in his personal power. Hence the discovery fell just short of a scientific generalization, and Mesmer's egotism was distrusted.

In the early nineteenth century mesmerism became a show phenomenon for the stage (as it is now), thus falling still further into disrepute. In 1837, however, John Elliotson, Professor of Medicine at University College, a pioneer and a radical in medical science, a man of great imagination and of many sound ideas, the originator and accomplisher of the idea of the attachment of a hospital to a medical school, the arch-defender of the use of the stethoscope, so much despised by medical men at first, but a man whose very force and imagination gained him opposition and enemies—in 1837 this John Elliotson witnessed a demonstration of mesmerism and at once set about trying out its therapeutic usefulness in the hospital. He was soon convinced of its value. Had he had the wit to call it by some other name than 'mesmerism' and the tact to have proceeded slowly, he might have won the case for the new phenomenon. Elliotson, however, had too much force to be tactful, and in 1838 the Council of University College forbade the practice of "mesmerism or animal magnetism" in the hospital. Elliotson immediately resigned from the hospital and from the university. Then followed a long period of propaganda for new things in general and mesmerism in particular. Elliotson started and edited the *Zoist* as an organ for this movement. Later mesmeric hospitals sprang up all over Great Britain. But, although there was a limited circle of respectable believers, Elliotson in general lost friends, money, and reputation. The medical world rejected him completely. Yet did he not discover all of hypnosis except its name (unless of course it was already discovered by Mesmer)?

While all this was going on James Esdaile, having read of Elliotson's work, was actually using mesmerism as an anesthetic agent in India. Here he met with some scientific opposition, but also with some encouragement. He performed successfully hundreds of operations, a great many of them major, between 1845 and 1851, when he returned to England. At one time he had a hospital created for him by special funds. Later the Government took him back into its hospitals to work out the relation of mesmerism to medicine. Esdaille could not claim to be a discoverer. He admitted Elliotson's priority as to the method. He was the first person to use mesmerism extensively for anesthesia, but the first case was that of the amputation of a leg in England in 1842. Yet why do we never hear of Esdaile? Perhaps because the anesthetic properties of ether were discovered in 1846 and of chloroform in the following year, and mesmerism or hypnosis did not therefore develop primarily as an anesthetic agent. But it is also to be observed that Esdaile, largely because he used the word 'mesmerism,' found himself in the disreputable camp of Elliotson.

James Braid (1843) antedated Esdaile but not Elliotson. In 1841 he undertook to expose a mesmeric performance on the stage, but, in attempting the exposure, was privately impressed by some of the phenomena. Then (like Mesmer and the magnets!) he remained open-minded and sought to experiment at home. He hypnotized his wife by having her gaze fixedly at the family sugar bowl. He found he could induce sleep in other members of his family and in his friends by having them fix their gaze upon an object. He elaborated a theory of visual fatigue and, only a few weeks after he had attempted the exposure of a 'charlatan,' appeared on the same stage to produce and to explain in physiological terms the same phenomena. In 1843 he published his book, *Neurypnology* (= "neuro-hypnology," hence "hypnotize" and the other derivatives); and thus in brief hypnosis was 'discovered.' Braidism grew, though it hardly flourished, was lost sight of, and was then rediscovered in France at Nancy and at the Salpêtrière, but with this later history we are not concerned.

Why was Braid the discoverer of hypnotism? Because mesmerism was rejected and Braidism was accepted, and Braid coined the word 'hypnotism.' And why was mesmerism rejected when the only real difference seems to have lain in the name? Because, I think, of the egotism of Mesmer and Elliotson, especially as they tended to assert peculiar power in themselves; because, in Elliotson's time, the name "mesmerism" was already established in disrepute; because Elliotson's vanity led him to oppose Braid and thus allied Braid with the medical profession; because Braid by temperament sought persistently to come at a 'normal' physiological explanation of the phenomenon even though his actual scientific advance was no greater than the advances of Mesmer, Elliotson, and Esdaile. In short personal values entered into the selection of a discoverer for hypnosis; but a careful scrutiny of history discloses mostly the continuity of scientific thought and only those small increments of originality that we have learned to expect.

Other Instances. These examples from the history of physiological psychology are surely enough to establish my thesis that mutations in scientific evolution are rare, perhaps almost unknown; that scientific thought, like individual thought, is sensibly continuous; and that creation or originality is not abrupt, nor mysterious. I may, however, mention a few other examples within psychology at large, which space would prevent including here even were further illustration desirable. The reader is free to solve these puzzles for himself, should he so desire.

Associationism. Who founded associationism? The historical break is between Hartley and James Mill. Hartley, I think, is generally regarded as the founder, unless one insists on going back to the germ itself; then it is Locke, if one takes the first great influence, or Hobbes, if one keeps strictly to priority. It is hard for me not to regard Berkeley and Hume as associationists, though the principle does not seem so important in Locke.

Physiological Psychology. Who founded physiological psychology? Wundt, who insisted upon it and wrote under the title and is evidently both chronologically and psychologically at the beginning of some great new thing? Or Bain who put chapters on the nervous system into his psychology? Or Johannes Müller who put chapters on sensation and the mind into his physiology? Or Lotze who wrote a medical (and metaphysical!) psychology? Or Hartley with his vibratiuncles and speculation without experiment? Or Descartes, who was a physiological experimentalist and gave us our mind-body dichotomy?

Or, if physiological psychology is simply *experimental psychology*, Wundt or Fechner or the physiologists themselves, especially in the persons of Müller and Weber? Fechner was a philosopher by his own intention and ambition. He was an experimentalist in the interests of philosophy! If he founded experimental psychology, he did it inadvertently. Wundt was an experimentalist by intention and ambition, but a philosopher and systematist by temperament. Wundt meant to found experimental psychology, and it was founded. Did he do it? Fechner has the priority, but *he* wanted primarily to disprove materialism.

Context Theory of Meaning. Who originated the context theory of meaning? Titchener, of course, if one intends the word "context" and the exact formulation that he attaches to it. Yet it is not clear whether, without losing significance, the theory can be divorced from association as a principle, and thus whether it differs greatly from some of the associational theories of meaning (or of the object). And, apart from association, did not Berkeley (1709, par. 8–15, 17, 45–51) essentially state this theory? Did Titchener (1915*a*, 26–30) perhaps then simply adapt it to modern systematic uses?

Behaviorism. Watson, I believe, claims to have founded behaviorism. Did he do more than add the "ism" to behavior? Certainly the attempt to get along without consciousness in psychology is as old as the Cartesian divorce of the mind from the body. But others have raised this question and I do not need to extend my queries here.[5]

Gestalt Psychology. Who began *Gestalt* psychology? (Calkins, 1926*a*; 1926*b*) Just at present in America the names of Köhler and Koffka are on everyone's lips. Both of these men refer the origination of *Gestalt* psychology to Wertheimer. Wertheimer modestly finds the roots in the school of *Gestalt-qualität* and points to Von Ehrenfels. He in turn certainly owed something to Mach. But what is the cardinal principle of *Gestalt* psychology that is so all-important? Is it that the whole is always more than a mere *Und-verbindung* of all its parts (the argument against the atomism of associationism)? Is not this the view of the mind that James (1890, I, 224–290) labored to convey? Is *Gestalt* a protest against Wundt and his influence? What about Wundt's *Aktualitätstheorie*, his creative synthesis and the law of psychic resultants? Was Wundt nearly so 'atomistic' as his critics would have him be, or did he too have a vision similar to James', and Ehrenfels', and Wertheimer's, and try to picture it in a similar way?

Conclusions

Scientific thought is a progressive unity. It evolves slowly, so slowly that the thought of an individual, incorporated within it, ordinarily does not represent a large increment of change. Nevertheless the rate of progress is very uneven and at times thought in a given subject-matter moves rapidly. Such an accleration may be due to the unusual originality of a single individual, but it is more likely to be the result of previous converging tendencies which render a given 'discovery' the next natural step in the process. Many synchronous independent discoveries are thus to be explained.

It seems to me that scientific thought is thus like the personal thinking of the scientist. The scientist has his brilliant intuitions, but the originality of the moment of insight is little more than the unexpected seeing of a relationship. Both kinds of thought are evolutionary, and their stages are marked off by the anastomosis of logical processes. Only in this somewhat artificial sense are there mutations in the evolution of thought.

The essence of originality seems then to lie, not so much in sheer novelty, as in the systematic aspects of a discovery or a theory, that is to say, in the selection of data or conditions, their collocation, and the establishment or exhibition of the resultant relationships. The first result is a generalization. Thus Braid surpassed Elliotson, not as a discoverer, but because he gave a more generalized meaning to the hypnotic phenomena than the earlier assumption that they depended upon the animal magnetism of some undefined persons. But the broader generalization is systematization. The originality in the theory of the specific energy of nerves was little more than the collocation of thitherto unrelated facts.

Just as genius tends to be measured by reputation, so mere originality may pass unnoticed unless it yields certain results. Some, though not all, of the factors that bring originality into scientific attention are extrinsic to the individual concerned.

There is in the first place the 'doctrinization' of theories. Clear and emphatic exposition tends to turn theories into 'doctrines' or 'laws.' When others accomplish this process for an investigator, he is entitled to what credit it brings him. When the emphasis is his own, we must beware lest we confuse scientific acumen with expository or polemical skill. Here lie all the cases from the man with a persistent conviction based upon insight to the 'promoter' of a view who is merely defending his own 'greatness.'

In all these evaluations we must not lose sight of the fact that a man's departure from current tradition is a measure of himself and not of extraneous conditions inherent in the times. If something is lost from originality when it is seen to be but a step in a larger evolutionary process, then any step that is against the trend of science must gain in originality. Thus negativism is often originality, but we should not, I take it, wish to measure greatness by negativism.

The fact is that we try to measure the value of discoveries by their correctness. This practice is justified as against the results, but it seems to me but a poor measure of a man. Correctness is not only relative and a matter of the times, but it is thus entirely external to the investigator or theorist. The originality of a discovery or theory within a given universe is not lessened when the universe is enlarged, though its 'truth' may be. In fact many great discoveries are great because they led to beliefs in great falsities (as viewed later against a larger universe), which nevertheless in turn led on to new discoveries.

This fact leads us to note another measure of greatness which is largely external to the individual. Discoveries are important when they are significant, when they yield the broadest generalization or most numerous relationships. It may be true that it is the great man who perceives significance, but it is also true that the significance shows the problem to the 'great' man. This is why great discoveries do not occur until the times are ready for them or, when they occur too early, are not great. In other words the state of the times works both before and after the discovery. It prepares the way for the discovery and it develops it into further research and discovery after it is made. Thus the discovery may become a mere point in the evolutionary process and not such an important event after all.

There are of course great men, who as creative scientists greatly excel others, and who represent thus an individual difference that is a truly psychological difference. It is easy to name persons who certainly differ in scientific ability from Helmholtz. My thesis is that much of the greatness that is attributed to the 'great,' is an artifact and depends upon matters that are not intrinsic to the mind of the 'great' man. We can not always evaluate the intrinsic and the extrinsic factors in a given case, but we can at least realize the problem. Moreover we can realize how small is the thought of an individual in comparison with the process to which it belongs, and we can turn our attention to the larger and more important matter of the stream of scientific thought. Could we thus even partially dehumanize science, a great deal of fruitless and really meaningless controversy about both the past and the present would be avoided.

NOTES

1. The entire history of science should properly be my subject-matter; but I am writing for psychologists, and the history of physiological psychology is a present interest with me.
2. For the theory of color vision (Young, 1807, I, 440) but the quotation concerning the three portions of the nerve filaments is an obscure isolated sentence, remote from the color theory (II, 617).
3. The law is that the sensory nerves arise in the posterior, and the motor nerves in the anterior, roots of the spinal cord. The controversy has, moreover, recently been quite satisfactorily discussed by Carmichael (1926b, 191–198).
4. There are various accounts of the history of hypnosis. Moll (1889) is the most detailed, but lacks perspective. Bramwell (1903) is the most relevant here. I forbear from giving the original references to Mesmer, Elliotson, and Esdaile. Bramwell and others give them. However, it is more with their activities than their writings that we are concerned.
5. Cf., especially, Diserens (1925), who, in discussing psychological objectivism, very clearly exhibits the continuity of thought from the Greeks to the present.

The Psychology of Controversy

𤭖𤭖𤭖𤭖𤭖𤭖𤭖𤭖𤭖𤭖𤭖𤭖𤭖𤭖𤭖𤭖𤭖𤭖𤭖𤭖𤭖 1929

IDEALLY, it might be argued, the psychologist is a superior being, for over all other scientists he has the advantage of being a psychologist. He alone, the argument would continue, knows the human mind without which there could be no science. The work of the exact sciences, as they are sometimes called, involves not only precise observation but also a loose admixture of personal prejudice, ambition and conviction. The psychologist, however, knows the human mind that is both the object and the subject of his work, and is superior to prejudice, to exaggeration, to vanity, and consequently to quarrelsomeness. Thus without these constant errors he serenely pursues his way, at peace with his fellow-workers, his hand alone grasping at fundamental truth with the personal equation of observation accounted for and eliminated by corrections. Psychology would thus be the one perfect exact science.

And it might be, though it is not clear that it could be. Certainly psychology has not been above personal bias. It is true that when psychologists battle they may hurl Freudian explanations of each other at each other. They may rise with scientific magnanimity against opponents and suggest that falsification is involuntary and unconscious, or that stupidity is inherited and therefore not a matter of individual responsibility. All this is, perhaps, delightfully scientific, and yet there nevertheless remains in such controversy a seeming lack of objectivity. For instance, some psychologists in writing for publication place the mystic symbol Ph.D. after their names, but none, as far as I know, has yet seen the value of adding the statement of his own I.Q. Stanford University now does that sort of thing posthumously for the great, but it has not yet undertaken a handbook of the living. The classical method of psy-

Reprinted with permission from *Psychological Review*, 1929, **36**, 97–121. Address of the President before the American Psychological Association at New York, December 28, 1928.

chology is introspection, yet not the behaviorist, nor the 'gestaltist,' nor the purposivist, nor the late functionalist, nor even the introspectionist himself has yet succeeded in maintaining clear vision with the eye rotated through 180° to see the mind that is at work. From this point of view we would seem to have a long way to go, and yet I must confess to you, attractive as my picture is, that I am not sure that we want to go, or can go, all that way. The scientific eye sees dimly when it turns through half a circle to look behind itself. The scientist, it seems to me, is limited by certain paradoxes of human nature and the psychologist shares these limitations with other scientists. It is therefore to two of these paradoxes that I ask your attention. The second follows from the first.

I. The history of science, like Hegel's view of the history of thought, is one long series of theses, set off by ardently advocated antitheses, with ultimate syntheses terminating controversy and marking a step forward. This picture, it seems to me, holds, not only for speculative, philosophical psychology, but also for the most rigorously observational work. Controversy has always been part of the method of science. A judge, or even a lawyer, might accept the statement that controversy, the clash of prosecution and defense, is the fundamental method for getting at truth. However, I do not think that the scientist would be quite so ready to subscribe whole-heartedly to this principle. He expects controversy as part of the scientific 'game,' but he generally engages in it under the principle that 'I am right and you are wrong.' We hear little in science of an able defense of a lost case. Only correct discoveries are held to measure scientific ability. There is little applause for the investigator who, by being brilliantly wrong, prevents his antagonist from being wrong at all, and thus contributes to the truth. Unfortunately this situation makes scientists tend to hold to lost causes, when they might know better, for no other reason—unconscious reason—than that the laurel commands no acclaim when shown to be artificial.

After much thought about the matter, I have come reluctantly to the conclusion that scientific truth, like puristic truth, must come about by controversy. Personally this view is abhorrent to me. It seems to mean that scientific truth must transcend the individual, that the best hope of science lies in its greatest minds being often brilliantly and determinedly wrong, but in opposition, with some third, eclectically minded, middle-of-the-road nonentity seizing the prize while the great fight for it, running off with it, and sticking it into a textbook for sophomores written from no point of view and in defense of nothing whatsoever. I hate this view, for it is not dramatic and it is not fair; and yet I believe that it is the verdict of the history of science.

The paradox then in science would seem to be that the more you fight for the truth the less you see it. If you are always trying to see it, you have no time to fight, and without fighting you get science nowhere; you are just the cautious critic who is afraid to venture research. Perhaps I can improve this doleful picture before it is done. Let us, however, turn our attention first to famous controversies, and, since discretion behooves us, chiefly to those of the dead.

If we are looking for controversy, there is of course the case of Mesmer, who participated in a battle royal with the conservative scientists of Paris at the end of the eighteenth century (Binet & Féré, 1887; Moll, 1889). Certainly the egotistic, opinionated Mesmer was an uncomfortable person for the scientific contemporary who did not believe in his theory; but, if science is, as is so often claimed, quite impersonal, Mesmer's personality ought to have nothing to do with the question of his demonstration of the truth of animal magnetism. Nobody knows whether Mesmer in young manhood was more conceited than the average of men who later become famous. It is quite clear, however, that, even had he been a modest and retiring person when young, his great theory that an important beneficent power resided in his own person would have made him into the sort of man that his opponents would regard as vain. In fact, conceit was involved in his scientific theory, since the theory had to do specifically with Mesmer. Yet nobody in the various investigating committees or in the Académie des Sciences was objective enough to see this crucial point. They denounced Mesmer, largely, so it seems to me, because of his personality, and thus mingled their own personalities with their scientific criticism.

The facts can be restated briefly. Mesmer was a physician in Vienna. As a physician he could not ignore the obvious influence of the celestial bodies upon human well-being, a fact well known then although not now. Mesmer asked himself how these remote bodies can act upon human beings from a distance, and it occurred to him that the astrological influence might be mediated by magnetism, a force that is capable of penetrating space. This was Mesmer's first theory, and if he had, then and there, written a book about it we could have put him down with all those persons, from the Greeks to the present day, who have held and advanced theories without resort to experimental proof. Mesmer, however, in good scientific fashion, used his happy thought as the basis for an experiment. He got himself magnets and tried passing them over the bodies of his patients with remarkable effects; the persons were benefited by the magnets or even cured of diseases. 'By the magnets'—it is a proper phrase to have used, and yet so often the supposed analysis of an effect into its causes turns out to be wrong. Presently Mesmer met a Swiss priest who was practicing the same kind of therapeutics as Mesmer, passing his hands over the bodies of his patients *without* the magnets. Mesmer had fixed upon the wrong cause of his effect.

There were two things for Mesmer to do. The more probable thing—so I am obliged by the history of science to conclude—would have been for Mesmer to have denounced the priest or at least to have tried to prove that he had concealed magnets up his sleeves, to have come out more vigorously in favor of magnets, insisting that they were essential to the true Mesmeric method, and to have enlarged, by the advertising that dogmatic assertion in the face of controversy gives, his medical practice. Mesmer, however, did the improbable thing: he discarded the magnets. It would have been lucky for all the people who have wrangled over this matter for a century after him, if he had discarded the word 'magnetism' also. Unfortunately Mesmer had begun with the notion that a mysterious influence without contact is likely to be magnetic, and the physiologist, van Helmont, a century earlier had expounded a theory of animal magnetism. So Mesmer called his new therapeutic means 'animal magnetism,' allowing the implication to stand that the influence was something like mineral magnetism. He now knew that he could cure people of certain diseases, or make them think themselves cured, which, in certain cases, is the same thing from the physician's point of view. Others could not effect these cures. Undoubtedly Mesmer's personality and his growing confidence in his power were the reasons for his power, but Mesmer did not know this. Not all minerals are magnetic; why should all persons be magnetic? Mesmer came to believe that he, unlike most other persons, was magnetic, and thus capable of influencing others. All this happened before Mesmer left Vienna for Paris in 1778.

Up to this point, it seems to me, we have nothing more than the account of the genesis of a scientific discovery that is without reproach. Mesmer's personality is irrelevant to the scientific fact. The Church opposed him; the scientific academies ignored him; his followers worshipped him; but none of these things matter. He had discovered hypnotism, that is to say, he had discovered the state of hypnosis, had arrived at a vague notion of its therapeutic significance, and was possessed of the practical means of inducing the state, although he had an incorrect theory as to the nature of the means. Thus Mesmer occupies a definite position in the history of the knowledge of hypnosis. Without him knowledge could not have advanced as it did advance, for it was the travelling mesmerists who interested both Elliotson and Braid, it was Elliotson who interested Esdaile and many others in England, it was Braid who started Liébeault on hypnotic work and Liébeault who convinced Bernheim who began the Nancy school. Mesmer, ordinarily neglected, occupies the important place at the beginning of the genetic chain of events. That his knowledge of the conditions, the nature, and the effects of hypnosis was incomplete is a situation that applies to almost all scientific discoveries at first; moreover our knowledge of these facts is still incomplete.

After Mesmer went to Paris it is not quite so clear that his discoveries can be divorced from his personality. Here he developed further the conditions of hypnosis, the mysterious baquet with its rods of iron that the patients held (iron, of course, because of its magnetic properties), the circle of sitters about the baquet connected by cords or hands (a circuit, because of magnetic analogy), the subdued light, the soft music, the hocus-pocus of Mesmer's speech and his magician's attire. It is no wonder that the scientific world was disgusted, but my question is whether this disgust interfered with its perception of the truth. Mesmer was the talk of Paris. There was a large band of enthusiastic disciples. The scientists appointed investigating committees, which investigated and found, so it is always said, 'against Mesmer.' Actually there was no denying the phenomena; all the committees did was to disapprove Mesmer's theory which he had formally embodied in twenty-seven propositions, and in particular to deny the identity of this influence with mineral magnetism and the existence of 'a responsive influence between the heavenly bodies, the earth, and animated bodies.' The view then developed that Mesmer, since he was not using mineral magnetism, was employing some secret force that he would not divulge. His disciples, who thought that they had been promised this secret, finally turned against Mesmer because he would not reveal it. Mesmer was discredited, driven from Paris by public opinion, and died shortly afterward. He had, of course, no secret to reveal. Everybody, the committees and his disciples, knew all that he did, but could not realize that a man can know how to use a power without understanding its nature.

The question of Mesmer's personality comes in here because we wonder whether he merited rebuke. The technique of the baquet was certainly an aid to the technique of hypnotizing, and Mesmer in a sense made this discovery. But was he sincere? Did he believe that all this mystery was an aid to animal magnetism, or did he induce it quite consciously to attract the crowds? The concept of sincerity is a dangerous one. Psychologists could well do without it, substituting the notion of dissociation. At any rate, it seems to me that psychologists who have thought about the problems of personality will have to agree with Mesmer's defenders that Mesmer at least thought he was sincere; and who but a psychologist could undertake to distinguish between a man's sincerity and his belief in his sincerity? However, the conviction or the exoneration of Mesmer hardly matters to us. What about the scientists who repudiated him? They shut their eyes to an important scientific discovery because they could not stomach the conditions of its demonstration. Mesmer was a nuisance. He was a propagandist and a demagogue, and, behold, the whole world had gone after him. Moreover he was making money out of his discovery. He was vain and opinionated, and had even achieved that summit of conceit of making the new force a property of his own person. It is thus no wonder that the scientists repudiated him, and it is also no wonder that the use of hypnosis passed from the hands of scientists to charlatans for nearly half a century. This is the scientific dilemma that I am discussing: does science preserve its purity and thus retard its progress by shutting its eyes to partial truths, and does it thus sometimes cut off its nose to spite its face?

I have dealt with Mesmer at length because I want you to be quite clear as to my problem. I could now go on with other instances from the history of our science keeping you here until early morning, unless, in spite of being psychologists, you should develop free wills and leave. As it is, my love of determinism is too great to risk such an *experimentum crucis*. I shall be brief with my other cases.

The history of Mesmer was repeated with John Elliotson in the forties of the last century, except for the fact that there can be no doubt of Elliotson's complete sincerity, that is to say, of the complete integration of his personality, with no divided knowledge about what he claimed to be the truth (Bromwell, 1903, 3–30). Elliotson was a physician of exceptional native ability who was a member of the faculty of University College in London in the thirties of the last century. Nowadays we should call him a radical. He was always, to the resentment of his colleagues, advocating some new idea, like the use of the stethoscope, just invented, of which they said, 'It's just the thing for Elliotson to rave about,' or the maintenance of a hospital in connection with a medical school, an idea which, however, he advocated successfully. He made some important contributions to *materia medica*, and did not hesitate to ridicule the fallacies of current medical dogma. He was too ardent to be tactful, and consequently he was disliked by most of his colleagues. In 1837 Elliotson acquired the inheritance of Mesmer by witnessing the demonstration of a travelling mesmerist. Within a few days he was mesmerizing the patients of the new University College Hospital and getting what he regarded as beneficial therapeutic results. He was urged to desist on the ground that he was injuring the reputation of the Medical School, but he refused on the opposite ground that truth is more important than a reputation. Within a year the Council of University College had passed a resolution forbidding 'the practice of mesmerism or animal magnetism within the Hospital,' and Elliotson had resigned from the Hospital and from University College never to enter either again. He kept up his crusade. No medical journal would print his papers so he founded the *Zoist* as an organ of free speech about new things, especially mesmerism. He was denounced. Medical men would not associate with him. He lost his practice. Feeling ran into intimate channels and he also lost most of his personal friends. Yet Elliotson kept on. Mesmeric hospitals sprang up all over England. He had a group of supporters, but the group did not include many of the reputable medical practitioners of his day.

How far this controversy penetrated into the emotional lives of its participants is illustrated by the following instance. Like Mesmer, Elliotson saw in mesmerism mostly a therapeutic agent, but it was also obvious that the new state might be used as an anesthetic—in those days just before the discovery of the modern anesthetics. In 1842 Ward, a surgeon, amputated a leg of a patient under mesmeric trance.[1] The patient had been suffering excruciating torture from the least motion of an ulcerated knee-joint, and could sleep little. A mesmerist, Topham, one of Elliotson's disciples, found that he could give this patient rest by mesmeric sleep. Later Ward amputated the leg at the thigh after Topham had mesmerized the patient, and tried, in the course of the operation, bruising the cut end of the sciatic nerve. The patient remained in relaxed sleep and denied all memory of the operation afterward.

Ward then reported the case to the Royal Medical and Chirurgical Society of London. The report aroused a storm of protest. Marshall Hall, whom we now honor for the discovery of reflex action, described mesmerism as 'trumpery which pollutes the temple of science,' and fell back on his own theory, arguing that the report was false because it did not show that the sound leg twitched reflexly when the other leg was cut. Eight years later Hall informed the Society that the patient had confessed to collusion, although the patient then signed a deposition stating that the operation had been painless. Other members at this first meeting of the Society contended that, 'if the account of the man experiencing no agony during the operation were true, the fact was unworthy of their consideration because pain is a wise provision of nature, and patients ought to suffer pain while their surgeon is operating.' At the next meeting of the Society, after violent discussion, it was voted to strike from the minutes the statement that such a paper had been read.[2]

Well? Intolerance does not beget tolerance. That is all. Hypnosis may not be the ideal surgical anesthetic, but it is a great deal better than none, as Esdaile, inspired by Elliotson, was in the same years proving in hundreds of cases in India, and against opposition almost as strong as was to be found in England (Bramwell, 1903). The medical men almost let the world suffer on in surgical operations for an indefinite period. They might have done so but for the fortunate discovery of the anesthetic effects of nitrous oxide in 1845, three years after Ward's use of mesmerism, and of ether, and chloroform a couple of years later (Smith, 1927). Against these anesthetics there is a story of similar opposition and of the contention that anesthesia interferes with God's plan for the universe; but I have cited enough instances of this sort.

In fact the history of science is full of such examples. Elliotson made them his text when, after much opposition, he was finally invited in 1846 to deliver the Harveian Oration before the Royal College of Physicians. He could begin most aptly with the story of the opposition to Harvey's discovery of the circulation of the blood.

In modern psychology we have so far been spared the violent controversy that engages public attention, except in psychic research, which represents today a case almost exactly like that of mesmerism. It seems impossible to undertake psychic research without emotion, and the emotions of the investigators are present in part because it is an egotistic hypothesis. Like mesmerism it claims that a peculiar power is localized only in certain individuals, and it defines this power in terms of its effects and omits the causal term that is necessary to every scientific correlation or fact.

However, although modern psychology lacks these dramatic controversies that enlist the lay public on one side or the other, it is lacking neither in controversy nor in intolerance. I trust that I am still treading safe ground if I ask you to recall with me the famous controversy between Wundt and Stumpf about the tonal distances.

Into the elaborate intricacies of this controversy we cannot enter, nor do we need to do so. As is well known, musical interval follows a law like Weber's Law. A given interval is divided into two equal portions by a stimulus which is, in vibration rate, the geometric mean of the stimuli for the two extremes. Stumpf, with a musical background, believed that musical interval bore a close relation to the simple sensory properties of tones. Wundt, basing his view on experiments in the Leipzig laboratory by his pupil Lorenz, regarded sense-distances as less closely related to musical interval. Lorenz's results showed that observers in bisecting a tonal interval tended toward the arithmetical mean and not the geometric. About this difference the controversy waxed.

We should perhaps bear in mind the fact that the difference in question is small with respect to the tonal distances involved. On the other hand— and this was Wundt's ground for assurance—these seemingly small differences were large with respect to the scatter of the judgments, much larger than modern statisticians are accustomed to require. Stumpf, however, could not accept this view. For one thing he appealed to the extreme case as a *reductio ad absurdum*; if tonal distance is directly proportional to vibration rate, as Wundt claimed, then a major second like c^3–d^3, must include the same distance as the entire octave, c–c^1, three octaves below. This proposition seems so manifestly absurd that we can understand why Stumpf felt that Lorenz's results must be capable of being explained away, as he undertook to do argumentatively, in part by questioning the meaning of Lorenz's observers in judging tonal distance and the degree to which they were influenced by musical relationships.

Wundt had espoused Lorenz's results by publishing some of them in the third edition of the 'Physiologische Psychologie' (1887). Lorenz's paper came out in 1890. Then followed controversy, altogether of one hundred and forty-one pages. Each published thrice. First Stumpf (1890) printed sixty-seven pages, in which he reprinted portions of many of Lorenz's tables and sought to reinterpret them. There was almost no personal invective in the paper; nevertheless it is hardly impersonal to reprint another man's results and, in a paper almost as long as the original, argue elaborately to opposite conclusions. It is easy to imagine Wundt's feelings when the significance of the observations was thus called in question. Wundt (1891*a*), therefore, replied with a paper which included some personal advice to Stumpf. Stumpf's

(1891*a*) rejoinder adopted more nearly Wundt's tone. It was called 'Wundt's Antikritik.' Then Wundt (1891*b*) printed 'Eine Replik C. Stumpf's.' Finally the controversy closed in verbal exhaustion with Stumpf's (1891*b*) 'Mein Schlusswort gegen Wundt' and Wundt's (1892) 'Auch ein Schlusswort.' The discussion became less calm as it progressed. The two final *Schlusswörter* dealt each almost as much with the psychological problem of how the other psychologist conducted argument as with the psychological problem of tonal distances.

This controversy must be read to be appreciated, but I can perhaps give you the flavor of it. As I have said, Stumpf in his original criticism had little to say to which Wundt or Lorenz could have objected, except that they were wrong and should have drawn exactly the opposite conclusions. The only definite resort to the method of psychologizing opponent psychologists that I have found in the entire paper is this: "This extension, however, certainly does not amount to as much as it should according to Wundt, who here, as he so often does, has exaggerated a correct idea into another that is falsely inverted with respect to it."

Wundt in his reply studied to be calm. He said twice that he would test Stumpf's conclusions 'sine ira et studio,' without anger and vehemence. Such a statement, however, carries a latent as well as a manifest content. When the orator says, 'I will call my opponent neither a liar nor a fool,' he is not doing just exactly what he says he is doing. There is not the least doubt at all that Stumpf had hurt Wundt's feelings, and that Wundt was thus moved to many of his remarks, including his final sentences, which read as follows: "Stumpf knows, I hope, as well as I, that whoever would further the psychology of tone must have something more than musical experience. However, it can do no harm, I believe, if he will strengthen himself in this conviction by the result which he now achieves [as the consequence of this criticism]. Somewhat sooner then will this polemic also have for him the further result, that he will learn to value, not only as the best but also as the most useful virtue for a scientific researcher, this: to be just toward others, to be severe toward himself." This peroration does not seem to me to clinch the problem of the tonal distances. I suppose, however, that Wundt thought it did.

I have not time to cull numerous examples from the remaining four articles. You can imagine what was said after Wundt has thus advised Stumpf 'without anger and vehemence.' To Wundt's personal advice about being just toward others and severe toward himself, Stumpf, everything considered, replied quite calmly. He said, "Wundt is accustomed to imprint on his polemics a kind of moral stamp. . . . It is distasteful to me to make many words about the matter." Wundt reiterated that he found nothing in Stumpf's rejoinder "from beginning to end but distortion and fictions. 'I have studied these things and you have not!' Upon these words I restrain myself from judgment," he concluded.

Finally Stumpf, who had been consistently the more reluctant to pursue the personal side of this controversy, was goaded in his *Schlusswort* into a frank characterization of Wundt's polemical method. He wrote: "I abstain from a detailed rejoinder to the new voluminous reply of Wundt. For it, which pours out his expression of blind thoughts, any word would be too much. Those, however, who wish to compare, point for point, his new article with mine and especially with the earlier one upon which it is based, will find therein for themselves, as in his preceding article, the same mixture of untrue assertions, of confusions, of mutilations of the course of my thought, of obscure imputations and negligences, of infirm evasions, of fallacies of every kind, and of frequent assurances of the incapacity and ignorance of his adversary." Each of the first six items of the list Stumpf supported with long footnotes, omitting only citations of his own alleged incapacity and ignorance.

Stumpf started the controversy, but Wundt made it personal. It is plain that Stumpf was drawn into this aspect of it with reluctance, and that, being more tender-minded than Wundt, he felt it keenly. More than thirty years later, in writing a short account of his life and thought, the affair still rankled. He devoted to the controversy a paragraph, which he placed in the biographical half of his article (Schmidt, 1924, 218). Stumpf regarded the controversy as an event in his life more than as a psychological contribution; but Wundt, the tough-minded, made no reference to this little affair in his 'Erlebtes und Erkanntes.'

Now I feel that most of you will be disposed to condemn this controversy and to blame Wundt the more for the part he took, and yet I believe that there are not so many of us who, on the next occasion when our work is attacked in print, will in reply studiously avoid trying to make our antagonist seem to our readers like the fool that we believe him to be. We have not yet solved my fundamental dilemma; we have only illustrated it.

However, before I discuss the major issue, let me point out that controversy of this kind is not limited to Germany. In the nineties there was the American controversy about reaction times, with Titchener and Baldwin the chief protagonists (Baldwin, 1895; Titchener, 1895). Titchener was upholding the Leipzig view that the muscular reaction is always about one tenth of a second shorter than the sensorial, provided you have subjects so well practiced that they can assume the two attitudes at will. Baldwin was contending that people are of different types and that some react more quickly in a sensory manner and some in a motor manner. Baldwin thought that Titchener was misrepresenting the truth by selecting subjects that would fit his theory. Titchener thought that Baldwin had wandered from the straight scientific path in concerning himself with a problem of human nature instead of the scientific problem of the generalized human mind. Of course, as Angell and Moore showed eventually, both were right; yet neither seemed to be able to see how the other was right, obvious as the matter is now. If Baldwin wanted to work with individual differences in true American fashion, what matter if Titchener thought that personal idiosyncrasies are not the problem of science. If Titchener got his difference with *general* practice (not, of course, with practice for giving the desired result), why did Baldwin mind that training in the direction of attention should counteract the effect of natural modes of attention? Yet each was so sure of his view that neither ever seemed in publication to understand the other. Each, like Wundt and Stumpf, made a moral judgment. Titchener thought Baldwin unscientific because he used subjects untrained, in the Leipzig sense, to precise observation. Baldwin thought Titchener unscientific because he closed his eyes to a problem of the natural world.

Nor is controversy of this sort limited to the ancients of the late nineteenth century. I could have taken my examples from the present decade, but I have thus far forborne because it must be hard for you to believe that my remarks carry with them no whit of praise or blame. Perhaps I can briefly make my point that the styles have not greatly changed by a few citations in which I obscure the source.

Only a few years ago one psychologist complained, in a long critical article, about the practice of a colleague, who, he asserted, would praise the work of his friends and condemn similar work by others. This controversy is full of instances germane to my subject-matter, but I shall content myself by citing only the closing sentence of the paper I have mentioned. It reads: "We live close to one another with our similar problems, which approach today as nearly as does all the community of work. If here, as in a thickly planted forest, conflicting growth occurs, it is a thing of the natural order. If, however, it falls out as in a horse-race, where someone uses the whip in order to lash the noses of the neighboring horses, then I must raise a protest against it in the name of fair play." [3] Recently a psychologist, usually very conservative in his utterances, actually likened a colleague to 'a soap-box evangelist.' Within the year another psychologist has said, in print, of still another: "To the charge of misunderstanding must now be added the charges of misreading, misinterpreting, and misquoting," and then, like Stumpf in his *Schlusswort* to Wundt, has proceeded in two pages to document these items. It sounds scandalous, that a scientist should not only misread and misinterpret, but actually misquote. Yet I doubt if either author is less well-intentioned than the other.

You may say, of course, that all this is but the scientific 'game,' that it is the way things are done. I submit, however, that these expressions are not mere stylistic conventions of writing; often there is even more real feeling than the words express. Wundt's moral prescriptions for Stumpf in 1891 were still disagreeing with him in 1924. We have all known psychologists who were supposed not to be able to meet each other socially lest something should happen. Most of us know what it is to feel bitter about published criticism, especially when it is personal; yet, if science is the dispassionate search for truth by the empirical method, can it flourish in the face of passion?

Let us go back to Wundt and Stumpf. The argument is, so far as it dealt with the tonal distances, very evenly balanced. Titchener said (1905, II, ii, 242) that he read the controversy three times, and decided twice for Wundt and once for Stumpf. Since we still do not know the correct answer to their problem, we might say that the chances are even for either of them being right; and thus the chances are even for either being wrong. It was a battle of giants; why discriminate? But, if scientists are seeking only for the truth and not to prove themselves right, then there are even chances that Stumpf would have convinced Wundt, or Wundt Stumpf, and only a twenty-five per cent chance that each would have convinced the other and have thus continued the controversy. I make this ludicrous use of the elementary principles of probability in order to show you how certain you would have been from the start that neither was going to be convinced. They both could not be right; each knew that; each, as a psychologist, knew about human fallibility and prejudice even in the pre-Freudian days, and could therefore realize that there was a good chance of his being somewhere in the wrong. Plainly there is a perseverative tendency in scientific thinking.

It would be easy now to draw the moral that the scientific value of an investigator varies inversely with his emotionality in scientific matters, but I do not believe that such a conclusion would be true. It is not only the lesser men who quarrel. The great are particularly adept at it, and the lesser may perhaps only be copying them. Rather it seems to me that we have a true dilemma, that the drive that urges men to laborious research and to the braving of public criticism with their conclusions, is the drive which perseveres and makes them persist against criticism. Thus the same thing that drives them toward the truth may also keep them from it. We still face, then, the uncomfortable picture with which I began. However, before I attempt even an incomplete solution, I want to deal briefly with the second of my scientific paradoxes, which I promised you long ago.

II. This second paradox is that new movements in psychology, and presumably in thought at large, are most obviously negative. That which claims to be progress, that which is presently accepted as progress, is nevertheless most patently an undoing of the progress of the past. How then is there any real progress in what appears on inspection to be a regress? The answer, I think, is psychological, but before I come to it, let me try to establish my point about the negativism of progress.

Recently I have tried to show for psychology that trite historian's point that nothing which is supposed to be new is ever really new (Boring, 1927). The course of scientific thought is gradual, as it is in individual thought. In the individual it is hard to distinguish imagination from memory; careful scrutiny of a creative imagination seems to reveal little that is brand-new. So it is in scientific thought. The ideas occur as the result of individual thinking, or the facts are found as the result of experiment, both are put forward, and nothing much happens. Then, perhaps many years later, someone comes along, sees relationships, puts things together, and formulates a great theory or founds a great movement. Often the formulator or founder is not even the compounder, but another man, who because of his personality or because of the times in which he speaks, has the capacity for gaining attention. So he originates, as we say, a step in progress, lending his name to a theory or a school, and it is left to dull historians to discover and reiterate the fact that de Moivre discovered the Gaussian law and Charles Bell the Müllerian doctrine of the specific energy of nerves. Founders are generally promoters, in science as elsewhere, and we have therefore here to consider the mechanisms of public attention.

With respect to scientific movements there seems to exist something like Newton's third law of motion: action equals reaction. You cannot move— in the sense of starting a movement—unless you have something to push against. The explanation of this law, I think, lies in the relation of movements to public attention. Science can actually, by the empirical method, so I am disposed to believe, lift itself by its own boot straps, but the result is not what we call a 'movement' because motion can be defined only with respect to a frame of reference. A movement must move with respect to something, and progress must move away from something, if the movement is to command observational attention. It is therefore the business of the founders of new schools, the promoters and propagandists, to call persistent attention to what they are not, just as one political party is forever emphasizing the short-comings of the other.

Thus we see that movements are founded upon controversy, and that all we have been saying about the effect of controversy on controversialists applies also to the schools. A school may be flexible and disposed toward change and growth in all directions except those against which it has set itself. Here it is hardened by its own drive. A movement cannot move backwards and persist, and the question as to which direction is backwards is decided by the opposition which brought the movement into being. Moreover the drive forward leads to an over-estimation of the distance moved. The negativism of progress is thus essential to observed progress.

Now let me illustrate.

The greatest foundation within modern psychology is Wundt's promotion of experimental psychology itself. The question is often asked: Did Fechner or Wundt found experimental psychology? Fechner came first and may be its father, but Wundt is certainy its founder. Fechner with his psychophysics was trying to found, not experimental psychology, but a spiritualistic metaphysics. Wundt, from within physiology, arrived at his view from a study of the relationships of the sciences, in a day when physiology was as self-conscious as psychology is now.

In the interests of the new movement Wundt had to overcome many obstacles. He had to write a scientific handbook for experimental psychology. He had to get himself a chair of philosophy and pervert it to experimental practices. He had to found a laboratory, a real laboratory of rooms with instruments in them. He had to get the experiments going, and then to found a journal for their publication. To make his point it was necessary for him, in all sincerity, to exaggerate. The new experimental science must be exhibited to the world as a lusty infant with none of its organs missing. Thus Wundt, when experimental results were lacking, resorted in his hand-book to speculation to fill the chapters. There was certainly an over-emphasis on apparatus, peculiarly psychological apparatus. If psychology was an independent science, it must have apparatus to distinguish it from philosophy, and special apparatus to distinguish it from physiology.

All this we can readily understand because we ourselves are still of this self-conscious school of Wundt's. The struggle to separate psychology from philosophy in American universities is still not quite yet over. The habit of writing complete text-books in the face of incomplete knowledge still persists. There is still, I believe, a tendency to collect and exhibit much psychological apparatus without regard to the immediate needs of research. If you do not know what it is like to be on the inside of a new movement, consult therefore your own minds.

Yet this movement for a scientific psychology was largely negativistic. It was primarily directed against philosophy. It was a long time before Wundt had done any experimental work equal in importance to Fechner's, and yet Fechner thought he was working in experimental philosophy. The experimental work of the sixties and seventies was performed mostly by physiologists. Of course, we say now that the final result has demonstrated the positive nature of the original idea, although there remain philosophers who do not agree. I do not believe, however, that the present outcome reacts upon the situation of sixty years ago. Whatever has happened since, there was a chance then that experimental psychology might prove sterile. But it is difficult to argue clearly where our own prejudices are involved. Let us consider the movements within psychology.

In the nineties there was the school of *Gestaltqualität*. It was a reaction against the current elementarism, although it did not itself avoid elementarism as successfully as does the modern *Gestalt*. The chemical combination of sensations was obviously inadequate for the explanation of perceptions. Nevertheless the form-qualities, the founded contents, the superiora, and the act of founding turned out to have no empirical definition and the movement failed. Or did it not fail, but live on to be reborn in *Gestaltpsychologie?*

The answer does not matter. My point is that it would not have been a movement if it had not been directed against something.

So it was also with Külpe's school of imageless thought. The very word 'imageless' is a negative term. The movement was nothing more than a protest against sensationism. It is easy to say this now, but what of the enthusiasm of the Würzburgers for the *Bewusstseinslagen* and *Bewusstheiten?* They did not think that their movement was negative. They thought they had discovered a new kind of mental stuff. You have only to read the controversial literature to see how the love of self-preservation sustained each side.

In America we used to have functionalism. It was a revolt of the colonial psychologists against Germany, their mother-country. The controversy between Titchener and Baldwin was a phase of the whole. Germany was more philosophical and America more practical, as America's rôle in the history of mental tests has shown. Chicago functionalism was the explicit movement, but I think it was but symptomatic of what was quietly going on all over America, except in some protected places like Ithaca, where Penelope still remained faithful to the marriage vow. Functionalism centered attention upon the individual and the individual organism. Leipzig could still work with the generalized human mind; in Chicago, and in Columbia too, they had *minds.* I think of this revolt as the most radical since Wundt's original heterodoxy, and I also recall that the explicit functional movement itself was largely negative and got little further along positively than did the school at Würzburg.

In those days the opposite of functionalism was structuralism, but nobody—except perhaps some graduate students—ever called himself a 'structuralist.' Titchener adopted the phrase 'structural psychology' and abandoned it long before it went out of use. No, the functionalists had to have something definite to push against, and it was they only who talked about 'structuralists.'

We have this same phenomenon in behaviorism. For years the American tendency has been to have two behaviorists growing where one grew before. Any number of psychologists have been willing to call themselves behaviorists and to be proud of it, but they missed badly a definite opposition to set them off. Words have been coined for the opponent school, words like 'introspectionism' or 'introspectionalism,' but I have never heard anyone apply such a term to himself. Someone once suggested 'Titchenerism,' which had the advantage of seeming to indicate at least one Titchenerist definitely. My point is that all along behaviorism has been seeking an enemy so that it could disprove the charge that it is fighting windmills, for it must fight something; it is a movement.

I know it is not fair to leave behaviorism so casually, but I must do so. Behaviorism is not new; this has been shown more than once. Yet Watson is right in thinking that he founded it. He could not have founded it if it had been new; it would not yet have been ready to found. It denies consciousness as the subject-matter of investigation, and therefore the so-called introspective method for investigating it. In this it is negative. It goes on investigating what is left, bereft of an enemy since many of those whom it woos for enemies would also investigate the same problems. It is unfortunately limited by its parental inheritance, for it cannot get over trying to translate consciousness and the sensory quale into behavioristic terms, as it has already translated association into the conditioned reflex. Respect for parents may be laudable and yet hinder the free development of youth. Behaviorism is already past its prime as a movement, because movements exist upon protest and it no longer needs to protest. Had it been less successful it might have lived longer as a movement and a shorter time as a method.

Gestaltpsychologie is in the same box with behaviorism. Born at the same time its development was hindered by the war, so that it is now less mature. Its infant cries of protest against an unkind world still persist. Everybody must know now what *Gestaltpsychologie* is not. It is not elementaristic or associationistic. It eschews the vague concepts of the past, like attention and attitude, and cultivates new vague concepts in their place, like insight, closure, and level. When Wertheimer and Koffka were describing it, they worked largely in negative terms. There is no general positive content of *Gestaltpsychologie* with which anybody disagrees. Still the voice cries in the wilderness, whereas the kingdom of God is already with man. *Gestaltpsychologie* was not new in 1912; it was quite ready to be founded. It is now a movement. Presently, I think, it too will become simply psychology.

I am now ready to form a conclusion.

I believe that I have shown that movements and the rise of schools are a form of controversy, often one-sided because directed against no particular antagonist. Thus, as controversy, the movement introduces all the psychological advantages and disadvantages of personal controversy.

Discussion is relevant to scientific work, but controversy is more than discussion. It involves emotion: and passion, while of itself irrelevant to scientific procedure, enters to prejudice reason and to fix the debaters more firmly in their opinions. If it were possible, scientific discussion should be dispassionate, not only in form but in spirit, for otherwise progress toward the truth is hindered.

Since the controversy of a movement is apt to be less personally pointed, especially when there is only one active party to the quarrel, participation in a movement may have the advantage of blinding the scientist less than participation in a personal controversy. On the other hand, movements, in so far as they are blind, have the further disadvantage of lending to blindness the social support of the group within the school.

As psychologists, we cannot, however, afford to condemn controversy, be it ever so emotional. If we could read out of the body scientific every investigator who lost his temper with an opponent and kept it lost, we should read out those very men who, because of their drives or prejudices or whatever we like to call that conative component of their personalities, had made the positive contributions to the science. Research is something more than a habit and it requires something more than patience. It requires, among other things, an irresistible urge, bolstered up, I think, not so much by curiosity, as by egotism. This urge may carry one to the truth, beyond it, or even directly away from it. Vision and blindness are here alike, for both are attention, and attention to one thing is inattention to another. The same urge helps and hinders progress.

Must the truth then forever transcend the individual? Is the stage of science like the court of law, where attorneys contend and only the judge speaks the truth? This is the view of research that I find so personally abhorrent and yet seem forced to accept.

There is, however, an incomplete solution for the dilemma. A scientist should, I think, cultivate dissociation. Too much has been said in favor of the integration of the personality, and too little in favor of dissociation. The scientist needs to be a dual personality. He needs to be able to become the prosecutor or the judge at will. He can then stand off and evaluate himself at times, and perhaps even arrange things so that the prosecuting personality will fare more happily when it returns to dominate his person. But I would not have him be the judge too often, for then the assured, prejudiced, productive personality might get 'squeezed out,' and science would be the loser.

I recommend this dissociation, not because it will make us happier, not merely because it is fun to be the judge as well as the prosecutor, but because I have no expectation that it could be so complete that there would be no interaction between the two personalities. I should hope for a tempering of the prosecutor by the judge so that there would really be more vision and less blindness, and so that psychology would benefit thereby. Then we should have less futile controversy, fewer people devoting their lives to lost causes, even more candid and thus more fruitful discussion, less talk and more research.

I have asked you tonight to play the judge with me. I think it is important for psychology, still so talkative a science, that we should all be practiced in being judge as well as prosecutor. Do I dare in closing to point you a moral, as Wundt so ungraciously did to Stumpf? If there is any precept that comes out of all this talk, it is rather that we should beware of precepts. Psychology needs both judiciousness and effective prejudices; and I cannot resist the impression that we shall do well to cultivate and welcome both.

NOTES

1. The full description of the Ward case and of the action of the R. M. C. S. upon it are given in a little pamphlet by John Elliotson, 'Numerous Cases of Surgical Operations without Pain in the Mesmeric States; with Remarks,' 1843. The 'remarks' are numerous and caustic. The pamphlet I have seen was published in Philadelphia, but I think it was also printed in London.
2. I have omitted all mention of James Braid, the reputed discoverer of hypnosis, on account of lack of time. See Braid (1843). Braid also met opposition, but he did not break with the medical profession because he refrained from criticizing it, because he laid no claim to a peculiar personal power but sought to explain hypnosis in normal physiological terms, because he avoided the word 'mesmerism,' because he opposed Elliotson, and because Elliotson attacked him. (See my remarks on this situation in Boring, 1927.)
3. The quotation is as literal as anonymity permits.

Dissent

▣▣ 1961

THERE is a sense in which partial achievement is better than complete success, a sense in which the unattainable is the best goal.
Human beings and other living organisms are adaptive systems. Their unremitting effort is directed toward an adaptation which is never perfect because the constantly changing environment in which the system operates
requires a perpetual compensatory adaptation. You would think that an
organism might sometimes achieve complete adaptation to rest complacent
with no adaptive activity necessary, but we know that such a psychophysiological nirvana would turn out to be failure and not success. Man and rat
seek activity; for either of them complete undisturbed adaptation would end
in neurosis or psychosis. Sensory deprivation does not come to an organism
as success, and release from responsibility is not what man or rat really needs.
It is for this reason that increased leisure is not a proper goal for Labor.

Long ago Richard Avenarius (1888) expressed this paradox in his conception of the life processes as vital series of changes set up by the perpetual
imbalance of the organism between the catabolic environmental forces and
the anabolic internal adaptive forces. The reason that this paradox is obvious and not preposterous is that life is a series of events within an ever-
changing system, and activity—change adjusted to other change—is the
essential and indeed the criterion of life.

A similar paradox occurs in the intellectual life. One gets ahead in the
kind of thinking that advances civilization by being forever remotivated by
frustration. We dislike frustration but we need it. We need it in order to
avoid it, and our dislike of it is useful in that it provides the motive to avoid
it. This is indeed how science goes on forever, how every success in research
poses more new problems than could be seen in the original undertaking, how
knowledge never comes anywhere near abolishing ignorance. An investigator

Reprinted with permission from *Contemporary Psychology*, 1961, **6**, 395.

welcomes and uses new problems like a rat in an activity cage. Science and scholarship constitute a perpetual struggle to advance wisdom, yet how horrible it would be were knowledge to become complete, were life-giving ignorance to be abolished!

It is such a view of intellectual avidity that suggests why dissent plays so crucial a catalyzing role in creative thinking. Dissent is a generator of energizing frustration. It is the occasion for renewed activity, the interjection that protects a thinker from the deprivation inherent in terminal success.

And it is here that you may perceive the explanation for one of CP's dominating motives during these first six years of its existence. CP has welcomed the frustration of dissent as a stimulus to the intellectual avidity that it has been striving to promote. CP—not without some bitter criticism—has been as much concerned in the dynamic undertaking of stimulating thought as in the duller service function of purveying information. That is why CP is so much less disturbed by disagreement within its pages than are the dissidents themselves. In science truth is not absolute—so CP keeps insisting— and CP would feel that it had accomplished a worthier mission if it had tortured its readers with a healthy contribution of indecision than if it drugged them with a full measure of the incontrovertible.

To this philosophy many of CP's readers will offer vigorous dissent. Good! The generation of dissent is part of CP's mission. It is from frustration that civilization emerges.

Science and the Meaning

of Its History

𒐪𒐪𒐪𒐪𒐪𒐪𒐪𒐪𒐪𒐪𒐪𒐪𒐪𒐪𒐪𒐪 1959

THE past is the vivarium of science, where we can see it actually at work. There are good reasons for studying the history of science, but the two most common arguments for doing so are both, I am convinced, wrong.

One should not study the past of science in order to project the trends and make a good guess about where science—or even *a* science—is going to be next year or in twenty years. A knowledge of history is not a crystal ball. It is true that the progress of thought is determined by psychological and social laws, and that we can often see after an event how it was predetermined by its antecedents. Specific prediction, nevertheless, almost always fails, or is right by mere chance, because the efficient antecedents are too numerous and too complexly related to be correctly understood. Laplace, for instance, thought that a complete knowledge of the present must necessarily, in a predetermined world, imply both the past and the future, and this is indeed the view of causal determinism, which is not a practical guide through the complexities of reality. The scientist's tomorrow constantly surprises him; we almost never know enough about the present to be sure of the future.

Nuclear physics, the scientific achievement of this midcentury, has a long and distinguished ancestry, but did the physicists of the 1930's suspect the impending revolution that is now an accomplished fact in the 1950's? Would anyone, looking over the American collegiate scene of 1800–1850—seeing the profusion of small sectarian colleges, with Presbyterian battling Baptist to infiltrate a board of trustees and make learning safe for righteousness—would any such observer have predicted America's relatively enthusiastic acceptance of evolutionary theory in the 1870's? Could anyone have foreseen how the

Reprinted with permission from *The Key Reporter*, 1959, **20**, No. 4. Edwin G. Boring was a Phi Beta Kappa Visiting Scholar in 1958–1959.

GI Bill would undermine athleticism at Harvard (to speak only of the university I know best), consign the once honorific gentleman's C to the museum of past curiosities, and, within limits, make learning respectable? Who would have predicted in 1930 that the professor's lecture on psychological sex-differences would become dull for lack of a sizzling feminist in his class to resent his conclusion? Indeed culture changes.

Or consider a case of failure eventually turning into success. The brilliant neuropsychologist Karl Lashley spent his life "in search of the engram," a phrase that in 1950 was the title of one of his last papers. The engram is the trace in the brain representing a remembered perception or idea. For twenty-five years Lashley seemed to wage a losing battle. He kept finding that nothing stays put in the brain's cerebral cortex. A particular spot has one function today and another tomorrow; or if one cuts the spot out of the brain, its owner presently learns to use a new spot for the same old function. At one time it looked as if Lashley's skillful, ingenious, and indefatigable labor was destined to dissolve in failure.

But the face of nature was then changing under the combined attacks of physicists and psychologists. "Field theory" came into physics, the realization that causality often does not work between little bits of stuff, but only between large patterns of activity. The Gestalt psychologists, who were rebels against conventional psychological atomism, made comparable discoveries for human preception; they found that one can understand an optical illusion only by considering it as a whole. And that was just what Lashley had also been proving for the pattern of communal excitation in the brain: one can get useful laws for the brain only by considering the whole and ignoring the parts of which it is made up. When Lashley died last year he was honored by all for his researches, which had changed the manner in which men think about the action of the brain, and honored by some who not so long ago had thought his life's enterprise would come to nothing.

Such are the reasons for the failure of prediction in a predetermined world. There are just too many surprises, there is too much ignorance of the many possibilities; one never knows half enough beforehand. Afterward one can see why events followed as they did; but that is afterward.

The other wrong reason for studying the past of science is to protect oneself from rediscovering something already known. This argument, like the other, fails because of the enormous complexity of science. Psychology, a young science, has listed more than 300,000 articles in its published bibliographies merely since 1894. The investigator must do his own historical research for each new topic he tackles. Published historical perpective shows only the high spots, the great trends, not the specific history; and even a small library has in it more facts than can ever be carried by a single brain.

So there we have two negatives. There is nevertheless a good reason for knowing the history of science. One finds that he needs to know about the past, not in order to predict the future, but in order to understand the present.

Enter the Psychologist. Such study is especially the psychologist's business, for science is a human activity that is both social and intellectual. Taken in perspective, it is the psychodynamics of the intellectual interaction between people, books, and nature. Men use observation and experiment to ask questions of nature and get back the answers; but the work of many men is required, and the books enable them to communicate across the centuries and also to remember more than their brains could ever carry.

There are at present no good texts on the psychodynamics of the history of science. A reader of the histories is supposed to induce for himself the general principles that facilitate or hinder discovery, that control the mind in its perpetual quest for new knowledge. Nevertheless, some of the basic principles are known.

It is obvious that discovery often waits until the times are ready for it. Then it comes, perhaps not easily, but often to more than one man at the same time. Both Briggs and Napier invented logarithms independently in 1614, and their work had been anticipated in 1611 by an obscure investigator. Why three men then and not someone else long before? Adams and LeVerrier both discovered the planet Neptune in 1845 by predicting its position from the irregularities of the planet Uranus. This must have been the right sort of thing to be doing in 1845, but was 1830 too early? Charles Darwin and Alfred Russel Wallace both formulated the same theory of evolution in 1858; although Darwin had worked out his theory through long years, it was still unpublished when Wallace sent his own paper to Darwin for comment.

There is something in the times that facilitates discovery and invention. Goethe called it the *Zeitgeist*. Some people call it the climate of opinion or of thought. Everyone thinks and speaks and writes under its influence; it is an enormous body of fact, opinion, prejudice, and attitude, the most plagiarized unwritten scripture in existence. The first principle in the psychodynamics of the history of thought is this unconscious facilitating effect of the *Zeitgeist* on belief and action.

But the *Zeitgeist* has a dual role. It pushes one idea into bloom but nips another in the bud. It is hard to think an idea before the times are ready for it; and when an independent soul actually does so, often he does not fully understand the new thought himself, and usually no one else accepts it. In 1604 Kepler concluded correctly that the crystalline body in the eye is a lens that casts an image of the outside world on the retina, an image that is reversed, right for left and up for down. Why, he asked, do we then see right side up when the information furnished the brain is upside down? The *Zeitgeist* said —and had been saying ever since the third century b.c.—that perception is the little man inside the head receiving the images that the outside world sends to him along the nerves, and this view is still to be found in common sense. Various wise men during the last three hundred years have seen, however, that the inversion of the retinal image does not matter, that one quickly finds out that excitation of the top of the retina means that its data come from the bottom of the outside world. The point here is that every one of these wise men had to fight the persistent *Zeitgeist* to substitute their rather simple wisdom for the simple error of common sense. Kepler himself never got past the *Zeitgeist*, but continued to believe that he had found a puzzle in need of explanation.

Independence, Prejudice, and Pride. Sometimes a man's greatness lies in his ability to resist the *Zeitgeist*. When in 1850 Helmholtz tried to measure the speed of conduction by the nerves, everyone else was sure that this feat could not be accomplished: that the speed of nerves must approximate the speed of light, that one does not will to wiggle his finger and then wait for the impulse to arrive and the finger to move.

Another principle is what has been called the scientist's motivational predicament. The predicament is that humility helps progress and egoism hinders it; but at the same time, egoism helps and humility hinders.

Humility's companion is objectivity, which is part of the scientific attitude itself. Science eschews prejudice and bias, and—formally at least—personal involvement. One advantage of the experimental method is that its logic helps the investigator escape from his own preferences in interpreting his results. He tries to be like posterity, the posterity that assesses yesterday's mooted problems with the assurance of having no investment of its own at stake. So much can prestige hinder progress that sometimes, the physicist Max Planck said, a theory will hang on after it has been discredited, continuing in use as long as its author lives.

The other horn of this motivational dilemma is that egoism—prejudiced, biased, self-assertive ego-involvement—is what usually furnishes the drive to get research done and the resulting papers published. There is nothing like a sense of rightness—or righteousness—to drive a man to work, even when posterity is going to turn thumbs down on his great endeavor. This rule holds for the isolated egoist, for the tightly knit school or in-group with its own special vocabulary that binds its members together and makes them almost unintelligible to out-groups, and for the great movement that characterizes a nation or a half-century. Attack and controversy always strengthen the will to achieve. Where has the wisdom of humility gone now, as we face the confident genius or the entrepreneurs of a new movement?

The motivational predicament is, of course, soluble in the large group and in the historical process, where there is a division of labor. One man's objectivity may then offset another man's drive. The basic contradiction can be partly resolved in the individual by a fluctuation of his attitudes: he can check his own enthusiasm long enough to take a critical look at it and experience pride when he succeeds in proving himself wrong. So it comes about that science gets along, driven and checked, in spite of this kind of difficulty.

Closely related to egoism is the dedication of so many successful scientists, the compulsive ones who keep confusing work with play, who look forward eagerly to a "vacation" so that they can "work." Compulsion is not, however, identical with egoism. A humble compulsive may labor for years and produce as wise and judicious an assessment as ever there was. Genius is not a capacity for taking pains, but taking pains can be very effective though genius be lacking.

Knowledge Helps Too. Certainly erudition helps the scientist. He whose memory is well packed with many items of many kinds and who can scan his stock quickly when something new is needed will help science most if other things are equal. Genius may be the habit of having useful insights, but insight depends on erudition. The boy in the experiment on productive thinking took one look at the task in mental arithmetic, $39 \times 41 = ?$, and said "1599." How could he know so quickly? He noted that $39 \times 41 = (40 - 1)(40 + 1)$, that the product of the sum and difference of two numbers equals the difference of their squares, so $1600 - 1 = 1599$. He was erudite. It is improbable that Archimedes, untutored in algebra, could have done so well.

If new insights are to occur frequently in science, then the investigators ought to be exposed as often as possible to other cultures, to other habits of thought. To occur with maximal frequency, new insights need more help than they can get from individual erudition, for they come most often when scientists can escape the conventionalizing restraints of the *Zeitgeist*. Interdisciplinary research tends to do just that. So does the internationalization of science.

From all this it follows that crash programs of research are not too likely to be successful, a fact that the public has failed to understand ever since an intense need produced the atomic bomb a few years after the need arose. Those years, however, followed several decades of deliberate basic research. The crash attack on cancer moves ahead but slowly. Seldom can we hurry history. Money will buy time, and history needs time, yet it is doubtful whether with twice the money and twice the manpower, the inhibiting *Zeitgeist* can move ahead twice as fast.

Science would be much better understood, even by investigators themselves, if this psychological frame of reference were always kept in mind. It is much too simple to think of scientists as right or wrong, as clear or muddled, as prejudiced or objective. Each individual effort is an eddy in the total stream of science; and we shall become much wiser, get much nearer the truth, if we remember always to look at the stream as a whole and notice the eddies only as they contribute to the sweep of the main current. "*La science,*" said the physiologist Flourens, "*n'est pas; elle devient.*"

Human Nature vs. Sensation:

William James and the

Psychology of the Present

🗌🗌🗌🗌🗌🗌🗌🗌🗌🗌🗌🗌🗌🗌🗌🗌🗌🗌🗌🗌🗌🗌🗌🗌🗌🗌🗌 1942

William James on Sensation

WILLIAM JAMES and the psychology of sensation: that is my topic. Yet the outstanding thing about James in this connection is that he did not like sensation as a chapter in psychology and neglected it as much as he could. Disliking it, he nevertheless entertained it with his usual conscientiousness, while he disapproved withal the labors of most of its sponsors. Their researches, from 1860 to 1890, seemed to him for the most part unimportant and the controversy which they aroused futile, although they were, nevertheless, the *raison d'être* of the new experimental psychology. For all that it is James' picturesque disparagement of them that is remembered and quoted by every student of his *Principles*. His apt *bons mots* have outlived the memory for their occasions.

At first glance James' attitude seems to present us with a contradiction. The new experimental psychology of 1870 and thereabouts was, for the most part, made up of the researches of Weber, Fechner, Helmholtz, Wundt, Aubert, Mach, and Vierordt—all investigations of sensation: Weber and the cutaneous *Ortsinn*: Fechner and the psychophysical methods; Helmholtz on vision and hearing; Wundt on the visual perception of depth; Aubert on light and color; Mach on vision and time; Vierordt on the *Zeitsinn*. This was the new physiological psychology which James had first heard about and then read, which he chose as his *Fach* in the early '70's. If it captured his thought then, why had he turned against it by 1890? He wrote then in the *Principles*:

> Within a few years what one may call a microscopic psychology has arisen in Germany, carried on by experimental methods, asking of course every mo-

Reprinted with permission from *The American Journal of Psychology*, 1942, **55**, 310–327. This paper was written for a Symposium on William James and the Psychology of the Present to be held at Harvard University in commemoration of the centenary of James' birth. The War prevented the Symposium. The paper was read before the Harvard Psychological Colloquium.

ment for introspective data, but eliminating their uncertainty by operating on a large scale and taking statistical means. This method taxes patience to the utmost, and hardly could have arisen in a country whose natives could be *bored*. Such Germans as Weber, Fechner, Vierordt and Wundt obviously cannot; and their success has brought into the field an array of younger experimental psychologists, bent on studying the *elements* of the mental life, dissecting them from the gross results in which they are embedded, and as far as possible reducing them to quantitative scales. The simple and open method of attack having done what it can, the method of patience, starving out, and harassing to death is tried; the Mind must submit to a regular *siege*, in which minute advantages gained night and day by the forces that hem her in must sum themselves up at last into her overthrow. There is little left of the grand style about these new prism, pendulum, and chronograph-philosophers. They mean business, not chivalry. What generous divination, and that superiority in virtue which was thought by Cicero to give a man the best insight into nature, have failed to do, their spying and scraping, their deadly tenacity and almost diabolic cunning, will doubtless some day bring about (James, 1890*a*, I, 192 f.).

If that is what James thought about the new psychology, why did he ever enlist under its banner?

The answer to that question has two parts. In the first place, James was not a man to enlist under any banner. He never wanted to join any movement. His curiosity and imagination had been captured by the possibilities of the new psychology, not by its achievements, and he saw in it, moreover, a means whereby he could remain secure in physiology, where he had had his training and held a post, and yet cultivate philosophy without assuming the full responsibilities of that more difficult discipline, as he conceived it to be. Others in those days had to make similar decisions. Wundt, starting in as a physiologist, had argued himself into his own synthetic brand of experimental philosophy—a chair of philosophy in a psychological laboratory, an experimental journal called *Philosophische Studien*, a set of systematic handbooks on physiological psychology, logic, ethics, and systematic philosophy. Stumpf, who loved music most and had been converted by Brentano to the rigors of philosophy, chose psychology for his *Fach*, because it was the only field, besides esthetics, where he could philosophize by experimenting with music. Like James he grew up into philosophy and away from the laboratory.

That is the second point about James' relation to the new sensory psychology: He grew away from it, and it grew away from him. In 1872, when James was only thirty, when Fechner's *Psychophysik* was only twelve and Wundt's *Physiologische Psychologie* was not quite born, James' imagination could be caught by the possibilities of a new science. Eighteen years later, when the *Principles* was published, James had been disillusioned enough to write the passage that I have quoted. Everyone knows how he said of Fechner and psychophysics:

> But it would be terrible if even such a dear old man as this could saddle our Science forever with his patient whimsies, and, in a world so full of more

nutritious objects of attention, compel all future students to plough through
the difficulties, not only of his own works, but of the still drier ones written in
his refutation (James, 1890*a*, I, 549).

There lay the trouble. Patient whimsies. Unnutritious objects of attention.
This new psychology, a promising adolescent in 1870 was growing up into a
dull intolerant bigot in 1890, or so it seemed to James. Where then lies the
truth? Was James at fault, or the new psychology, or both or neither? Just
how much more nutritious could the new psychology have been? Wundt's
meat was James' poison. Was James' Wundt's?

In the first place, let it be said that James hated sham and that there was
a very considerable amount of false scientification in this period when the
new psychology was being formed. Someone has said that the members of a
community could not manage to subsist by taking in each other's washing,
and for similar reasons science cannot live by mutual criticisms alone. If the
scientific process is not kept wet from the fountain of empiricism, it shrivels
and dries up. James called Fechner's law "an 'idol of the den,' if ever there
was one," because the respect shown it in both attack and defense was out of
all proportion to the validating evidence for it. It became, in fact, an In-
stitutional Principle, which psychologists preserved by characterizing all its
refutations as its exceptions. James was right about these idols, but, being so
close to them, he failed to see what use it is that idols have.

The point here is that the new psychology was not, *an und für sich*, a discovery, but a movement. If it had been a discovery, it would have been hailed
for what it was, have been doubted by some critical skeptics, and have
stimulated a flurry of other lesser discoveries which grew out of the facts of
the first or else used the method of the first. There was, in fact, a great deal
of this sort of fertile discovery by Helmholtz, Fechner, and the others, but it
was not in itself what made the new psychology into a movement. The
movement was formal. It had a name: *Physiologische Psychologie*. It claimed
status as a science and thus definitely set itself off against the non-experimental empiricism of philosophy. Wundt wrote a handbook to demonstrate
its nature and adequacy as a new science, and was the first to found a psychological laboratory, for James' laboratory three years earlier was not founded: it
came into being because his instruction in psychology required demonstration.
Wundt also founded a journal. A movement is thus more than an idea because it needs all these impedimenta. It does not merely grow; it marches
against opposition.

A formal movement is thus a protest and the psychological reason for protest is, of course, insecurity. No established science feels insecure or protests,
for, being secure, it turns to work without attention to itself. But the new
psychology of James' day was insecure, self-conscious, protestant, and full of
the business of founding itself. It exaggerated the immediate importance of
its tools and methods, and, in a way, it had to, because that is the state of

mind of a new science. It was aggressive, and the aggression got into the experiments and into the publications. Out of this situation there arose among the 'new' psychologists a strong faith in the validity of certain basic experimental methods, like psychophysics and introspection, and in the reality of certain hypostasized entities, like the mental element, apperception and feeling. These were the idols to which James objected.

In short, James objected to time spent on pseudo-problems. To decide whether feeling is an attribute of sensation, or an element, and whether it has attributes of its own is to learn nothing new about man (Perry, 1935, II, 123). To argue as to whether the magnitude of a sensation is given by the number of j.n.d. by which its stimulus is above the threshold is equally futile when one does not know whether all j.n.d. are equal and when sensations seem to introspection to have no magnitude. Of such matters, James, upholding no school and furthering no movement, was impatient, necessary as they may have been to make the movement move. They were indeed the impedimenta. It is easy for us today to sympathize with James' impatience, to see why he felt they were not "nutritious objects of attention." Was that the only reason for his dissatisfaction with the new psychology that was so predominantly sensory?

No.

A sense-physiologist could find within this same literature, after all the carapace of argument and systematic artifact has been removed, no end of "nutritious objects of attention"—all the facts about color and tone with which Helmholtz's treatises were packed, for instance. Were not Newton's laws of color mixture nutritious—that absurd and unbelievable discovery that white is not simple but is a mixture of colors? And was not this a law of psychology since white has no physical existence and Newton knew nothing of retinal physiology? Yet James did not mention color mixture in the *Principles,* and put the topic into the *Briefer Course* only under protest (Perry, 1935, II, 125). If it was the broader generalizations that James wanted and not mere facts, then he had such things as Helmholtz's resonance theory of hearing, which had in it a bit of genius, a lot of scientific precision, and enough nutriment to feed to generations of the sort of psychologists who can thrive on such a diet. Not James, however. The laboratory psychology disappointed him. It was accurate, but its program made it look so "small" (Perry, 1935, II, 122). He wanted a functional psychology, which could discover the forces that govern the moral and religious life and bring them under control (Perry, 1935, II, 121 ff.). In fact, the whole conception of a functional psychology is that it considers the adjustment of the total living organism to its environment, and is not primarily concerned with the description of the functioning of small parts of its mechanism.

In other words, what you find nutritious depends on what kind of digestion you have—a physiologist's or a philosopher's. James had a philosopher's.

Many of his contemporaries who called themselves psychologists had the physiologist's kind. A psychologist could turn out to need one diet or the other, but no stomach could prosper on both. Let us, therefore, examine more closely this dichotomy, where James made a choice. And let us consider it in the contemporaneous situation, where we may be able to understand it more easily. We do not have to go far from home to find what I take to be the Jamesian preference still expressed.

Hocking and the Near-Mind

Some years ago Professor Hocking (1926) made his position on this matter quite clear. He said, first, that the new psychology had better be called Near Psychology—or rather, if I am to speak precisely, he said that the new psychology deals with Near-mind, not Mind. What is a Near-mind? Well, in the first place, a Near-mind is not the causally determined mind of the physiological psychologists. "Most crudely stated," said Hocking of this dichotomy, "it is that *causes are not reasons, and reasons are not causes.* And since mental process is at least partly rational, no system of causes such as a physical-psychology aims to establish can be equivalent to mind. Two series of events, one of which is purely causal, the other of which has an admixture of reason, can neither be congruent with each other nor parallel with each other. A causal system can at best be but a Near-mind" (Hocking, 1926). To this rejection of causality as applied to Mind it is fair to ask: "But what is reason?" It is fair, because Professor Hocking had an answer. "The mind, then, differs," he said, "from every object of nature in being in addition a hold upon the possible, the future, the valuable—or, to put these together, upon possible future value. Its essential activity is to bring possible future value into connection with actual present fact; and my proposition is that it is the *only agency for doing this.* Mind is the only organ for making future possibility actual" (Hocking, 1926, 211). If the Near Psychologist finds this statement, thus wrested from its context, bewildering, he can be told to remember Brentano, of whom he has certainly heard. Value and the future inexist intentionally within the Mind, Hocking seems to say.

That such inexistence is existence and such intention a tension would also seem to lie within this argument. Let me give just one more of these extracted passages. "We have described," said Hocking in summary, "what the mind is in terms of an activity which we term, for lack of better words, a tension of hope. We have said that this activity eludes scientific measure, because it lies not within the world of nature, but plies between nature and the world of actual possibility" (Hocking, 1926, 213).

A tension of hope! It lies surely in the world of Brentano's intention, of James Ward's conation, of McDougall's purpose, and, I suspect, of the 'dynamic' principle in psychology wherever it is found. How does one validate the existence of "a tension of hope," of an activity "for making future possibility actual"? Ostensively, I think. No simple formula of words will do it. Hocking took thirteen pages on the occasion from which I quote. But ultimately, if such words are to have meaning, one has got to see that entities like implication and effort exist or are actual, and perhaps one has also to become at least a little impatient with those others who remain persistently blind to tensions and values and possibilities and who are forever resorting to the substitutes of the Near-mind.

My point here is that Hocking, whom I am letting stand for the philosopher-psychologist, is in this respect a nativist, a phenomenologist. He knows a given when he sees it and neither wants to reduce it to other terms nor thinks than anyone can. The Near Psychologist has, of course, also his ultimates, as well as the epistemological problem which they create, but that problem is not relevant here. I am saying that there are phenomenologists in the world, that James was one and that Hocking is another, that phenomenologists are satisfied with psychical givens, and that Near Psychologists, to continue with Hocking's phrase, are not, but feel the urge to reduce these givens to other givens. The dilemma is not one of truth, I think, but one of value or motive. And since men are so consistent in respect of this difference, we have to ask what it is that each kind of man prefers, and perhaps eventually why he prefers it.

Murray and the Needs

A similar complaint about conventional psychology has been expressed by another colleague of mine, this time a psychologist by title as well as by interest. Professor Murray, conjuring up a few years ago an ideal picture of the place of psychology within a university, remarked:

> The truth which the informed are hesitant to reveal and the uninformed are amazed to discover is that academic psychology has contributed practically nothing to the knowledge of human nature. It has not only failed to bring light to the great, hauntingly recurrent problems, but it has no intention, one is shocked to realize, of attempting to investigate them. Indeed—and this is the cream of a wry jest—an unconcerned detachment from the natural history of ordinary mortals has become a source of pride to many psychologists (Murray, 1935, esp. 805).

Those sentences are almost Jamesian, could almost have been in the *Principles*. Murray knows what he wants and says what he has to say with a frank enthusiasm and in apt phrase. The point of my quoting him lies, however, in what is implicit in his remarks. He knows that "human nature" is "a nutritious object of attention" and thus presumably he knows what human nature is. For Murray on human nature we should turn, therefore, to his *Explorations in Personality*.

There it becomes evident that human nature has to do with needs, that needs are the possessions of persons and can be satisfied, that an unsatisfied need leads to action which is terminated by the satisfaction of the need. A psychology of needs is, if I understand it correctly, a dynamic psychology. My point about the needs is, however, that they are given—presumably phenomenologically given in the first instance, although transferred eventually to others outside the solipsistic barrier as sophistication about them grows. One can speculate about the physiology of needs—whether hunger contractions or endocrine secretions have anything to do with certain needs—but a physiological account of the needs is not, in Murray's estimation, necessary to a useful comprehension of human nature. A study of many persons in many situations shows primarily that the organism is needy. Then Murray and his colleagues sit themselves down with all the available data about the person before them, and they undertake to describe his neediness. Eventually they come into agreement about a convenient set of terms to use in communication with one another and with that portion of the professional world that will trouble to acquire their special vocabulary. So Murray comes out with thirty odd names for needs—needs for abasement, for achievement, for acquisition, for affiliation, and so on down the alphabet to the need for understanding.

Murray's use of symbols for the specific needs, like "n Aff" for the need for affiliation, "n Blam" for the need for avoidance of blame, gives at first the impression that he has done just what James condemned, has dissected human nature into elements. Examination of Murray's procedure shows, however, that he is making no analysis into elements. These needs of his are aspects of human behavior. They form a new system of descriptive communication, a system mortised into conventional language. The needs are not separate or mutually exclusive. Who could always, in every case, distinguish affiliation from succorance, acquisition from achievement, blame-avoidance from harm-avoidance? Murray, it seems to me, stands clearly on the side of James in this basic dilemma, as indeed his outburst against academic psychologists indicated at first.

Köhler and Values

If, by choosing Hocking and Murray as contemporaneous examples of James' attitude toward the importance of the problems of sensation, I have implied that this issue exists primarily in Cambridge, Massachusetts, let me correct that impression at once. James did not, I think, particularly influence Hocking or Murray in their impatience with that which Helmholtz did so well. Rather is it that this harmony is preëstablished in some basic system of values which some men hold and some do not. Let us get away from Harvard and look at Gestalt psychology.

When Gestalt psychology was still new in America certain similarities between it and James' psychology became evident (Calkins, 1926, 154–157; Boring, 1929a, 499–502, 576 f.). The two systems were similar as protests against atomism and, on the positive side, both undertook the delineation of mind as a whole. The stream of consciousness, as depicted by James, could have been a concept presented in Wertheimer's early papers (Wertheimer, 1921, 1923). There was no direct influence, however, even though Stumpf and James were intimate and Wertheimer, Koffka and Köhler all had some roots in Berlin. One can say, however, that James was a nativist, that Gestalt psychology is phenomenological, that phenomenology is the modern substitute for nativism, and that the problem now before us is the question as to why some men prefer the immediate givens of nativism, whereas others feel insecure without some genetic account of the givens. In examining this dichotomy we are getting, I think, close to fundamentals. We are indeed fortunate in having had a full discussion of the difference by Köhler in his William James Lectures.

Köhler devotes the first chapter of his *The Place of Value in a World of Facts* to what he calls "the case against science." In it he holds a long and very telling conversation with his Alter Ego, in which he himself takes the difficult position of the conventional scientist and his Alter Ego puts to him with trenchant specificity his doubts about a *Wissenschaft* which does not contribute to a better knowledge of man. The problems of human nature that Murray called "hauntingly recurrent" are formulated by Köhler with some precision—much more precision than they had in the happy invective of James' *Principles*. This is no occasion for me to diminish the effectiveness of Köhler's clear and apt exposition by a fumbling attempt at abstraction. Let him, who would know about the *Krise der Wissenschaft* of which Köhler speaks, read Köhler to see just what that crisis is, how the "patient whimsies" of the German *Gelehrter* and of those other scientists who have accepted them as models failed a post-war world (and, as it turns out, a pre-war world!) in dire need of "more nutritious objects of attention."

Köhler undertakes to show where the problem lies and then, using Gestalt psychology as a paradigm, to point the direction in which science must move if human nature is eventually to be understood. The direction is, of course, toward Value, away from the facts that are manufactured for science with all immediate human value polished off of them. One cannot, however, hope to follow this new course unless he knows what to avoid.

The problem—says Köhler (1938, 1–34) with a flash of insight—is the problem of the Nothing But. Nothing But! Natural science has become the science of the Nothing But. Whatever is given, whatever is native, has been reduced, he has his Alter Ego tell himself, to Nothing But the common ultimates, the constructs of natural science. The scientific process of the scientific age has been a process of "debunking," and the Alter Ego thinks that it is now high time to begin debunking the debunkers—that is to say, to devalue the value of valuelessness to which the scientists have held so long for security or from habit or for whatever other motive which can explain their highly artificialized modes of thought.

For instance, the Alter Ego complains to Köhler, the scientist, that the effect of science upon the study of man has been to eliminate man from the study of man by reducing him to Nothing But the inhuman data of physical science. "None of these disciplines," says the Alter Ego of mathematics and the physical sciences, "tries to solve problems which refer to the essential characteristics of man, to the dynamics of society and of history. In this respect we have made a most depressing discovery: Whenever the scientific mind tries to handle *these* topics it loses its bearings; its methods fail to yield any valuable results, and mere opinions take the place which in real science is occupied by knowledge. Evidently all these problems have one element in common which makes them inaccessible to your technique. This common element is man. Whether considered as an individual or in groups, i.e., in society and in history, it is man to whose nature you are unable to do justice. There is something in him which you cannot conquer by procedures which are quite successful in present natural science. For this reason your achievements begin to sink to a much lower level when your thinking merely approaches human affairs. . . . In certain departments the customary technique of science is practically powerless and . . . nobody knows how to find new methods which would apply in these fields. On the *program* of these departments, man is the main item. Unfortunately he is *only* on the program. . . . In the departments which are supposed to study human life, discussion of this program apparently serves as a substitute for actual insight and factual knowledge" (Köhler, 1938, 9 f.).

Köhler's thesis is that man is primarily concerned with values, that science is concerned with fact, and that science, in turning man's values into the kinds of facts with which it is accustomed to deal, deflates the values into something that is less than what they were. He wishes that science might come back to man and his values, taking the values as they exist or are given without reduction to the common terms of natural science. He presents his book as an example of how it can be done within a limited field. In doing so he is giving, it seems to me, general meaning to what Murray wants in psychology, to what Hocking wants, to that aspiration of James' which made him so impatient with the Wundtians and with the early researches of the new psychology. Even sensation once had a 'functional' connotation of which modern psychology has quite divested it. Hunger used to be a sensation which was as sensation a desire for food. Now hunger is *either* a pattern of algesic qualities aroused by slow rhythmical contractions of the stomach *or* the need for food and its consequent activities whether or not the hunger pangs are felt. 'Value' has gone out of the sensation, although value is kept in psychology by the needs.

Modern Positivism

At this point we ought, it seems to me, to introduce that confused and dangerous word *positivism*. Mach was a positivist. James at times favored positivism—of the Machian kind. Recently, however, the Vienna circle have been the positivists, and modern psychology, influenced more by behaviorism and Bridgman's operational definitions than by Schlick and Carnap, often likes to express fealty to 'logical positivism' or to what it sometimes calls 'operationism.' It is plain that the modern positivists are descended from the older positivists in two ways: both groups are antimetaphysical and both believe in the reduction of constructs to the more primary data involved in observation. There is, however, a difference in the nature of the ultimates of reduction. For Mach experience was ultimate. To achieve safety and understanding one reduced the scientific entities to the basic data of observation which is experience. Thus Mach fits into the phenomenological tradition and can properly be regarded as a grandparent of Gestalt psychology. The Machian descendants seem, however, to constitute a Kallikak family, for Mach is also grandparent to the logical positivism which seeks reduction, not to experience, but to the operations of the observing process. Modern positivistic psychologists, instead of regarding phenomenal experience as ultimate, ask for a definition to be expressed in terms of the processes by which experience is observed. No longer do they believe that to have an experience is in itself to know about it.

The consequence of this change in the atmosphere of positivism has been that phenomenology, instead of finding support in positivism as it could with Mach, is now utterly opposed to the current brand of positivism. Listen to Köhler in the preface of *The Place of Value in a World of Facts*.

> Never, I believe, shall we be able to solve any problems of ultimate principle until we go back to the sources of our concepts—in other words, until we use the phenomenological method, the qualitative analysis of experience.

At this point one might, thinking of Mach, put Köhler down as a good positivist. But read his next sentence.

> In this our Positivists show hardly any interest. They prefer to deal with concepts which have acquired a certain polish in the history of scientific thought, and they think little of topics to which these concepts can not be directly applied (Köhler, 1938, vii).

That sentence shocked me when I first read it, for it completely reversed the accepted meaning of positivism. The concepts polished by much use in scientific thought are what one finds in metaphysics which all positivists have agreed to eschew. Positivism tries to get back to the simple data or processes of observation. How can Köhler charge it was using only the popular shopworn articles? He can, though, and does. His book, moreover, makes clear what he means. Phenomenology and positivism parted company early in the present century, and now they can hardly speak to each other. Köhler is on the side of phenomenology and I think James would have been too.

The problem whether to choose values or facts, minds or near-minds, needs or sensations is in itself a matter of relative values. Köhler is at pains to point out that the modern positivists are not incorrect but merely insufficient. What is correct may not, however, be enough, he notes; and—if one asks, enough for what?—the answer has already been given. Enough for the understanding of man and for what man thinks is most important about man.

Phenomenology and Reduction

It might be possible simply to leave the whole problem here, to say that there are in the world both phenomenologists and reductionists, that neither gives the whole picture and both together are more complete than either alone. Such a view implies a certain symmetry between the two positions. It asserts that, if something of the whole is lost by reduction, then the whole itself must lack what reduction adds. Certainly a case could be made for emotional symmetry between the two positions. The phenomenologists, it is true, are thoroughly disturbed by the failure of conventional science to leave the values alive when dealing with man, but then conventional science has itself been often disturbed by the way in which the phenomenologists leave the values in. Anyone who is familiar with the history of the way in which science first and psychology later—from Copernicus to John B. Watson—accomplished the reduction of man's irreducible values knows that science has felt neither complacent nor assured about its value of valuelessness. Both parties to this controversy must have felt insecure, else they would have lacked the motive for the aggression of moral judgment and apt invective. Perhaps the best solution of this dilemma is to admit the existence of an individual difference, describe it, approve it and rest content with the interesting fact that one man's meat is another's poison. Certainly such a solution is easiest. Nevertheless let us see if we cannot come to some understanding of this difference in the value of value.

The difference is old. For instance, Goethe, the phenomenologist, denounced Newton, the experimentalist (Boring, 1942, 28–34, 49 f., 112–117, 123 f.). This animadversion of Goethe's had nothing to do with man, but I bring up the matter because I think that the issue between James and Wundt, between phenomenologists and positivists, is more fundamental than Köhler makes it. Newton was cautious; Goethe was bold. Newton had the insight that the moon is forever falling to the earth, but he delayed publication for many years while he tried to get his calculations to confirm his insight. Goethe had the insight of the metamorphosis of homologous parts as he examined the sheep's skull on the Lido and that was enough for him. Newton demonstrated by a few simple experiments with prisms that white is a mixture of colors, and Goethe with a prism in hand but no experiment impeached Newton as having denied the obvious. Perhaps this instance is not fair since it exhibits Goethe wrong and thus at a disadvantage, but there is hardly any other event which shows so clearly that the phenomenologist must have faith in himself and his own observation, whereas the experimentalist mistrusts himself and is forever looking to controls and mediacies to correct his own errors.

Starting with Newton we can come on down the line of history. Goethe derided Newton because he used experiments to distort the obvious. Helmholtz ridiculed Goethe as a victim of his own vain obstinacy. James (1879, 10) found that Helmholtz's "indefinite and oracular statements about the part played by the intellect [in perception] have momentarily contributed to retard psychological inquiry." Sully objected to the "dazzling effect" of James' *Principles* as obscuring "the sharp boundaries of scientific thought" (Perry, 1935, II, 104). Since then there has been the opposition between Watson and McDougall, and between behaviorism and Gestalt psychology. The most famous opposition of this nature was, however, the mutual disapproval of Helmholtz and Hering each for the other, an antagonism that gives us at once the key to the difficulty, for Helmholtz was an empiricist and Hering a nativist. In this dichotomy James, of course, belongs on the side of Hering as do also all the Gestalt psychologists.

It is usual to refer to the issue of nativism vs. empiricism as a dead and futile controversy of the late nineteenth century, but now we begin to see that the controversy is alive and still with us. The dislike of the Gestalt psychologists for Helmholtz is based upon his empiricism, his constant appeal to past experience for the explanation of present phenomena. Similarly the phenomenologists mistrust operationism because it goes beyond the given to the conditions of givenness, asserting that the given is not ultimate since the giving of it has to be understood. These operationists do not take experience as self-validating; they want to know what experience is and they answer their own question by submitting the process of observation to description. So there lies the issue: nativism vs. empiricism; Hering, Stumpf and James vs. Lotze, Helmholtz and Wundt; phenomenology vs. reductionism. Are we to give up the problem with the admission of the existence of a difference in tastes, or can we say something more about it?

In the course of the development of this opposition the initiative would seem to have passed from the nativists to the reductionists. If such an individual difference in respect of values is given, what nativist could question the validity of a given? The reductionist, on the other hand, might reasonably be asked to do something more than to describe the difference. What is it that he could say, with James, Hocking, Murray, and Köhler all speechless now that they have discovered the primary fact of this difference in nutritious scientific diets? Not much, I fear; yet I, who was born to feel safer with Helmholtz than with Hering, venture a first step along the path of reduction. Since the path is known to be an infinite regress, no one must expect me to approach its end.

Nothing But and Something More

In the first place, let me say, then, that Nothing But is also Something More. The phenomenologist takes the given and rests. Even Lotze said that nativism is not a theory of space because it does nothing but accept space. The reductionist takes the given and asks for Something More about it. The argument for Nothing But is merely that the Something More is always in the same general direction—Something More is Nothing But the same direction of reduction. Is that poverty or is it riches? That question need not, perhaps, be answered; yet there is a fact in psychology that suggests the answer, suggests that the answer may depend in part upon an individual difference as to what provides a presentation, meaningless in itself, with an adequate meaning.

What happens in perception? What is the general rule? It is that a stimulus gets the focus of attention, is completed or built upon by the organism until it is adequately meaningful, and then is allowed to make room for a next comer. Most potential stimuli have no effect, and nearly all of those which are effective remain marginal—like the words on a page which is quickly read and easily understood. If, however, you confront the perceiving mind with a sensory pattern that lacks adequate meaning and get that pattern focal, then the inevitable result is that the perceptual core gets further specification by the organism. The strange is what lacks sufficient meaning and the business of perception is to make the strange familiar. That is, if you like, the context theory of meaning, and nothing is surer than that the organism, faced with too little meaning for a focal core, will manage to find some context to add, enough to give itself a sense of competence and security. If the core is a face, then a name may be sufficient context. If the core is a face that floats in air without a body, then the context may be "magic" or "hallucination." That is the manner in which mere classification seems to the organism to provide understanding.

There will not be much objection to my insistence that accrual of context supplies meaning, but I have been speaking here of adequate meanings. When is a meaning adequate or sufficient?

Thirty years ago Jacobson (1911) and Titchener (1912, esp. 174–181), working on the problem of meaning and understanding, found—at least Titchener found it in Jacobson's data—an individual difference as to what constitutes sufficiency of meaning. Jacobson gave his observers letters, words, and sentences, asking them to state the meaning. Now what is the meaning on a letter A presented in a visual exposure apparatus? One observer in particular—Titchener called him "logical"—was obsessed with the difficulty of knowing where to terminate a meaning. The letter A is a letter—black—typed—on white paper—in an apparatus—in a psychological experiment—at Cornell—where *Bewusstheiten* can be analyzed—and where there is criticism of Würzburg—which is Külpe's school—and not Wundt's. Altogether there is an infinite number of infinite regresses that can be used to explicate the context of the original core. How much of how many of them constitutes a meaning for A? Even this observer found with practice that he did not have to go along the path of explication forever in order to get *the* meaning; he could recognize what was too much meaning or too little though he never felt sure just where the proper boundary lay. Other observers, however, had no difficulty in stating meanings. They seemed to intuit how much Jacobson wanted in the way of meaning and were not troubled by the logical problem of indefinite explication. Titchener called these observers "subjective," because they ignored the logic of the situation to do what the experimenter wanted of them, to give a simple determinate verbal meaning.

Although this ancient experiment proves nothing by itself, it serves as an illustration of the nature of one kind of meaning and of its indeterminacy. To understand something is to do something more than to accept it. One must make specifications about it, bring it into relation with other somethings. One must, moreover, know when to stop, to know when enough meaning is enough. All that seems clear and simple. Now let us apply the context theory of meaning to the question of nativism vs. reductionism.

Tastes in Scientific Meanings

The nativist accepts the given, takes what comes. He has every right to say that there must be primaries, that acceptance of the given without further specification is the normal process of perceiving. Mostly the mental life is too busy for the accrual of contexts to its multitudinous cores. Most perceptual items remain marginal. The reductionist, on the other hand, finds himself insecure in the mere acceptance of a focal item. Understanding for him is something more than acceptance or even description. The object must be put into relation to other objects, and, the larger the relational system into which he can introduce the object, the more secure he feels. Reductionists tend to be physicalists because they have a sure technique for reducing all mental concepts to physical by specification of the mechanisms of observation, the defining operations. The physical system, being a large system, thus furnishes for them maximal security. Reduction does not, however, have to be physical. As one studies the empiricism of the theories of space in the late nineteenth century, one is struck with the satisfaction which the authors felt at being able to *do* something about space. A nativist *as nativist* has nothing to do but accept the given. The only way in which nativists got any fun out of their theories was by becoming geneticists enough to show how complex space is built up out of the native givens—as James' discussion of theory of space shows so clearly.

The choice between modern phenomenology and modern positivism would seem thus to be of this kind. The positivist finds phenomenology empty. There is not enough to it. He wants Something More. The phenomenologist, on the other hand, finds physicalism too full, too full of the wrong things. He objects to Nothing But. The phenomenologist holds that the positivist's reduction is unrepresentative and, therefore, a false surrogate for the real thing. The positivist says that he cannot understand aspects of the real thing except in so far as they can be put into relation with something else, that relating is never destructive, and that the unrelatable is a useless mystery. Yet even he has to quit relating at some point in the relational process, and it might be argued that he could have stopped at the start, with the phenomenologist. It is all a question as to how much context it takes to make a scientific entity understandable, and on that matter scientists do indeed seem to differ.

There is little more for me to say. In leaving you thus with an unreduced individual difference on your hands, with the mere assertion of its existence, I am, of course, playing the nativist. The empiricist should ask: How is nativism generated, and how empiricism? Perhaps some future empiricist will, indeed, solve the problem, will show that a phenomenologist must have had a happy childhood with love and security to spare, a childhood in which it was natural to accept the givens without demanding accounts of their origins. The empiricists and reductionists would then turn out to be the insecure children, who learned early to look beyond the given, suspecting a catch in what is free. If to this remark the phenomenologist replies that positivism is, therefore, founded on nothing better than the sensed inferiority of the positivists, these latter are still free to assert that sensed insecurity is nevertheless the sanction for science itself.

In all this discussion we have not really gotten away from James except in respect of chronology. It is a century since his birth and half a century since the *Principles,* which he wrote during the decade in which I was born. Although some of the problems were different then, others have stayed with us.

Their permanence seems to argue that they are fundamental and perhaps referable, at least in part, to the relative permanences of human temperament, rather than that they are questions of right and wrong in science. It was the reductionists—Helmholtz and his kind—who first caught James' interest for the 'new science.' He refused, however, to go along with these founders. His drive derived not from his concern with the processes of understanding but from his concern with the mystery of human nature. A reductionist might say that James would be unimpressed by an understanding of a mystery that removed the mystery, since a mystery can be described, though not understood, without loss of its charm. Certainly it is plain where James would stand in the controversies of today. He would stand, of course, now as always, on his own feet. In general, however, he would take a position on the side of the Gestalt psychologists and phenomenologists. He would belong with Hocking and Murray and Köhler and all those distinguished others whom I have not named. The psychology of sensation has, nevertheless, advanced more than the psychology of motivation during the last fifty years. Just think what has happened to the scientific knowledge of the mechanism of hearing in the 1930's alone! Yet James still would not like sensation. He would approve of it and call it presumably, as others do now, "physiology." He would still be the nativist, accepting the given; nor would he even now wish to "saddle our Science forever" with the psychophysiology of sensation, when he could see before him "a world so full of more nutritious objects of attention." After all, even a rat knows how to choose his own vitamins (Richter et al., 1938).

The History of Psychology

░░

*E*DWIN G. BORING *is best known as an historian of psychology. His
papers, taken alone, cannot do justice to his work in this area. His monumental History of Experimental Psychology (1950a) is the standard text
and reference source throughout the world. Sensation and Perception in the
History of Experimental Psychology (1942) is the most thoroughly documented account of this particular field.*

*A distinction may be made between the contentual and the methodolog-
ical aspects of the history of psychology. The two books just mentioned are
primarily contentual in nature, and a roughly chronological order is followed.
Among the papers in the present section, three illustrate the methodological
approach; they are concerned with the history of introspection, experimental
control, and measurement.*

*The dynamics of history have also been the concern of E.G.B. both in
A History of Experimental Psychology (1950a), Psychologist at Large
(1961a) and in various sections of this book. It has been seen that history
often serves him as the vehicle for considering many other problems such
as the Zeitgeist and multiple discovery.*

*Selection from among E.G.B.'s papers for the present section was made
in respect of still another theme. Articles were selected to bring out the
various ways in which the history of a science may be approached. Special
ways in which historical material may be used are illustrated in some of the
other papers in this book, particularly those in the preceding section.*

History may be used to show the development of various meanings of a concept. E.G.B. does this in "The Nature and History of Experimental Control" by tracing the various meanings—a check in the sense of verification, a restraint in the sense of maintaining constancy, and a guide in the sense of producing a constant or precisely determined change.

History may be expressed through an acount of the work of a given individual. While history is a smooth flow, it is necessary to atomize it with the eponymy of individuals. By speaking concretely of the events of a life of a man, by selection of events, implicitly relevant, one gives the necessary body by which to grasp the nature of his contributions. E.G.B. has demonstrated how "Fechner: Inadvertent Founder of Psychophysics," guided by a spiritualistic, metaphysical goal, aimed at measuring sensation independent of its physical stimulation, but, instead, hit the experimental target of giving magnitude to sensation. Fechner's intentions for his work were in conflict with the Zeitgeist, and the Zeitgeist won out.

History may be used to establish relationships of "Masters and Pupils among the American Psychologists." Lines of influences are thereby traced. Boring and his daughter made an empirical, historical analysis of the teachers that American psychologists, living and deceased, acknowledged as primarily responsible for their thesis and degree.

In still another paper, "The Beginning and Growth of Measurement in Psychology," E.G.B. shows how the demand for quantification and measurement in psychology arose from the nature of the problems of psychophysics, reaction time, learning, and individual differences.

How a theory derived from another scientific field, in this case the "Influence of Evolutionary Thought," helped to make psychology a biological discipline, is still another approach he utilized.

History may be used to demonstrate that old ideas died hard, or, rather, do not die at all, but metamorphose in new forms suitable for the changed Zeitgeist. This is the case with "A History of Introspection" as a special method of psychology, which E.G.B. in Psychologist at Large (Boring, 1961a) traces from dualism to the modern verbal report advocated by John B. Watson. Watson's approach is followed in modern guise by the acceptance of an operational definition of introspection, with consciousness emerging as a construct. Introspection also persists in the reports of sensory experience in psychophysics, in patient protocols, in phenomenological descriptions in the study of perception and Gestalt psychology, and in that great portion of social psychology which is devoted to cognition.

History may be used as a vehicle to register protest against erroneous views. Through historical and logical argument, Boring protests vigorously against some of the psychologists' conventional, statistical assumptions. This protest is found in "The Logic of the Normal Law of Error in Mental Measurement," reprinted in Psychologist at Large (Boring, 1961a).

The Nature and History

of Experimental Control

丂丂丂丂丂丂丂丂丂丂丂丂丂丂丂丂丂丂丂丂丂 1954

SOLOMON (1949) has discussed the history of the concept of control in experimental work with especial regard to the use of control groups in the design of experiments, finding no instance of the employment of a control group before the study of transfer by Thorndike and Woodworth (1901) [1] and no extensive use of control groups in experiments on transfer until Winch's study (1908). It is easily shown that the concept of control is basic to all experimental design and is, indeed, inherent in the essential relational nature of a fact. The purpose of this note is to analyze the concept more fully and to say something more about the history of both the concept and the word.

The word *control* has three meanings: (1) a *check*, in the sense of a verification but thus also in the sense of a restraint, since verification restrains; (2) a *restraint*, in the sense of a checking and thus also in the sense of maintaining constancy; and (3) a *guide* or *directing*, in the sense of producing a precisely predetermined change, a constant and thus a restrained change. The word *check* itself has the first two meanings, though not the last, and the original meaning of *control* was *check*, for the word was *counter-roll* (*contre-rolle*), a duplicate register or account made to verify an official or first-made account and thus a check by a later roll upon the earlier. (Hence *controller*, which is misspelled *comptroller* because it has been thought of as meaning an accountant instead of a checker.) So the thought of correctness or conformity achieved by restraint runs all the way through the history of the word, even though what the psychologist hears nowadays about 'controlling behavior' suggests the promotion of action more than its restriction.[2]

The term *control* in the sense of a check or test observation or experiment came into scientific parlance in the latter half of the nineteenth century, as we shall see presently. By 1893 we find the *New English Dictionary* defining

Reprinted with permission from *The American Journal of Psychology*, 1954, **67**, 573–589.

control as "a standard of comparison used to check the inferences deduced from an experiment by application of the Method of Difference," which is the name of John Stuart Mill's second method of experimental inquiry. The *New English* goes on to define *control-experiment* as "a test experiment with this end in view." So *control-experiment* was definitely in the language before *control groups* had been thought of, and this concept takes us back to Mill's four methods of experimental inquiry in his *Logic* of 1843 (vol. 1, bk. III, chap. 8).

Mill's first method is the *Method of Agreement*: if A is always followed by *a*, then A is presumably the cause of *a*. Mere agreement does not, however, furnish rigorous proof, although you may be limited to it when you lack the voluntary variation of events—the independent experimental variable—and are reduced to description only. For this reason the establishment of causal relations in biography, history, geology, paleontology, and even astronomy is less sure than in experimental science. Mill remarked that mere agreement would indicate that night is the cause of day, and day the cause of night, since the sequence is universal, and he noted that we can be more certain that agreement indicates cause when the antecedent term in the conjunction of events can be established at will without dependence upon other events. Mill was right in mistrusting the Method of Agreement, since the concurrence of A and *a* in sequence may mean only that both are effects of the same sufficient cause, and, since if that other cause is sufficient but not necessary, it takes the Method of Difference to show that A and *a* are not necessary concomitants. It is for this reason that Mill suggested that the Method of Agreement is strengthened if A can be varied "at will," that is to say, if A is a freely independent variable. Such a caveat, however, actually constitutes an extension of the Method of Agreement to include the Method of Difference (when variation of A includes its elimination) or the Method of Concomitant Variation (when A is merely changed in degree). The inference of causation is never safe when based upon agreement alone.

The *Method of Difference* is Mill's second method: if A is always followed by *a*, and *not-A* is always followed by *not-a*, then A is certainly the cause of *a*. This is equivalent to adding the control observation: if *not-A*, then *not-a*. Mill used the word *control* once: "It thus appears that in the study of various kinds of phenomena which we can, by our voluntary agency, modify or control, we can in general satisfy the requisitions of the Method of Difference; but that by the spontaneous operations of nature those requisitions are seldom fulfilled." This use of *control* is, however, in the sense of direction or guidance, whereas the Method of Difference provides *control* in the sense of a verifying check, although Mill did not make that use of the word. He recognized, however, the fundamental relation of his first two methods, speaking of the *Joint Method of Agreement and Difference*, which is essentially the modern scientific procedure for treating contingencies when continuities are not observed.

(The third method, the *Method of Residues*, need not concern us. If ABC is known to be the cause of *abc*, and BC the cause of *bc*, then A must be the cause of *a*, even though A can not be produced without BC nor thus *a* without *bc*.)

Mill's fourth procedure is the *Method of Concomitant Variations*. Nowadays we think of such observation as basic to all experiments and thus of Agreement and Difference as special cases of Concomitant Variation. Concomitant variation exists when there is a series of differences, and in any pair of concomitances one concomitance furnishes a comparison or control for the other. So we could get along with this method alone, if it were broadly enough conceived, except for the historical fact that the concept of control actually grew out of the consideration of the Method of Difference, which Mill's prestige established as independently important.

Mill is usually taken as the authority on this matter. Thought about these principles is, however, historically continuous. A century earlier Hume (1739–1740, bk. 1, III, sec. 15) had a similar, less specific discussion, which laid down rules equivalent to the Method of Difference and to the Joint Method of Agreement and Difference. Still another century earlier Francis Bacon (1620) discussed the collection of data by the finding of instances that agree, and of negative instances and cases to furnish comparison.[3] In these authors the anticipation of Mill is quite clear if one but remembers what a century or two can do to both thought and its expression.

At this point it is important to remark that every statement of fact expresses some kind of a difference. Even such description as is not experimental, being specific and thus discriminative, differentiates what is from what is not. Jevons (1874, II, 44; 1883, 433) offered as the formula for a fact: "Where A is, X is; and where A is not, X is not"; and that, of course, is also a statement of agreement and difference. Jevons (1874, II, 43; 1883, 433) remarked: "Every correct and conclusive experiment necessarily consists in the comparison of results between two different combinations of circumstances." It is plain then that in scientific description we are not going to get away from the concept of control, although the idea appears with different degrees of specificity and formality in statements of experimental design. If you have an observed datum, there is always some point or frame of reference in respect of which the datum makes sense, and it might aid clarity of thought if one were to think always of a datum set over against a relatum. (If A, then *a*) would be a datum, and (if *not-A*, then *not-a*) would be the relatum and the control observation, which might indeed depend upon a control-experiment to establish it. Again and again when agreement seems to yield certainty, it is because the control-observation is implied or even included in the experiment.

Now let us examine some instances of the use of the concept of control and of the word *control* in the scientific literature of the last one hundred years.

Control as Restraint or Guidance. The meaning of *control* as restraint or guidance is the common, though later, meaning of the term, and in science it applies to keeping experimental conditions constant and also to altering the independent variable in accordance with precise known predetermination. We do not need to hunt out instances of the scientific aspiration to keep conditions constant, to maintain controlled conditions or to vary a parameter under controlled conditions. In these contexts control, constancy and precision are of the essence of experimental science. Thus Titchener (1910, 20; 1915, 22–25), in describing the nature of experiment, emphasized the necessity for repetition, isolation, and variation in the interests of good observation, constancy of conditions and exact variation, although he did not use the word *control*.[4] In similar sense Murphy and Murphy (1931, 201 f.) have spoken of the "relatively uncontrolled observational and biographical studies" of children and the later "new experimental and highly controlled observation studies worked out" after 1915.[5] We can also go back to Fechner who sought constancy of conditions by control of experimental procedures and the treatment of data: "The arrangement of experimental conditions," he wrote, "the recording of observed values, the enumeration of errors or of right and wrong cases, as well as all the calculations based upon them, must be so arranged and controlled (*controliren*) by repetition and otherwise that, as far as possible, errors are avoided by the multiplication of data, by calculation when error is otherwise unavoidable, and by observing an immutable integrity in the recording and conversion of data." [6]

Control of the experimental independent variable, moreover, implies guidance as well as the maintenance of constancy, but the same admonitions and aspirations apply to this kind of control as to the control of conditions fixed throughout a particular experiment.

> *Control* enters into psychic research with two different meanings. Holding hands and touching feet with each of your neighbors in the spiritistic circle may be thought to promote psychic continuity, but the practice also acts as a control against fraud. There is also, however, the *spirit control*, who or which guides and directs the medium. This use of the term seems to have come in late, for Podmore (1902) makes no mention of it in his excellent and thorough two-volume history of spiritualism. Nor did the *New English Dictionary* give this meaning in 1893, although the *Standard Dictionary* by 1913 was saying for one meaning of *control*: "The intelligence (whatever its nature) which regulates the communication of messages through a medium or psychic."

Control Observations, Series, and Experiments. We come back to the special use of the word *control* in its original meaning as a check or standard of comparison, a relatum. If separate observations have controls interspersed (e.g. single points introduced among the double points which are used in determining the two-point limen upon the skin), then we have what may be called *control observations*. When the controls are organized into series, then we have a *control series* with which the *experimental series* is compared, as in various memory experiments. If the dissociation of the terms for comparison is greater and the organization of each more elaborate, then we begin to speak of the *principal experiment* and the *control experiment*. The term *control experiment*, as a standard of comparison, has now got into most of the dictionaries. Its synonym is *test experiment*. Logically there is, however, no difference between one kind of relatum and another except in degree of organization and formal independence. The basic conception, of course, appears early in experimentation, whereas the use of the word *control* comes later.

> The concept of control is pretty old and was quite obvious once the Renaissance had turned men's thought from theological fiat to experiment as the

means for penetrating into nature's secrets. Here is a story that makes the whole matter clear.

In 1648 the Torricellian vacuum was known to physics in general and to Pascal in particular. This is the vacuum formed at the upper closed end of a tube which has first been filled with mercury and then inverted with its lower open end in a dish of mercury. The column of mercury falls in the tube until it is about 30 in. high and remains there, leaving a vacuum above it. Pascal was of the opinion that the column is supported by the weight of the air that presses upon the mercury in the dish (he was right; the Torricellian tube is a barometer) and that the column should be shorter at higher altitudes where the weight of the atmosphere would be less. So he asked his brother-in-law, Perier, who was at Clermont, to perform for him the obvious experiment at the Puy-de-Dôme, a mountain in the neighborhood about 3000 ft. ("500 fathoms") high as measured from the Convent at the bottom to the mountain's top. On Saturday, September 19th, 1648, Perier, with three friends of the Clermont clergy and three laymen, two Torricellian tubes, two dishes and plenty of mercury, set out for the Puy-de-Dôme. At the foot they stopped at the Convent, set up both tubes, found the height of the column in each to be 26 old French inches plus 3½ Paris lines (28.04 modern inches), left one tube set up at the Convent with Father Chastin to watch it so as to see whether it changed during the day, disassembled the other tube and carried it to the top of the mountain, 3000 ft. above the Convent and 4800 ft. above sea-level. There they set it up again and found to their excited pleasure that the height of the mercury column was only 23 French inches and 2 Paris lines (24.71 in.), much less than it was down below just as Pascal had hoped it would be. To make sure they took measurements in five places at the top, on one side and the other of the mountain top, inside a shelter and outside, but the column heights were all the same. Then they came down, stopping on the way to take a measurement at an intermediate altitude, where the mercury column proved to be of intermediate height (26.65 in.). Back at the Convent, Father Chastin said that the other tube had not varied during the day, and then, setting up their second tube, the climbers found that it too again measured 26 in. 3½ lines. These are reasonable determinations for these altitudes, showing about the usual one inch of change in the mercury column for every 1000 ft. of change in altitude.[7]

In this experiment there was no elaborate design, and it took place 195 years too soon for the experimenters to have read John Stuart Mill's *Logic*, but the principle of control and of the Method of Difference is there. How important it was for them to have left a barometer at the base of the Puy-de-Dôme to make sure that changes in the tube that they carried up the mountain were due to elevation and not to general atmospheric changes or to other unknown circumstances! How wise of the party at the top to have made the measurement under as many different conditions as they could think of with altitude constant! How intelligent of them to take a reading on the way down and thus to turn the Method of Difference into the Method of Concomitant Variation!

When Jevons was writing his section on "Blind or Test Experiments," he missed this paradigm from Pascal, 1648, but gave one from Faraday, 1848, and another from Tyndall (1863).[8] Neither of these examples is in any formal sense a blind experiment or, as we should say today, a control experiment. They are simply examples of the basic principle that a fact is a relationship and that you are not ready to make a scientific statement until you have a comparison to

present. Thus Faraday, in the research cited by Jevons as including blind experiments, was really trying out what he called magnecrystallic action on a
variety of different substances, finding that certain rules of magnetic orientation
hold for crystals of bismuth and similar metals and that there is no magnetic
action of this kind at all for the crystals of certain other metals, of which lead
is one example.[9] Faraday was engaged in what might be called the experimental
taxonomy of metallic behavior, and, now that his results are available to us, we
can separate them into data and relata, into experiments and controls, though
Faraday did not see his problem thus. Tyndall (1863, 21), in the place cited by
Jevons, was describing an experiment in which 19 lb. of water were brought
from room temperature to a boil in $2\frac{1}{2}$ hr. by the constant rotation of a steel
cylinder fitting tightly inside another steel cylinder and kept by a horse in
rotation while immersed in the water—a demonstration that mechanical power
can be turned into heat by friction. Presumably Jevons believed that the control here was the initial condition of the water at room temperature, but actually this experiment was an example of the Method of Concomitant Variation, for the temperature of the water was taken from time to time and found
steadily to rise as equine energy was continuously converted into heat.

In 1870 a new kind of control observation appeared in psychological experimentation, the V*exirversuch* that Vierordt (1870)—and later Riecker
(1874)—used in their determinations of the cutaneous two-point threshold.

If you keep putting two points simultaneously down upon the skin with
varying separations between them and keep track of the number of times each
separation is perceived as a single impression and the number of times it is
perceived double, then, if your chosen separations are proper, you can compute
the separation at which a *two* would be felt as often as a *one*. That is the
threshold. The observer, well trained to give phenomenal reports, can participate in this experiment quite successfully, but the naïve observer is apt to
make what Titchener called the stimulus-error, to report *two* often or always
because he knows or guesses that the stimulator often or always puts two points
to the skin. So Vierordt and then Riecker introduced single stimuli as checks
upon the observer, calling them V*exirversuche* or puzzle trials—actually control
observations. Riecker worked with the method of constant stimuli which was
still called then, after Fechner's original title, "the method of right and wrong
cases." It is 'right' to call two points *two* and one point *one*, and 'wrong' to call
two points *one* and one point *two*. Actually the observers often did call one
point *two* for there is a special physiological disposition for getting a two-fold
impression out of a unitary stimulus, and these errors with the V*exirversuche*
were called V*exirfehler* (paradoxical errors).[10]

Later McDougall (1903a) formally introduced the requirement that there
should be as many single stimuli as double and that the threshold should be
80% right for both kinds of stimuli taken together. That was good functionalism at the time and is nowadays good modern behaviorism: you see how
adequate the subject is to his environment (stimulus-world) when without
further knowledge he relies for information upon the sensitivity of his receptor
apparatus, but Titchener (1916, esp. 206–215) still thought that a trained
observer should be able to judge sensory impression accurately in its own right,
whatever he suspected of the stimulus. McDougall stuck by his guns even for
educated subjects, and Henry Head and his associates used McDougall's
method in the experiments which set up the distinction between protopathic

and epicritic sensibility.[11] It is only recently that the V*exirversuche* have come to be regarded as control observations, and indeed they are somewhat special for they function as straight checks or controls for objective behavior, whereas they may also become directing guides in an introspective psychology where a trained observer needs to be checked as to whether he is reporting only on sensory impression or whether, committing the stimulus-error, he is trying to infer or guess the true nature of the stimulus-object.[12]

It was along in the 1870s that the word *control* began to be used in the sense of a check or a standard of comparison in respect of which a difference is expected to lie.

In 1874, in the first edition of his famous *Physiologische Psychologie*, Wundt said that the fall-apparatus, used then to calibrate the Hipp chronoscope, is a *control*. Later the fall-apparatus changed its form and became and was called a *control hammer*. Product procedure is to run a series in which the times of the successive falls of the control hammer are measured by the Hipp chronoscope, and that series, which Wundt (1874, 772; 1911, III, 367) actually called a *Kontrollversuch*, gives you the variable error of the chronoscope and, if you have measured the true time of fall on the chronograph, the constant error too.[13]

Thus Wundt was ready enough to control a piece of apparatus with an objective check, but the only control he admitted as valid for the human observer was rigorous training in psychological observation. For psychological experimentation he registered objection to *Kontrollversuche*, *Prüfungsversuche*, *Probeversuche* and *Vexirversuche* (1911b, III, 399).

Also in the 1870s this meaning of the word *control* entered biology by way of Darwin (1875, XVII, esp. 413). In 1875 he reported on Utricularia, plants that float on foul water and that carry tiny bladders with valves that trap the insects and organic matter that get within the orifices of the bladders. It is a study in the taxonomy of plant behavior. After observing the reaction of the bladders to their normal food, "four bladders were tried as a control experiment," Darwin wrote. He fed them gum arabic and also sugar, neither of which produced the normal feeding reaction, whereas nitrate of ammonia did. Later Darwin (1881, III, esp. 160–163) is found describing the movement of plants in response to irritants. He performed experiments with the radicles of peas, attaching to them as irritants bits of cardboard "which served as standards of comparison or controls." In 1890 there was an article in *Nature* (Hankin, 1890) on the immunization of mice against tetanus. Immunized mice were inoculated with tetanus and failed to show its symptoms, but "control mice [not immunized] died within 48 hours." When a word can be used thus casually, it may be assumed to have become established in the language—in this case in the vocabulary of biology.

As experimental psychology developed, the design of its experiments became more rigorous and elaborate. Speaking approximately, we may say that formal design first developed in psychophysics, then in the reaction experiments, then in the experiments on memory.

In 1900 we find Müller and Pilzecker (1900) in their classical study of right associates using comparison series (*Vergleichreihen*) as controls (but not so named) for the principal series (*Hauptreihen*). They also introduced fore-series (*Vorreihen*) and after-series (*Nachreihen*) and thus in a way they anticipated some of the design that Thorndike and Woodworth employed shortly after for their study of transfer. You even find in Müller and Pilzecker *Hauptvorreihen, Vergleichvorreihen, Hauptnachreihen* and *Vergleichnachreihen*, but the *Vergleichreihen* are control series used on the same observers. The control groups come later (Wolf, 1950; Abbot, Mack, & Wolf, 1952; Hardy, Wolff, & Goodell, 1952).

There can be no doubt that use of control observation, either implicit or explicit, is essential in sound experimental work. There has to be a relatum to give the datum significance. More definitely designed control series and control experiments have at the present time come into common use, even when control groups are not called for. Such controls go by a variety of names. For instance, in medical research one sometimes sees nowadays mention of the use of *placebo* (a dose that pleases the patient but has no pharmacological effect; *placere*, to please) introduced as a control in comparison observations or in control series.

When there is no acceptable hypothesis as to the independent variable in an experiment, it may be impossible to have a control, which may become available only when a good hypothesis comes along. Thus, in the experiments on extrasensory perception (*ESP*), control is very difficult. Control by restraint and guidance is common enough for every effort is made to keep conditions constant and to prevent fortuitous leakage of information to the percipient, but control as a check requires a knowledge of what is to be omitted if the Method of Difference is to be used. The reading of cards in an invisible pack is supposed to have been extrasensory when the reading deviates from 'chance' by an amount that can be accepted under current statistical conventions with a high level of confidence. But what is 'chance'? Good statisticians nowadays do not accept, as they did thirty years ago, the principle of insufficient reason as meaning the a priori presumption that wholly unconstrained coincidence will give correct guesses in only 20% of the cases when there are equal numbers of five kinds of cards in the pack. In this case there needs to be a control experiment, one that would show empirically what the 'purely chance' frequencies are. Usually the parapsychologists attempt such controls, but the ideal is to have the same subject guess the same pack of cards both with and without *ESP*. How do you turn off *ESP* in a subject and turn it on again and know what it is you have done? It is not impossible that some of the heated argument about *ESP* would disappear if there could be a clearer understanding of what a control is and when one is being used.[14]

Control Groups and the Measurement of the Differences between Groups. There is an advantage in using an entirely different set of subjects in the control experiment from those employed in the principal experiment. When the same subjects are used in both experiments, you can not be sure that the one experiment, whichever is performed first, has not affected the other, and especially is that danger great in experiments upon learning where it is expected that initial events will affect later ones, since that consequence is exactly what learning is. It is no wonder then that the first use of control groups in psychological investigation came about in experiments on the transfer of training, nor that the control group is now so prevalent in the design of psychological investigations, since learning is at present so frequent a topic of research and rats, cheap and plentiful, are the chief class of subjects.

> There is, however, also a disadvantage that comes with the use of the independent control group. The use of separate subjects makes sure that there is no spurious cross-effect between the principal experiment and the control, for Peter's memories do not reflect Paul's learnings when there has been no social contact between the two. Thus you are safe in respect of the parameter under investigation; but what, one may ask, about other parameters? How do you know that your control group is the equivalent of your principal group in every relevant attribute except in respect of the independent variable, for which a difference is intended and assured? You have to have equivalent groups. You may match them individual for individual in respect of what seem to be their most important determinable and presumably relevant characteristics. You may make both groups very large, hoping that the law of large numbers will change your ignorance into assurance of equivalence. You can match litter-mates in body-weight if your subjects are animals, and you can advertise for twins when your subjects are human. Still your subjects in the two groups will not be identical, and you must on that account accept a loss in confidence to set over against the gain that led you to resort to control groups in the first place. There lies here a principle of complementarity from which you can not escape.[15]

Since Solomon (1949) has already traced the early history of the introduction of the control group into experimental psychology, there is no need for us to repeat his comments, and we may rest content with recapitulating his important points.

> The earliest example of a control group mentioned in the present paper is the control mice who died of tetanus because they were not immunized, but that is not a psychological investigation.[16] Solomon makes much of the fact that Thorndike and Woodworth (1901) were the first to see the need for a control group in the study of the transfer of training, but they did not fully appreciate its importance, for what they describe is only an incidental control experiment, to which they give eight lines of description in a paper of 1400 lines. The classical experiments on transfer without a control group are open to the criticism that you can not tell how much practice in skill A affects skill B unless you have tested B before the practice, and then this initial testing of B may itself have acted as practice on B to vitiate the results. You can measure this special practice effect of the initial testing on a control group, however, and then accept as significant the difference between the groups. Examples of well known investigations of transfer without control groups are

Volkmann's on bilateral transfer long ago (1858) and much later Swift's (1903) and Ebert and Meumann's (1904). Dearborn (1909) criticized these papers, showing that improvement in the after-test was due largely to learning in the fore-test and not, as had been supposed, to the intervening practice on the alternative task. The first investigation to use the full design of (fore-test→practice→after-test) in the experimental group, to be compared with (fore-test→nothing→after-test) in the control group was Winch (1908), and the general use of control groups in these experiments begins then. Sleight (1911) used a control group (not so named) in 1911. Later Ewert's study of bilateral transfer (1926) is representative of good work, and Bray (1928) gives a good historical account of experimental design in bilateral transfer. Woodworth's 1938 summary of the requirements in studying transfer is well known.[17]

As we have already remarked it is hard to establish causal relations in the study of history, for we have there only the Method of Agreement and no controls. Nevertheless historical agreements are interesting. Even if they do not show that one event is cause and another effect, they tend often to support the Zeitgeist conception of progress by showing that related conceptions are apt to emerge at about the same time. Thus we may note as a pertinent example of historical simultaneity that the use of group controls requires the comparison of two groups and that the statistical techniques for measuring the significance of group differences were being invented or discovered just about the time group controls came into general use. The year 1908 saw an early important paper in both lines of development—Winch's experiment with group controls and "Student's" paper on the significance of differences.

The history of the measurement of differences between groups runs approximately like this. The mathematicians—Laplace, Gauss, Bertrand, Poincaré—and the early statisticians—Quetelet and Galton—all had the formulas for the probable error or standard error of a mean and for the variability of the difference between two such means. They sometimes wrote the ratio of the difference to its variability, which was much later called the critical ratio.[18] In England in the last quarter of the nineteenth century there was great interest in the study of quantitative relations between groups, but concern centered on regression and correlation and not on differences. Galton's best known paper on regression appeared in 1886 and his paper on co-relation in 1888, whereas Pearson first described product-moment co-relation in 1896. Then (1900) Pearson published what was to become a basic paper in the measurements of group differences. He called it: "On the criterion that a given system of deviations from a probable case of a correlated system of variables is such that it can be reasonably supposed to have arisen from random sampling." Pearson gave here a chi-square table and prepared the way for what came later. His problem was really the one that R. A. Fisher took over much later: How significant is the deviation of a mean from the null hypothesis? The crucial though not the first paper was, however, the one in 1908 by the modest "Student," who only much later came to be identified as W. S. Gosset (1908). It dealt with the probable errors of means and of the differences of means and gave the famous t-tables for assessing the significance of differences. Pearson published again on this matter (1911), and the practical measurement of differences and the assessment of their significance was well under way. It is interesting to note that in those days—the decade of the 1910s—Pearson used six-place tables and a difference was regarded as 'certain' only if the probability of its being in the direction found was 1.000000, that is to say, somewhat greater than 0.999999 or less than one chance in a million of being wrong.

It was not until the 1920s that the three-place tables came to be accepted for this purpose and that McGaughy (1924) could assert that it was safe to accept differences when the critical ratio is only 3 or greater. Of course, nowadays we all follow R. A. Fisher who in the 1930s introduced the concepts of degrees of freedom, the null hypothesis, fiducial limits and levels of confidence.

That is a rough sketch of what was going on at this time in respect of the measurement of differences between groups. That the problem was in the air and that the times were right for its advancement is further indicated by the fact that Victor Henri in Paris in 1898 published a paper on the probability of differences, referring to a table of probabilities for critical ratios which he had already printed in his earlier and more fundamental paper of 1895.[19] This 1898 paper of Henri's anticipated Pearson's similar one by two years but it received almost no attention, for the main movement was going on in London and in English, and Henri's voice was little more than a murmur in remote Paris. Besides in France there was no one to push this sort of investigation, whereas London after a bit had the new Galton Laboratory. Nineteen years afterward an American psychologist did discover Henri's paper. He commented on it, corrected it, explained it, and invented the phrase "probable correctness of a difference," but his paper too was peripheral to the main stream and perhaps no one but he, his wife, and the editor ever read it (Boring, 1917). Still these eddies at the side show how the main stream is flowing, out in the center of history. That is the way the Zeitgeist works.

Now we ask: Did the use of group controls wait upon the development of the statistical methods for measuring differences between groups? That is a hard question to answer, for, as is usual in historical questions, we have only Agreement for evidence and no control observation. Winch with his good design for group control in 1908 used none of the new statistics. He compared individuals in the groups case by case and drew his conclusions. Besides Gosset did not even publish his paper until 1908 and it took time and help from the Galton Laboratory before psychologists found out how to use it. It seems instead that the initial relation between the two developments was coordinate, not causal. Nowadays, however, when scientific assurance can be had for only a 5-% chance of being wrong and truth exists at the 1-% fiducial level, half the experimental papers can use group controls and many of them use the new statistics. Even though neither development caused the other, there has certainly been a circular positive feed-back between the two technics, one that helps to keep them both in use.

Prevalence of Control, Explicit and Implicit in Scientific Activity. We shall say little here of *control* in the sense of restraint or guidance. Of course, experimental conditions must be kept constant. Every experiment has an independent variable and preferably only one, though an experimental design may involve many experiments with different independent variables. The independent variable must be constrained to vary in a predetermined way, and all other possible variables must be kept constant. The following paragraphs, however, consider *control* only as a check and as it is related to the Method of Difference.

At first it seemed worth while to find out how much psychologists are thinking about controls in their experimental work, so I took one of the 1951 volumes of the *Journal of Experimental Psychology* (vol. 41) to assess the situation (Table I, columns 4 and 7). I was astonished to find that 52% of the 58 experimental articles in this volume used control groups, so I analysed the contents of the 1916 and 1933 volumes of the same journal. No control groups were used in 1916, only 11% in 1933. I also checked on the first volume of the *American Journal of Psychology*, 1887, and, to get something simple before experimental psychology existed, volume 73 of Gilbert's

TABLE I

Frequencies of Experimental Articles in Which Chief Facts Depend on Use of Controls or of Observed Differences in Three Volumes of the Journal of Experimental Psychology

	Frequencies			Percentages		
	Vol. 1 1916	Vol. 16 1933	Vol. 41 1951	Vol. 1 1916	Vol. 16 1933	Vol. 41 1951
(1) Control groups; group differences	0	6	30	0	11	52
(2) Control series; control observations; observed differences	4	18	16	17	34	27
(3) Concomitant variation	15	18	11	62	34	19
(4) Factual description	5	11	1	21	21	2
Total	24	53	58	100	100	100

Annalen der Physik, 1823, which most psychologists know in later years as Poggendorf's *Annalen*. There were no group controls in them. That is, of course, as expected.

Next I counted experimental articles which had in them explicit reference to control series or control observations or which were concerned with establishing a difference between two conditions (not individual differences). It is impossible to distinguish these two kinds of differences between compared conditions—as to whether one condition provides a second datum (case of two principal sets of observations) or merely a relatum (case of principal observation and control observation). Line 2 of the Table shows these frequencies. When three or more conditions are compared, you come to the various experimental patterns which may be called concomitant variation, some of them quite complicated. See line 3 of the Table. About three-fourths of the experimental articles in the 1887 *American Journal* and half the experimental articles in the 1823 *Annalen* were of these two kinds: studies of a pair of concomitant differences or of more involved concomitant variations.

There are also the experimental articles which provide factual descriptions like determinations of the predominant frequencies of vowel sounds, or the spectral specification of the stimulus to white, or the examination of the sensitivity of the blind spot, or the establishment of the cues to the perception of moisture (line 4 of the Table). These descriptions constitute a kind of experimental taxonomy and are characteristic of the early stages of the development of an experimental field. Nearly half of the experimental articles in the 1823 *Annalen* are of this sort, a fifth of the articles in the 1916 and 1933 *Journal of Experimental Psychology*, but only one article out of 58 in 1951. What has been happening in experimental psychology is that psychologists, perhaps especially under the stimulus of R. A. Fisher, have been becoming more conscious of experimental design. Thus they are aware of the relata, and either they investigate differences between phenomena or they introduce experimental control observations, making the comparison of events explicit and measuring the significance of the difference between them.

In making these counts I have ignored non-experimental articles—factual discussion, theoretical discussion, polemics, and papers describing apparatus, techniques, and methods. In the volumes examined these kinds of articles are more common in the earlier years and that seems proper in view of what we know about the history of sciences, although particular editorial policy also has something to do with these frequencies.

The prevalence of group controls in recent psychological experimentation is undoubtedly due in part to the greater availability of subjects. In Germany and America in the 1890s the students worked with each other and even with the professor as observers. Such studies remain important but are supplemented nowadays by researches which utilize large numbers of rats and school-children, subjects which, besides being inexpensive and plentiful, make the sample examined more representative of larger populations and less dependent upon possible idiosyncrasies.

Summary. Control in the sense of restraint has always been used in experimentation to keep conditions constant and is thus an essential part of the experimental method.

Control in the sense of guidance is involved in causing an independent variable to vary in a specified and known manner and is thus also essential in experimentation.

Control in the sense of a check or comparison, the original meaning of the word, appears in all experimentation because a discoverable fact is a difference or a relation, and a discovered datum has significance only as it is related to a frame of reference, to a relatum.

The methodological status of control as a check or comparison is to be understood by reference to J. S. Mill's Method of Difference.

Control or the frame of reference is often only implicit, as it is in factual description.

The control observation is often only implicit, but the control series or the control experiment is generally explicit, being taken into consideration in the design of an experimental investigation.

The explicit control experiment is not new. Pascal used it in determining the weight of the air in 1648.

The experimental use of control groups is new, being found in biological research in the late nineteenth century and in psychological research since the early twentieth century. Its use at the present time, especially with animal subjects and school-children, is very common.

Although the use of the control experiment is early, the use of the word *control* in the sense of a check or comparison does not seem to appear in the scientific literature until the latter part of the nineteenth century.

NOTES

1. Especially the eight-line paragraph on p. 558 where the use of a control group is described.
2. Cf. B. F. Skinner (1953), where the conception of control seems to me to be more positive than negative in the chapters entitled: The controlling environment; Self-control; Personal control; Group control; Economic control; Culture and control; and The problem of control. Certainly Solomon's *control group* has little relation to Skinner's *group control*. Even in discussion of experimental design the meaning of *control* is apt to vary. For instance, C. E. Buxton (1948, 73 f.), in the course of two pages uses the word thrice as meaning maintenance of constancy of conditions and once in the sense of a test-observation.
3. Bk. II, Aph. 11–13, deals respectively with the three principles.
4. The only use of the word *control* that I can find in these books is in *Text-Book*, 22, where Titchener remarks that "experimental control is still possible" even when introspection interferes with consciousness.
5. They also give examples of systematic arrangements for the recording of exact behavior and the maintenance of constancy of conditions on pp. 214–227.
6. G. T. Fechner (1860, I, 85); and there is another example of the use of the word farther down on the same page: "die Wiederholung oder sonstige Controle an sich langweiliger Operationen."
7. Pascal (1937, 103–108), which is mostly Perier's letter to Pascal about the experiment. For short accounts, see I. B. Cohen (1948, 71 ff.); J. B. Conant (1951, 72–74). Cohen says that Perier noted the continuous drop in the height of the column as he came down; if three points make a continuity, he did. Conant says that Pascal was at the foot of the mountain watching the control barometer, but that was Father Chastin. Pascal was waiting in Paris to hear what happened.
8. Jevons (1874, II, 43–45), in the section called "Blind or test experiments," in the chapter on "Experiment"; but the mention of Faraday's and Tyndall's experiments does not appear until 1883 (433 f.).

9. Michael Faraday (1855, III, series xxii, 83–136). The experiments on magnecrystallic action were performed in 1848.
10. On this experiment, the *Vexirversuche* and the *Vexirfehler*, see Henri (1898*b*, esp. 61–66). On the nature of *Vexirfehler*, which are no more "errors" than is any compulsive illusion, see Kincaid (1918); Helson and Burgert (1936).
11. Henry Head (1920, I, 26–29). The original experiment was Head, Rivers and Sherren (1905); Head and Rivers (1908).
12. Cf. Boring (1921), which, paradoxically, interprets Titchener's conception of the psychological point of view functionally.
13. See also Titchener, *Experimental Psychology*, 1905, II, pt. ii, 340–344.
14. Pratt, Rhine, Smith, Stuart & Greenwood (1940, esp. chaps. 1–3). P. 26 says: "It can be demonstrated mathematically that so long as the target deck patterns contain five of each design, the average number of correct matchings with any call pattern is invariably five." You can not, however, demonstrate any empirical event mathematically. All you can show mathematically in this case is that 1/5 of the possible patterns would give 1/5 of the matchings correct, but that is not to say that the actual patterns would average out to 1/5 correct matchings. For a given call pattern the decks could be rigged to give any desired frequency of correctness. A control experiment might show and might not show what effect *ESP* has on frequency of correct matching, depending on how much in each of the two situations to be compared is left uncontrolled (in the other sense of that word). On the difficulty of using the probability model to fit an empirical situation, see Boring (1941).
15. Andrews (1948, 10–15) distinguishes five methods of control: (1) the control test, which is simply the Method of Difference; (2) the control group as described above; (3) matched pairs, in which equivalence of control groups is assured by matching every individual in the experimental group to one in the control group in respect of all conceivably relevant parameters except the crucial one under investigation; (4) the practice method, in which learning is made maximal before the experiment so that further improvement in the fore-test is improbable; and (5) the rotation method where the orders of tests are counterbalanced, for instance, the tests A, B and C are given for one group in the order ABC, for another in the order CAB, and for a third in the order BCA. When these orders are combined, it is hoped that practice effects due to priority will cancel out but, of course, you can not be sure. Counterbalancing is not constancy, and the principle of complementariness applies here too. Similarly the method of practice gives up the attempt to study effects of early practice.
16. Hankin (1890).
17. Woodworth (1938, 178–181). In the new edition, see the long chapter on transfer, Woodworth and Schlosberg (1954, 733–778, esp. 735–738).
18. Walker (1929, 55 ff., 179); Henri (1895, 466–500 passim). The statement in the text is too general, but it serves to set the stage for the late 1890s.
19. Henri (1898*a*). For Henri's 1895 paper, see note 18.

Fechner: Inadvertent Founder
of Psychophysics

᠁᠁᠁᠁᠁᠁᠁᠁᠁᠁᠁᠁᠁᠁᠁᠁᠁᠁᠁᠁᠁᠁᠁᠁ 1961

CERTAINLY the most interesting tool that science employs in its perpetual pursuit of knowledge is the scientist, with his enthusiasms, egoisms, and prejudices, his inevitable unconscious attitudinal orientation in the consensus of contemporary opinions, which we call the *Zeitgeist*. One wonders what science would be like if automation could take over completely. Are there mechanical equivalents for jealousy and pride and pigheadedness and insight, and those other interacting personal forces that contribute to contemporary truth in the scientific field?

Fechner [1] never tried to found psychophysics or a new experimental psychology. He was, in his own estimation in those last forty-five years of his life, a philosopher, fighting what he regarded as the crass materialism of his day, the *Nachtansicht* or "night view," as he called it, and promoting the faith that mind and soul are the ultimates of reality, the *Tagesansicht* or "day view." This favoring of the clear philosophical vision in the day view as opposed to the materialistic darkness of the night view is Fechner's panpsychism, a faith that seems mystical to most modern scientists, partly because the German word *Seele* does not distinguish between mind and soul, between that which compares the sensory intensities of two lifted weights and whatever it is that persists after the body's death.

Let us take time to recall what Fechner did with the 86 years of his life between 1801 and 1887. At the age of 16 he went to Leipzig to study physiology, which in those days meant taking a doctorate in medicine. He stuck to physiology for only seven years and then turned to the study of physics and mathematics. He began work in this new field humbly, making his early reputation by the translation into German of French handbooks of physics

Reprinted with permission from *Psychometrika*, 1961, **26**, 3–8. An invited paper presented at the Twenty-fifth Anniversary Observance of the Psychometric Society, Chicago, Illinois, September 6–7, 1960.

and chemistry. At the age of 33, after some research in the new physics of electricity, he was made professor of physics at Leipzig; he held that post until 1839, when he resigned for reasons of poor health.

For 15 years he had been a physicist, but three other interests were emerging. Under the nom de plume of Dr. Mises, he provided scope for his humanistic interests by beginning a series of essays on various topics, the first of which was a satire on the current medical faith in the potency of iodine: *Proof that the Moon is Made of Iodine*, 1821. Out of this side of Fechner's nature emerged his vigorous support of spiritualism as opposed to materialism: he wrote *The Little Book on Life after Death* in 1836. On the scientific side there was his growing interest in sense-physiology, and presently his papers on subjective colors and afterimages in 1838 and 1840. It must have been then that he permanently injured his eyesight by gazing too long at the sun through colored glasses.

There followed from 1839 to 1851 a dozen years of retirement in Leipzig. During the first three or four years he suffered from some form of psychoneurosis, and it would seem that this German academic never quite escaped from unusual seclusiveness as he lived on in Leipzig outside of the University. It was during this period that his concern with the "day view" of reality, with panpsychism, emerged. In 1848 he published *Nanna*, a volume named for the goddess of flowers, in which he argued for the mental life of plants. Then in 1851 came the *Zend-Avesta*, with a subtitle specifying that the volume was about the things of heaven and the life to come.

Actually this philosophical period of Fechner's life extended altogether over 43 years from 1836 to 1879, during which, in writing in 1861 on the problem of the soul, he remarked that he had already called four times to a sleeping world which had not awakened, and he was now calling a fifth time, and "if I live, I shall call yet a sixth and a seventh time, 'Steh! auf!' and always it will be the same 'Steh! auf!'" He did call twice more, the seventh in 1879 in the volume on the "day view and the night view."

Fechner's philosophy won him little respect among the scientists, nor any great acclaim by the philosophers. William James took him seriously, hailed the *Zend-Avesta* when he belatedly discovered it, told Bergson that Fechner "seems to me of the real race of prophets." James described Fechner's philosophy in *A Pluralistic Universe* (1909, 131–177) and related Fechner's views to his own. It was this excitement about spiritualism that pushed Fechner into psychophysics—strange parentage it was for psychophysics.

On that now famous morning of 22 October 1850, Fechner, lying in bed and puzzling how to do away with materialism, had the thought that, since conscious events are necessarily related to events in the brain—at least in the living person—an equation between the two systems would have the effect of identifying them and of abolishing the dualism, abolishing it in favor of a psychic monism which was what Fechner wanted. If he knew about Weber's law, he did not think about its relevance then. Later, however, he realized the significance of Weber's experiments and also of Daniel Bernoulli's contention in 1738 that *fortune morale* (psychic) is proportional to the logarithm of *fortune physique* (physical). Now Fechner thought: sensation is a function of its stimulus; you can measure stimuli, but how can you measure sensations? He concluded that sensory magnitude can be measured in terms of sensitivity, and he laid down the general outlines of his program in *Zend-Avesta*, the book about heaven and the future life. Imagine sending a graduate student of psychology nowadays to the Divinity School for a course in immortality as preparation for advanced experimental work in psychophysics! How narrow we have become!

After the publication of the *Zend-Avesta* Fechner had 14 years of intense activity in psychophysics, the first 9 of them in experimentation. After that came the epochal event, the publication of the *Elemente der Psychophysik* in two parts in 1860, the occasion that we celebrate today. It was the psychophysics, not the panpsychism, that attracted attention. Fechner's alleged measurement of sensation met with criticism and objection which indeed showed its importance in the current scientific belief that belonged to the mid-nineteenth century. History was now ready for a scientific psychology, but how can you become scientific unless you can measure your phenomena? Fechner's scheme was plausible and the need for sensory measurement led some to overlook its defects. He argued that sensation cannot be measured directly but can be indirectly. What you do is to measure sensitivity by determining differential thresholds; then, to find the magnitude of the sensation, you calculate the number of just noticeable differences (jnd) from zero sensation at the absolute threshold to the sensation that is being measured. Of course, this business of counting up jnd to measure a sensation met with the question: How do you know that all jnd are equal? And indeed, when measured by certain other scales, jnd may turn out not to be equal.

About 1865 Fechner turned from psychophysics to a new interest in experimental esthetics, publishing his classic in that field in 1876. The world, however, would not leave him free. Applause from some reinforced criticism from others, and Fechner was forced—for it was not easy for a German scholar to let criticism go unanswered—to reply to objections and to defend his measurement of sensation. He must have thought that he would himself have been content to go on crying to a sleeping world that the measurement of sensation had now made plausible man's grasp on immortality; but when the world at last awoke, it was to the wrong cry—unfortunately for Fechner, fortunately for us.

Tolstoy, speaking of History in his *War and Peace* and arguing for cultural determination—and thus indirectly against the importance of Great Men in the determination of History—remarked that "History, the unconscious, general hive-life of mankind, uses every moment of the life of kings as a tool for its own purposes . . . A king is History's slave." History itself is the sum of the myriad of events that make it up, and every one of these is caused, though there be so many that prediction from a knowledge of them becomes impossible. As to the Great, Tolstoy imagined a young cavalry commander who achieved high honor because, exuberant with good health, unaware of danger but without orders, he led his men at a gallop across the level plain in what turned out to be a successful charge. So with Fechner. He attacked the ramparts of materialism and was decorated for measuring sensation.

Scientists, for the most part, believe in the operation of deterministic causality between events, yet they also like in ordinary professional conversation to leave room for the originality of Great Men. There is a contradiction here. To see the Great Man's important contribution to thought, as a consequence of the combination of commonly accepted knowledge, plus certain ideas or discoveries of other men, plus one or two coincidences of the kind of insight that brings thitherto unrelated ideas into useful connection, is largely to reduce greatness to a link in a complex causal chain. When the whole story is told of an invention or a discovery or the founding of a school, when as much attention is given to the antecedents as to the consequences of the great event, its greatness seems to diminish, its importance becomes less as it spreads over a broader range of activities and a longer span of time.

The case with Fechner goes about like this. The times were ready for scientists to get hold of mind by measuring it. Sensory thresholds had been determined as much as a hundred years before Fechner. The physiologists were already experimenting with sensation—Johannes Müller with specific nerve energies in 1826, Ernst Heinrich Weber with tactual sensibility in 1834. To contemporaneous thought Herbart had contributed the notion of the measurement of ideas, while denying the possibility of experimenting on them; and he had made Leibnitz's concept of the threshold well known. Lotze published his *Medical Psychology: The Physiology of the Mind* the year after Fechner's *Zend-Avesta*. It was in this setting that Fechner had on 22 October 1850 his important insight about measuring sensation and relating the measures of sensation to the measures of their stimuli.

Fechner's claim to originality of epoch-making magnitude lies in this insight. His claim to honor lies in his careful and laborious work through the decade of the 1850's, and the crucial character of the *Elemente* when it finally came out in 1860. He is credited with having given experimental psychology the three fundamental psychophysical methods still in constant use today, but actually the method of limits goes back to 1700 and may be said to have been formalized by Delezenne in 1827, whereas the method of constant stimuli was first used by Vierordt in 1852. Only the method of average error belongs to Fechner, and that only half, for he and his brother-in-law,

A. W. Volkmann, developed it in the 1850's. What Fechner did in the *Elemente* was to present the case for sensory measurement and write the systematic handbook for psychophysics, a new field of scientific endeavor. In this sense he founded psychophysics as a field that is ancillary to the establishment of the philosophy of panpsychism.

It is conceivable that the *Elemente* might have fallen flat, as the laborious production of a queer old mystic in Leipzig who went to endless pains to prove a point that most wise men do not believe. The times, however, were ripe for psychophysics. Immediately the methods began to be used, and new facts began to accumulate, while the argument waxed about Fechner's interpretation of what it is that the methods do, about whether sensation had actually been measured after all.

In general, the greatness of Great Men is a subjective addition to history which posterity adds in order to understand history. History is continuous and sleek. Great Men are the handles that you put on its smooth sides. You have to simplify natural events in order to understand them, and science itself is forced to generalize in the interest of economy of thinking. Just so the history of science singles out events, schools, trends, and discoveries and eponymizes them, that is to say, it names them for a central figure. Fechner has become the name for a change in the newly developing scientific psychology, for the gradual acceptance of the belief that the fleeting and evanescent mind—consciousness—can be measured. That had to happen before anything else could take place in respect of scales and measurement in the psychological sphere.

William James admired Fechner, the philosopher, but deplored Fechner, the psychophysicist. Almost everyone knows how he said, "But it would be terrible if even such a dear old man as this could saddle our science forever with his patient whimsies, and, in a world so full of more nutritious objects of attention, compel all future students to plough through the difficulties, not only of his own works, but of the still drier ones written in his refutation . . . The only amusing part of it is that Fechner's critics should always feel bound, after smiting his theories hip and thigh and leaving not a stick of them standing, to wind up by saying that nevertheless to him belongs the *imperishable glory*, of first forming them and thereby turning psychology into an *exact science*." Well, say I, isn't that sort of glory as nearly imperishable as one could expect ever to get? But then, of course, James did not agree with Tolstoy. He thought that there are Great Men.

Only this year Henri Piéron has expressed a thought quite similar to James' except that Piéron and James are on opposite sides of the Fechner fence. Piéron wrote in concluding a centennial article about the importance of Fechner's psychophysics: "And thus the shade of Fechner does not cease in our day to hover over many American laboratories of experimental psychology which without doubt never hear tell of Fechner except when Stevens declares that nothing of Fechner's work remains." That is hardly fair to us Americans. Stevens' students hear about Fechner, and scattered over America are a small coterie of psychologists who seldom miss noting the date when 22 October comes around.

And now here are we celebrating the centenary of the *Elemente*. In complimenting Fechner we compliment ourselves, of course. A centenary is virtually a religious rite. We could not be pleasing Fechner now, even if he had justified his contribution to psychophysics by eventually finding himself immortal. What we need for our own use are symbols of our faith, our faith in science and measurement and quantification. It is right to hang Fechner's picture on the wall. It is a symbol of what we will to have important. It is right to be glad when your son is born on 22 October. It is right to atomize the smooth flow of History by the eponymy of great names. The scientist may be a determinist in his model-making, but as an active scholar and experimenter he needs more motivation than simple description and the generalization of observation can provide. He needs humor and reverence, as well as a little distortion of the complacency of history, to keep his prime-mover going, and what good is the scientific machine without a prime-mover?

It was given to Fechner to have the idea of measuring sensation independently of the measure of its material stimulus. In his opinion he succeeded. Posterity doubts the validity of his procedure or even condemns it. Yet, if posterity has something better, it grew out of what Fechner provided. All honor then to the man who, resolved to achieve one goal, actually reached another, who because of his patient insistence remains the central figure at the absolute threshold at which measurement entered psychology. It may be said that he gave to sensations their magnitudes.

NOTES

1. For references on Fechner see Boring (1950*a*, 275–296); Brett (1921, 127–139); Hall (1912, 123–177); James (1909, 131–177); Kuntze (1892); Lasswitz (1896); Murphy (1949, 84–92); Perry (1926, 81–96); Ribot (1886, 134–187); Titchener (1905, II, XX–CXVI); Wundt (1901).

Masters and Pupils among
the American Psychologists

◫◫◫◫◫◫◫◫◫◫◫◫◫◫◫◫◫◫◫◫◫◫◫ 1948

WITH MOLLIE D. BORING

PLEDGE, in his *Science since 1500*, gives three master-and-pupil charts which show the presumptive intellectual genealogy of scientists.[1] These charts make interesting reading. Here, for instance, is Pavlov, who was a student of Heidenhain's and also, along with Pflüger, a student of Ludwig's. Ludwig has no ancestry showing on this chart, but the line through Heidenhain (whose sibling was Ehrlich) goes back through Cohnheim to Virchow to Johannes Müller. Would it not be interesting, we thought, to attempt to make a similar chart for modern American psychologists? This paper shows the result of our attempt.

There arose first the question of how to select American psychologists for study, and it seemed natural for us to take the 119 psychologists who have been starred in the first seven editions of *American Men of Science*.[2] Of these persons 47 were dead and 72 were living.

For the dead we filled in the names of the teachers with whom they 'took their degrees,' or we looked up the relationship in biographical data about them, or, when still in doubt, we wrote to some living person who had been associated with the deceased psychologist in the laboratory in which he did his doctoral research and asked which older man seemed to have been primarily responsible for the younger man's thesis and degree.

Our experience with the living shows that we may easily have made some errors with the dead. There can be no doubt that Cattell was Wundt's student, even though he resisted so many influences of the Leipzig Institute and disapproved of them. Both Wundt and Cattell have told us of this relationship in print. Thinking of him as analogous to Cattell, we should also have assigned Witmer to Wundt, for he went to Leipzig and took his degree with Wundt. To this inference, however, Witmer remains available to pronounce

Reprinted with permission from *The American Journal of Psychology*, 1948, **61**, 527–534.

TABLE I

Psychologists and Their Teachers

Eighty-four pupils who came under the principal influence of a single teacher in the formative period up to the time of the Ph.D. The pupil's name comes first, the teacher's second. (The pupils are listed in the order of the dates of their Ph.D.s or equivalents.)

H. H. Donaldson—G. S. Hall
Hugo Münsterberg—W. Wundt
J. McK. Cattell—W. Wundt
Joseph Jastrow—G. S. Hall
H. K. Wolfe—W. Wundt
G. T. Patrick—G. S. Hall
E. C. Sanford—G. S. Hall
Frank Angell—W. Wundt
E. B. Delabarre—H. Münsterberg
Livingston Farrand—J. McK. Cattell
Herbert Nichols—G. S. Hall
E. A. Pace—W. Wundt
E. W. Scripture—W. Wundt
W. L. Bryan—G. S. Hall
E. B. Titchener—W. Wundt
Lightner Witmer—J. McK. Cattell
M. W. Calkins—Wm. James
H. C. Warren—J. M. Baldwin
T. L. Bolton—G. S. Hall
M. F. Washburn—E. B. Titchener
J. H. Leuba—G. S. Hall
Robert MacDougall—H. Münsterberg
C. E. Seashore—E. W. Scripture
Raymond Dodge—B. Erdmann
C. H. Judd—W. Wundt
Max F. Meyer—K. Stumpf
E. H. Lindley—G. S. Hall
Boris Sidis—H. Münsterberg
E. D. Starbuck—G. S. Hall
Madison Bentley—H. K. Wolfe
L. J. Martin—G. E. Müller
E. L. Thorndike—Wm. James
S. I. Franz—J. McK. Cattell
H. H. Goddard—G. S. Hall
A. H. Pierce—H. Münsterberg
R. S. Woodworth—J. McK. Cattell
Walter Dill Scott—W. Wundt
H. T. Woolley—J. R. Angell
G. M. Whipple—E. B. Titchener
E. B. Holt—Wm. James
Ethel Puffer Howes—H. Münsterberg
Knight Dunlap—H. Münsterberg

R. M. Ogden—O. Külpe
J. B. Watson—J. R. Angell
Max Wertheimer—O. Külpe
Bird T. Baldwin—H. Münsterberg
H. A. Carr—J. R. Angell
Arnold Gesell—G. S. Hall
Daniel Starch—C. E. Seashore
F. L. Wells—J. McK. Cattell
June E. Downey—J. R. Angell
Joseph Peterson—J. R. Angell
W. V. Bingham—J. R. Angell
K. Koffka—K. Stumpf
C. E. Ferree—E. B. Titchener
H. S. Langfeld—K. Stumpf
Herbert Woodrow—W. B. Pillsbury
Rudolph Pintner—W. Wundt
S. W. Fernberger—F. M. Urban
E. R. Guthrie—H. K. Wolfe
K. M. Dallenbach—E. B. Titchener
J. F. Dashiell—J. McK. Cattell
W. R. Miles—C. E. Seashore
E. G. Boring—E. B. Titchener
T. L. Kelley—E. L. Thorndike
K. S. Lashley—J. B. Watson
Kurt Lewin—W. Köhler
Donald G. Paterson—R. Pintner
John E. Anderson—H. Münsterberg
Floyd H. Allport—E. B. Holt
C. P. Stone—M. E. Haggerty
M. S. Viteles—L. Witmer
Elmer Culler—H. A. Carr
H. E. Jones—R. S. Woodworth
Leonard Carmichael—W. F. Dearborn
Carney Landis—K. S. Lashley
J. A. McGeoch—H. A. Carr
E. G. Wever—E. G. Boring
J. P. Guilford—K. M. Dallenbach
C. F. Jacobsen—K. S. Lashley
R. C. Tryon—E. C. Tolman
B. F. Skinner—W. J. Crozier
D. G. Marquis—L. M. Terman
S. S. Stevens—E. G. Boring

his emphatic negative, for he went to Leipzig and took his degree with Wundt only because Cattell sent him there with money from the Seibert Fund. Witmer resented Wundt and Leipzig and acknowledges Cattell, not Wundt, as his early professional mentor. Similarly Bentley acknowledges his debt to H. K. Wolfe, not to Titchener, but we have no choice but to put Whipple down as Titchener's student because Whipple is not here to comment on our inference.

To the 72 living we wrote and all but three of them replied. We told each our belief or guess as to his 'master,' and asked each to correct us or to comment on the proper answer to our question, "Who was it who influenced you most in psychology up to the time you got your Ph.D.?" We treated the three who did not reply as if they were dead: we wrote to persons who were closely associated with them at the time they received their Ph.D.s. We think these relationships are essentially correct, but they are not incontrovertible. There was, for instance, one delinquent for whom we thought we had surely obtained through collateral correspondence the correct 'master'—until he wrote in late to claim a quite different filiality.

The term *master* is, of course, anachronistic. The modern American psychologist neither knows nor ever knew a master. On the other hand, two-thirds of them (84 of our 119) acknowledge, some with great gratitude, the predominant influence of a single senior man in getting them started in their professional development. See Table I. A sixth more (18) divide the predoctoral influence between two mentors, whereas Hollingworth and Strong place three men *in loco magistris*—Cattell, Thorndike and Woodworth. Altogether we have four psychologists with three 'masters' each. See Table II.

There are also the honorable mentions. As we classified our data, there were 28 older psychologists who received honorable mention from 22 younger psychologists. We note this fact and forego comment on it. These mentions depend not only upon the susceptibility of the pupil to many influences but also upon his generosity.

Still another class of respondents are those who acknowledge the intellectual influence of older savants who were not psychologists. Christine Ladd-Franklin, for instance, recognized the influence of the philosopher, C. S. Peirce, as well as of other less famous teachers. Yerkes mentions G. H. Parker and some other Harvard biologists. Max Meyer and Köhler both acknowledge a debt to the physicist, Max Planck. Langfeld notes the importance of W. Nagel to him in his Berlin student days. Thurstone calls Dexter Kimball, the Cornell engineer, "the best teacher I have ever known." Kimball affected Thurstone's professional orientation, as did also Richtmyer, the Cornell physicist. Skinner's debt to Crozier can also be listed in this category—or is Crozier really a psychologist in physiologist's clothing?

Some of the respondents report being influenced by the writings of men with whom they had not been in more personal contact. James' *Principles* influenced John Dewey toward functional psychology before the men had known each other personally. W. L. Bryan, Wm. McDougall and Gardner Murphy all mention the importance of James to their thinking. Murphy adds Freud and Janet. Terman claims Binet.

Often psychologists come under strong postdoctoral influences. J. R. Angell notes such a debt to Wundt, Hull to Thorndike, Stone and Klüver to Lashley, and it is clear that Miles had a similar relation to Dodge. Koffka, just after his degree on rhythm with Stumpf, experienced a Damascene light

TABLE II

Psychologists and Their Teachers

The eighteen pupils who acknowledge two principal teachers in the pre-Ph.D. period, and the four who acknowledge three teachers. The pupil's name comes first, the teachers' second. The pupils are listed by date of Ph.D.

J. R. Angell—Wm. James, J. Dewey
W. B. Pillsbury—E. B. Titchener, H. K. Wolfe
G. M. Stratton—W. Wundt, G. H. Howison
W. F. Dearborn—R. Dodge, J. McK. Cattell, E. L. Thorndike
L. M. Terman—G. S. Hall, E. C. Sanford
Warner Brown—J. McK. Cattell, K. Dunlap
F. N. Freeman—C. H. Judd, R. Dodge
H. L. Hollingworth—J. McK. Cattell, R. S. Woodworth, E. L. Thorndike
E. K. Strong—J. McK. Cattell, E. L. Thorndike, R. S. Woodworth
W. S. Hunter—J. R. Angell, H. A. Carr
A. T. Poffenberger—J. McK. Cattell, R. S. Woodworth
E. C. Tolman—H. Münsterberg, E. B. Holt
A. I. Gates—E. L. Thorndike, R. S. Woodworth
Mark A. May—R. S. Woodworth, E. L. Thorndike
Clark L. Hull—V. A. C. Henmon, D. Starch
E. S. Robinson—J. R. Angell, H. A. Carr
H. E. Garrett—R. S. Woodworth, A. T. Poffenberger
Florence Goodenough—L. M. Terman, R. S. Woodworth, E. L. Thorndike
Heinrich Klüver—Wm. Stern, Max Wertheimer
C. W. Bray—L. Carmichael, H. S. Langfeld
C. H. Graham—W. S. Hunter, J. P. Nafe
E. R. Hilgard—R. Dodge, E. S. Robinson

that came from Wertheimer—*Gestalttheorie*. James' influence keeps bobbing up everywhere. We have not, however, attempted to assess postdoctoral influences, for that could land us in a quagmire.

It is plain that the question "Whose student were you?" was difficult for many of our respondents to answer. Most of the psychologists could manage a simple reply, but many wished to put two (or even three) names into the record. When all is said and done, however, there remains a group (13 of our 119) who do not find that they were inducted into psychology by persons other than themselves (see Table III). We have called these persons—thinking that we know better how to use this phrase than even the French themselves—*les enfants du bon Dieu*. Who got William James into the then new psychology? Agassiz? Bowditch? No one who reads the fully adequate accounts in James' letters thinks that. James is responsible for James. Who started G. Stanley Hall in? Not James really, though Hall took the first American Ph.D. in psychology at Harvard in 1878. What about J. M. Baldwin and G. T. Ladd? And then, to move on two decades, what about William McDougall? Would it be Rivers or G. E. Müller? Hardly. McDougall himself acknowledges James, but that was James the book. Can you have a book for a teacher? Among the living we have placed in this category of self-starters Dewey, Yerkes, Köhler, H. M. Johnson, Thurstone, G. W. Allport and Gardner Murphy. This distinction is not, of course, black and white; perhaps others belong in this group.

TABLE III

Psychologists without Principal Teachers

The thirteen psychologists out of the total 119 who seem to have had no principal teacher in the pre-Ph.D. days, the self-starters

William James	Robert M. Yerkes
G. Stanley Hall	William McDougall
George Trumball Ladd	Wolfgang Köhler
John Dewey	H. M. Johnson
J. Mark Baldwin	L. L. Thurstone
Christine Ladd-Franklin	Gordon W. Allport
Gardner Murphy	

With these reservations made, we have little to do except to leave our readers with the tables and charts. Table I is for the 84 psychologists whom we regard as having had a single principal teacher in pre-Ph.D. days. Table II is for the 22 men with two or three predoctoral mentors. Table III is for the 13 self-starters.

The size of the Chart (1A and 1B) has made it necessary to divide it and place it on two pages. Nor will it go together in plane space. There have to be some crossing lines. The interlocking instruction of Cattell, Thorndike and Woodworth makes most of the difficulty in Chart 1B. It has also been necessary to repeat in Chart 1B six of the names which appeared in Chart 1A: James, Judd, Dunlap, Cattell, Thorndike and Woodworth. For these repeated names we have used the subscript "1" in the first chart and "2" in the second chart; e.g., "James$_1$," "James$_2$."

Some persons, like Wundt, whose names were not starred in *American Men of Science*, are introduced because they are acknowledged principal

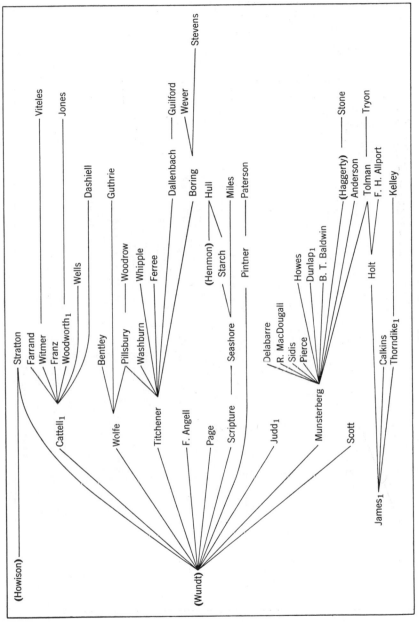

Chart 1 A

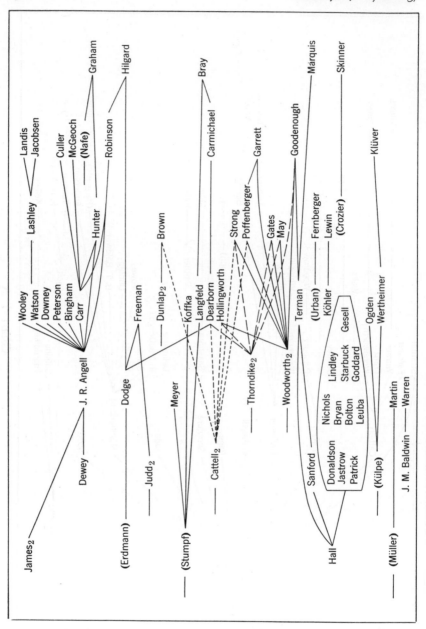

Chart 1 B

teachers. Their names have been placed in parentheses. We have resisted the further complication of carrying all the lines back until we reach a teacher who seems to have been a self-starter. We could take Külpe back to Wundt and G. E. Müller, G. E. Müller and Stumpf back to Lotze. We could hardly go back of Wundt and Lotze.

The names in the charts are arranged from left to right by seniority, with only a few slight deviations. In general, the chart has eight columns and a man appears in the column for the decade in which he obtained his Ph.D. (or its equivalent). Thus Wundt is practically alone in the initial column at the left. James heads the column for the 1870s, Cattell the column for the 1880s, and so on to Stevens who heads the column for the Ph.D.s of the 1930s. The vertical ordering represents mostly our cleverness in arranging for a minimal number of crossing lines. When possible we have placed seniors above their juniors, but usually geometry has controlled. In view of the uncertainty of the master-pupil relation in democratic America, we find ourselves somewhat surprised that we were able to construct the Chart without more confusion. Perhaps even an American feels more secure if he can choose and exhibit an ancestor or two.

NOTES

1. Pledge (1939), shows connection of master and pupil: Chart I, 16th century, 29 names, p. 28; Chart II, 17th and 18th centuries, 46 names, p. 106; Chart III, 19th century, 63 names, p. 200.
2. See Visher (1947). For the 134 starred psychologists (Visher's figure of 132 is wrong), see pp. 141–143. We have omitted from this list as not being properly classified nowadays as psychologists 15 names: A. C. Armstrong, E.F. Buchner, J. E. Creighton, G. S. Fullerton, H. N. Gardiner, W. T. Harris, H. M. Hurd, J. H. Hyslop, H. R. Marshall, A. Meyer, W. Newbold, J. Royce, G. Santayana, J. G. Schurman, C. A. Strong.

The Beginning and Growth
of Measurement in Psychology

🮖🮖🮖🮖🮖🮖🮖🮖🮖🮖🮖🮖🮖🮖🮖🮖🮖🮖🮖🮖🮖🮖🮖 1961

A SCIENCE has to undergo a good deal of development before it is ready to be founded, before it can be recognized as a distinct social institution with its separate books, journals, and appointments, as an independent enterprise to which some men devote their lives. A science, once founded, develops and changes, and sometimes the changes involve the addition of new fields to the old science, new fields that have histories of their own that were not part of the history of the science as it stood previously. In this way the history of psychology changes as psychology's present becomes enlarged, and it is not always clear just which events in the history of science belong to psychology. For instance, there are those who feel nowadays that psychology, as it moves over into the field of linguistics, should claim part of that history for its own, and there are others, but by no means as yet a majority, who think that psychology has now moved so far from physiology that it ought to give back some of its older history to the physiologists. Be those things as they may, there is, nevertheless, a pretty clear history of the entry of measurement into psychology and into those activities that eventually became psychology, and these events we find falling naturally into four fairly independent histories.

(1) In the first place, there is the history of *psychophysics*, which may be thought of as founded in 1860 with the publication of Fechner's *Elemente der Psychophysik*, but which goes back nearly a hundred years more to the measurement of sensitivity and of the discriminatory capacity of the senses as accomplished by physiologists and other natural philosophers (Boring, 1942, 34–45, 50–52).

(2) Then there is the history of *reaction time*, which is at first the astronomer's learning to measure and take account of the personal equation in the observation of stellar transits, and then, when the discovery of galvanic elec-

Reprinted with permission from *Isis*, 1961, **52**, 238–257.

tricity and electromagnets had made chronographs and chronoscopes available, the determination of actual individual differences in reaction times. First the physiologist Donders (1862) used these procedures to measure, as he thought, the times of various mental acts, and then the psychologists built an elaborate mental chronometry on these methods, generating an excitement about mental measurement that collapsed after thirty years (Boring 1950a, 134–153).

(3) There had been no quantitative measurement of *learning* or *remembering* until Ebbinghaus (1885), stimulated by Fechner's achievement in psychophysics, described the first measurements. In its early days this new field of endeavor flourished with no awareness of Pavlov's work on conditioning in Russia at the turn of the century. Along about 1913, however, the two sets of activity were brought together in America, coming presently to dominate the field of experimental psychology. Skinner introduced operant conditioning early in the 1930's (Boring, 1950a, 386–392, 431 f., 625–631, 636–638, 650–652; Murphy, 1949, 174–183).

(4) And then finally, under the aegis of Francis Galton, there was the beginning of the measurement of *individual differences*, mostly by means of the mental test. This trend was generated in the enthusiasm caused by Charles Darwin's theory of evolution. Galton, Darwin's cousin, undertook to establish the fact of mental inheritance in 1869 by the publication of his *Hereditary Genius* (1869). Later in his *Inquiries into Human Faculty* (1883), he established the facts of great differences in individual capacities. He devised simple tests of these capacities which James McKeen Cattell (1890) in America named *mental tests*, promoting them vigorously. Binet's tests of intelligence came just after these initial efforts, and thereafter the testing of individual capacities became one of the primary undertakings of the rapidly growing American psychology.

Here, however, we have an instance of another new development that is not independent, the emergence of *statistical method*. The roots of modern statistics lie in mathematical probability theory with Jacques Bernoulli (1713) and other great men, including Laplace and Gauss. The father of statistics in Quetelet (1835), and Galton (1869) got from him his idea of measuring hereditary genius. It was Galton who invented the concept of "co-relation," and Karl Pearson who, taking the problem over, developed the methods of correlation. The early work in biological statistics was concerned chiefly with the establishment of relationships, and it was not until about 1908 that the methods for computing the significance of differences came into vogue. Ever since Galton, statistical method and the psychology of individual differences have developed in mutual support (Boring, 1920b, 1–18; 1950a, 468–488, 498–501, 532–540, 548 ff., 560 ff., 570–578, 581–583).

Before we proceed further with our four histories of quantification, it is worth while to note here the nature of some of the very early scientific contributions that belong in psychology's history and were nearly, though perhaps not quite, measurements.

The astronomer Kepler in 1604 reinforced the opinion, already held by some, that the crystalline body in the eye is not a sensitive receptor but a lens which must, Kepler noted, form on the retina an inverted image of the external world. How is it, he asked, that we see rightside up when the immediate source of our information is upside down? Descartes supported Kepler by fixing the excised eye of a bull in a hole in his shutter, scraping off the sclerotic coat at the back of the eye, and letting you see on a paper at the back of the eye-ball the inverted image of the world outside. Was not this measurement? Is it not a kind of measurement to show that the image is inverted, that the top goes to the bottom, and the bottom to the top (Boring, 1942, 222–225)?

Then in 1638 Galileo published his measurement of the relative frequency of the different pitches. Pythagoras had already shown how pitch is dependent on the length of the plucked string that sounds the pitch, and that too was measurement. What Galileo did was to run an iron chisel across a brass plate so that it made a whistling noise. He judged by ear the musical relation of two tones thus produced and then counted the relative frequencies of the successive "streaks" which the chisel made on the brass as it "screeched" across. This observation, added to Pythagoras's, established the frequency theory of pitch and the octave relation (Boring, 1942, 322–324).

There seems to be no reason why these discoveries—the inversion of the retinal image, the frequency of pitch—should not have been made earlier. In general, though, the Zeitgeist had been against experimentation. Archimedes thought of pure reason as the highest human endeavor and was contemptuous of his own use of physical knowledge to achieve practical ends, and that view had continued through medieval times. It takes originality, the determination of genius sometimes, to transcend the Zeitgeist; yet every time genius breaks through, it becomes easier for others to resist the standard values of the time, and the growth of this habit of experimenting with nature is clearly a part of how science entered into civilization and did so much to form it.

Psychophysics

It is usually not easy to say what determines a trend in the Zeitgeist, what establishes a steady change in the values that affect science. This trend progresses slowly and steadily and is more often recognized after it has progressed for some time than while it is in progress. If it does not persist, it is not even seen as a trend.

In the seventeenth and eighteenth centuries, natural philosophy was becoming more and more experimental, and the study of the functions of the human body advanced with the rest of science. It is surprising how much Albrecht von Haller (1757–1766), who is sometimes instead of Johannes Müller called the father of experimental physiology, had to say about sensation. Especially were the phenomena of vision, stimulated by Newton's *Opticks* (1704), the subject of description. The big names are William Porterfield (1759), Joseph Priestley (1772), and Thomas Young (1807). In the nineteenth century the poet Goethe, turned natural philosopher in his bitterness against Newton's theory of color, polemized on vision (1810), and then there were Purkinje (1819–1825) and Johannes Müller (1826*a*), whose early researches were on vision (Boring, 1950*a*, 96–115). Some people said that this flurry in research upon sensation was due to the discovery that the motor and sensory nerves are different—the law of the spinal nerve-roots (Bell, 1811; Magendie, 1822*a*, *b*)—that now sensation as well as movement needed to be studied. It is, however, more likely that this discovery, made independently by Sir Charles Bell (1811) and Francois Magendie (1822), was itself a natural function of the Zeitgeist; someone else would have made it if they had not (Boring, 1950*a*, 31–33).

Now you can not describe visual phenomena and optical systems without being quantitative and making measurements. There were, however, certain early experiments which are especially interesting because they were thought —at least later—to have measured sensation.

Bouguer (1760) performed an experiment that anticipated Weber's Law. He had two lighted candles and a vertical rod, and he moved one candle away from the rod until its shadow on a screen was only just noticeably different (jnd) from the background on which both candles shone. Then he determined another pair of distances for another jnd and finally concluded that two illuminations are just noticeably different when they differ by about $\frac{1}{64}$. This ratio for the jnd was independent of the total illumination.

Fraunhofer (1815) undertook to measure the relative brightness of the spectral colors. He used a divided field and matched in brightness a band of the spectrum in one-half of the field with a variable white light in the other half. The resulting curve with its maximum in the yellows is the ancestor of the modern luminosity curve (Boring, 1942, 176–182).

It was in 1834 that the physiologist, Ernest Heinrich Weber (1834), discovered what was later to be called Weber's Law. He concluded that for pressure on the skin, the jnd is a constant fraction (about $\frac{1}{30}$) of the weight, so that you may speak of 29 and 30 being just noticeably different without saying whether you mean ounces or drams. Weber extended his views (1846), and immediately others began trying to establish Weber's Law for senses other than touch and for dimensions other than intensity. Weber's Law was quantitative. It was a measurement in the sense that it measured in terms of the stimulus a sensory distance judged quantitatively. It did not, however, imply a sensory scale (Boring, 1942, 495–498).

It was Fechner who turned Weber's Law into a psychological scale and into what is nowadays called Fechner's Law. He made the assumption that all just noticeable differences are equal. You count up jnd to find the magnitude of a sensation, its distance above the sensory zero, which is, of course, the absolute threshold. If S is the magnitude of the sensation and I (intensity) the magnitude of the corresponding stimulus, then Fechner's Law is $S = k \log I$. Weber's Law is $dI/I = $ constant, where dI is the stimulus value of the jnd. The former comes from the latter via Fechner's assumption of the equality of all jnd (Boring, 1950a, 284–296).

Fechner's experiments on sensory measurements during the 1850's were published in his *Elemente der Psychophysik* (1860), the book that some think marks the beginning of the new experimental psychology because it brought sensation, the representative of impalpable, immaterial, unextended consciousness, under the requirements of measurement. The three methods of measuring absolute thresholds, differential thresholds, sensory equivalents, and sensory distances that Fechner established are still the three fundamental methods today. Fechner did indeed introduce measurement formally in the new psychology, and he helped in this way to found a new science—for it was thought that the fact of being able to measure phenomena secured the status of an activity as scientific.

In the 1860's and 1870's there was, principally in Germany, great activity in measuring sensation, in establishing Weber's and Fechner's Laws. There was also great controversy, interminable Teutonic polemical talk, which led William James (1890a, I, 533–549) to his well-known satirical summary of it all:

> "And what good came of it at last?"
> Quoth little Peterkin.
> "Why that I cannot tell," said he,
> "But 'twas a famous victory!"

The other objections were three:

(1) The facts do not support the laws. Often Weber's Law seems to hold fairly well in the middle range of intensities, but fails at the extremes, especially at low intensities. If Weber's Law fails, so does Fechner's. Yet many held fondly to them because they had nothing else so good with which to replace them—the horror vacui in scientific theories.

(2) The assumption that all jnd are subjectively equal was denied. That was fair enough, and Fechner's Law was vulnerable because of this assumption. The way out was to measure supraliminal sense distances directly without reference to the jnd, but there were few such measurements available in the nineteenth century. Today we have plenty, and we know that jnd of intensity do not correspond to equal subjective increments (Stevens, 1957).

(3) The third objection was introspective and was called the quantity objection. Sensations do not, it was argued, have magnitude. They differ only in quality. "Our feeling of pink," said William James, "is surely not a portion of our feeling of scarlet; nor does the light of an electric arc seem to contain that of a tallow candle within itself." "A low tone," said Ebbinghaus, "sounds different from a high tone, and in like manner a loud tone different from a soft." The objection was vigorously urged and at the time no one seemed to see that the argument against sensation can be applied equally well to the stimulus. True that a scarlet does not look more complex than a pink, but neither is a heavy weight more complex than a light one, nor a bullet more complex than a cork (Boring, 1921). After the turn of the century, this argument lapsed with the demise of introspective psychology and the rise of operationism.

The measurement of supraliminal sense-distances would be the way to determine whether the Fechner function were the logarithmic relation of the Fechner Law or something else. Psychologists seemed to be slow in taking up these determinations. Plateau (1872) in the 1850's asked artists to paint a gray half way between black and white. He did not report his results until 1872, and then the next year he got Delboeuf (1873) to undertake and publish experiments on the bisection of sensory distances. Delboeuf reported again on this work (1883), G. E. Müller (1903) lent the weight of his prestige to the procedure in 1903, and then Titchener (1901–1905, vol. II, pt. ii, 194–232) coined the phrase *sense-distance* in 1905. The standard procedure was bisection. You had a faint sound *a* and a loud sound *c*, and you varied the intensity of an intermediate sound *b* until $ab = bc$. Then you could divide *ab* in half, or *bc*, and so on to any degree of fineness of scaling. Is such a sensory scale a logarithmic function of the scale of the stimulus? No, it is not.

Psychology had already been facing the problems of scaling human abilities. They came in at the turn of the century with the effort to establish scales of intelligence and to rate individual differences by mental tests. Mostly the scales for the tests were ordinal scales; they ranked people in order without indicating what intervals on the scales were equal to each other. It was Stevens' interest in psychophysics, beginning in the 1930's and carrying on to the present, that made psychologists aware of the various kinds of scales and of the possibility of purely subjective scales, which could, in a test of the Fechner function, be studied in relation to physical scales.

Stevens holds that there are three kinds of scales, or better four if you include the initial limiting case. (1) The *nominal scale*, the beginning of quantification, is a labelling of items without ordering them, as is done for football players. (2) The *ordinal scale* places the items in rank-order, as in the raw data of mental tests. (3) The *interval scale* ranks the items and also arranges them so that the intervals between different pairs can be compared in magnitude. The method of bisection, of equal sense-distances, yields an interval scale. So does thermometry when it results in Fahrenheit or Celsius scales. These scales admit of statements about the differences between magnitudes, but, having no true zero, they do not admit of statements about the ratio of one magnitude to another. (4) The *ratio scale* is the most powerful of all, having all the properties of the others and also a true zero, which allows us to make statements about the ratio between two magnitudes. The ratio scale is familiar in physics (length, absolute temperature) but its introduction into psychophysics was a great step forward (Stevens, 1951; 1958).

To measure subjective intervals directly, you ask a subject to say which of two intervals appears greater to him, or else to change one until the two are equal. To measure ratios subjectively, you ask the subject to state how great one magnitude is in relation to another, or else to vary one magnitude until it has a given relation to another (is twice as great or half, or ten times as great).

Stevens did not originate the ratio scale for subjective magnitude. It seems to have been an innovation of Merkel's (1888, 1889, 1894) in Wundt's Leipzig laboratory in 1888, but it had almost no use until the 1930's, when the development of electronics had made possible the control of the loudness of tones and at least eight researches between 1930 and 1936 employed ratio judgments of loudness. The one in 1936 was Stevens' (1936*a*).

You would think that interval-scaling and ratio-scaling for the same sensory magnitudes would give consistent results, that the latter procedure would simply supply the missing zero for the scale of intervals, and Stevens presumably thought so too. He soon found, however, that the two procedures set up different attitudes in the subject and that the results do not agree. Interval judgments may, under some conditions, give results consistent with the old Fechner function, $S = k \log I$, but the outcome is generally less curved than a logarithmic function. Stevens has found for a very large number of different sensory modalities and dimensions that ratio judgments yield scales that can be described by a power function, $S = k\,I^n$, where n is a constant whose value varies with the sense department and with conditions of stimulation. Since the ratio scale has much more meaning than the interval scale, and since the observed data from many experiments can be described by a simple formula, Stevens (1957) thinks of the power function as the true form of the function sought by Fechner. It almost looks as if this problem might at last be regarded as settled, a full century after the publication of Fechner's *Psychophysik* in 1860.

What we have been saying about psychophysics does little more than indicate the temper of the times. The new experimental psychology may be said to have been founded by Wundt because he played the role of entrepreneur for it. The novel science was begun formally about 1860, with Fechner's *Psychophysik* and Helmholtz's monumental three volumes on physiological optics (1867) and his classic on tones (1863), which showed how scientific and quantitative the field could be. The researches—not the system of concepts but the experiments—grew out of experimental physiology, and Wundt actually called the new science *physiological psychology* and represented it as a Zwischenwissenschaft between physiology and philosophy. Naturally then the early phase dealt with the physiology of consciousness, and that meant with sensation and perception, topics which lent themselves readily to measurement. Later complaints were to be heard that the new psychology was nearly all physiology and had skimped learning and the cognitive mental processes; but of course that was the way it had to be. Experimental psychology had to begin somewhere, and the historical fact was that sensory physiology was there to draw upon.

Eventually, before the end of the century, there were available many measurements in every department of sense, quantitative data on quality, intensity, duration (the so-called "time-sense"), and on spatial relations for vision and touch. There was a big body of measured fact to show before Ebbinghaus brought learning under measurement in 1885, and even before there had grown up the chronology of higher mental processes which were based upon reaction times.

Reaction Times

Psychology's self-conscious effort to become "founded" as a new experimental science—an effort that derived from Wundt but was reinforced by Helmholtz, Ernst Mach, and some of the great or soon-to-be-great investigators of the 1860's—produced in Germany a group that was trying hard to advance quantitative investigation, that was on the lookout for psychological variables that are measurable. It was not so much that measurement intruded itself upon psychology as that these new psychologists were seeking out psychic measurables and dragging them triumphantly into psychology. Those were the circumstances under which both the mental chronometry and the experimental psychology of learning began.

The reaction times came from astronomy. In 1796 the Astronomer Royal at the Greenwich Observatory dismissed his assistant because his observations of stellar transits had been half a second in error and increased to nearly a whole second when he was admonished to improve—at least such was the difference in time between the measurements of the Astronomer Royal and of his assistant. Since the calibration of the Observatory's clocks depended upon this kind of observation, the discrepancy was serious.

In 1820 F. W. Bessel (1823), the astronomer at Königsberg, undertook to compare his own observations of stellar transits with those of another equally eminent astronomer. He knew about the incident at Greenwich. He was interested in errors of observation and had been talking to Gauss about them. The difference of his own observations from the other astronomer's turned out to be so large that he set about getting still other comparisons made as astronomers visited each other's observatories. There was great variability in the results; no one astronomer's deviation stayed constant. Nevertheless a great many of these discrepancies were recorded, and the phrase *personal equation* was introduced. The equation, "A-S = 0.202 sec.," means that on the average Argelander observed transits 0.202 sec. later than Struve. These personal equations are relative. No one knew at that time, moreover, why there should be these individual differences.

Later the development of electrical knowledge made possible the invention of the chronoscope (1840) and the chronograph (1859), so that the measurement of absolute personal equations became possible. You let an artificial star make the transit of a cross-hair in the field of view and measure electrically the elapsed time before a subject has pressed a key as soon as he observes the transit. These measures are, of course, reaction times. Since these personal "constants," like the relative equations, also showed too much variability to satisfy the astronomers' need for accuracy, they developed other means of observation, yet not before the psychologists had discovered that the personal equation is measuring a psychological phenomenon (Boring, 1950a, 134–142).

Wundt was aware of this problem of variability in reaction time and spoke about it at a meeting of astronomers in 1861 (Titchener, 1923). In 1863 he discussed it in his *Vorlesungen über die Menschen- und Thierseele* (Wundt, 1863). Because the transits were determined by the observer's listening to a clock ticking seconds while watching the star move across the hair-line and his estimating the fraction of a second at which the transit occurred, Wundt called this observation a *complication,* a term that Herbart had used for a perception that is composed of elements from more than one department of sense. In Wundt's laboratory the "complication experiment" was standard for a good many years, and complication clocks were built to provide the conditions under which a subject could determine the subjective synchronism of a sound and a sight, or a touch and a sight, or a sound and a touch (Boring, 1950a, 142–147).

The more important development was, however, the way in which the absolute personal equation became a reaction time, and further the manner in which the Dutch physiologist, F. C. Donders (1862), established what came to be called the subtractive procedure. Donders proceeded to complicate the simple reaction, the immediate response to a stimulus by the movement of a finger. First, he added several stimuli but limited the response to a single movement for only one of the stimuli. He called this reaction Discrimination. It took longer than the simple reaction and the difference in time was, he thought, the time that Discrimination takes. Then he complicated the reaction still further by using several stimuli with a different finger to react to each stimulus. This was Choice, and the time that Choice takes he got by subtracting from the total time the time for Discrimination.

The Leipzig Institute under Wundt took up this procedure and the 1880's saw an elaborate development of what some called *mental chronometry*. We can put everything together into a table to show what the maximal complication at Leipzig was at one time thought to be. This table is a hierarchy. The total time for each reaction included the time of the process at the right, which is added by the conditions of the experiment, to the preceding reaction. In other words the time of each process alone is got by subtracting from the total time for the reaction the total time for the preceding reaction. Discrimination and choice were obtained by different complications.

Reaction	Conditions	Process	Subtraction
1. Reflex	Inherited reaction	Reflex	(1)
2. Automatic action	Learned automatic action	Voluntary impulse	(2-1)
3. Simple muscular reaction	One stimulus, one movement, attention on movement, stimulus perceived	Perception	(3-2)
4. Simple sensorial reaction	One stimulus, one movement, attention on stimulus, stimulus apperceived	Apperception	(4-3)
5. Cognition reaction	Many stimuli, each apperceived, one movement	Cognition	(5-4)
6. Association reaction	Cognition reaction with association added	Association	(6-5)
7. Judgment reaction	Association reaction with judgment added	Judgment	(7-6)

For more than a decade this manner of measuring the time of conscious processes was one of the excitements of the new psychology. Measurement had come into the new psychology in a grand way to give it unassailable scientific status. Then Külpe (1893) leveled against the subtractive procedure a criticism that presently deflated the balloon. He appealed to introspection, the same introspection that had said that a scarlet is not so many pinks, that sensations, since they are not complex, lack magnitude. Külpe noted that the change of conditions, indicated in the second column of the table, means a change in the attitude of the subject and in the whole conscious process. For instance, you do not add apperception to perception, you substitute it for perception; and so with the others. It may seem odd that so grand a dream of measurement could have been so easily dispelled, but it must be noted that nothing important emerged from these measures of reaction times. It was also true that the times for the various processes were not constant. Not even the sacred 0.1 sec. for the time of Apperception (4-3) was reliably substantiated. So, between the verdict of introspection and the unreliability of the times, the dream of measurement faded. What was left was the method of measuring reaction time, used in a hundred different ways in psychological research ever since (Jastrow, 1890; Titchener, 1901–1905, II, pt. ii, 356–392; Boring, 1950a, 147–150).

Learning

The new experimental psychology was born in the mid-nineteenth century of two parents: physiology and philosophy. Sense-physiology, as we have seen, furnished the experimental research on sensation and perception with both facts and methods. Philosophy contributed British empiricism, which seemed to make the study of sensation especially appropriate for an understanding of the mind, and British associationism, which grew out of empiricism and constituted at first the fundamental synthetic principle for the new science.

The development of the doctrine of association, from John Locke (1690), through Bishop Berkeley (1710) and David Hume (1739–1740), to Alexander Bain (1855) and Herbert Spencer (1855), took up Aristotle's four principles for remembering the forgotten and made them into formal laws of association. Two ideas become associated so that the recurrence of one evokes the recurrence of the other, when the objects of the two are similar or contrasting or are together in space or in time. Ultimately it was seen that contrast is a form of similarity, since disparates do not even contrast, and that spatial contiguity is a form of temporal contiguity, since objects can not be together in space unless they are also together in time. When William James was writing his *Principles* (1890), the four laws had become reduced to two psychological ones: similarity and temporal contiguity, with the former debated and the latter pretty generally accepted. Two ideas that once concur in thought tend to recur together, either evoking the other—such was the basic law.

Nevertheless that law can not be universal. The recurrence of one idea can not arouse every other idea that has ever concurred with it. There are too many. There has to be selection, and for this reason philosophers, beginning with Hume, came more and more to think of associations as having different strengths dependent on the frequencies of the past contiguities. When you heard about the law of contiguity and the law of frequency, what was meant was the law of the frequency of contiguity. Although the philosophers spoke of associative strength as depending upon the frequency of concurrences, they never got around to actual measurement, to using frequency as a measure of association. That advance waited for Ebbinghaus (1885).

In the late 1870's, Ebbinghaus picked up at a Paris bookstall a second-hand copy of Fechner's *Psychophysik*. He was fascinated by it. He saw that Fechner by measuring sensation had made psychology scientific, but that measurement had not yet been applied to the higher mental processes. So he undertook to make the application to learning and memory, working out the requirements carefully, with his eye on Fechner, Quetelet, and theory of probabilities. You can measure, he noted, the difficulty of learning a material, like prose or poetry, by counting the number of repetitions it takes to learn it. Thus he set up repetition as a measure of learning. Because prose and poetry, being in the culture, are already partly learned by those who know the language and its literature, he invented the nonsense syllable—two consonants with a vowel between, like *zat, bok, sid*, not a word—and taught himself lists of these nonsensical and thus more uniform materials. He counted the number of repetitions necessary just completely to master nonsense series of different lengths. He compared the difficulty of poetry, prose, and nonsense. He studied repeated learning of the same material. He measured the strength of backward associations by observing how many repetitions were necessary to learn backwards a series that had just been learned forwards; and by a similar rearrangement he measured the strength of remote associations (syllables next but one, next but two, and so on). He measured forgetting by seeing how many repetitions were required to relearn, after different lapses of time, a series that had originally just been learned perfectly. His classical forgetting curve shows the losses of learning (repetitions necessary to relearn) for intervals varying from 20 minutes to 31 days (Murphy, 1949, 174–181; Boring, 1950*a*, 386–392).

Ebbinghaus' contribution was a scientific break-through. He did not follow up his success but left that to others, of whom the most distinguished in the early days was G. E. Müller (Boring, 1950*a*, 371–379). Methods and research multiplied rapidly, producing too huge a literature to outline here. The present writer in 1920 listed 15 standardized, approved, almost classical methods for measuring learning and memory. All depended on the same simple relationship.

If W is the amount of work done in learning, usually measured by the number of repetitions, and if M is the degree of mastery achieved, usually expressed as a percentage, and if D is the difficulty of the material learned (nonsense, prose, poetry, long materials or short), then the relation between these variables is $DM/W = a$ constant. You can keep anyone of these three variables constant, vary a second as the independent variable to be measured, and use the third, the dependent variable, as the measure. Ebbinghaus' method of complete mastery kept M constant at 100 per cent and measured D by observing W. The method of retained members measures learning in terms of M, the per cent learned, when D is varied and W is constant. How many of 10 words can you remember as compared with 10 nonsense syllables, when you have only five repetitions of each? The method of memory span uses D as a

measure: how long a series of syllables or digits can you remember perfectly
($M = 100$ per cent) with 1 repetition, with 2, and so on?

These methods have tended to die out in the last three decades as American
psychology has been becoming more and more behavioral in its outlook and
the concepts and terminology of conditioning have been replacing the concepts and terminology of association.

The observation of what was called the conditioned reflex began in Russia
with Pavlov (1927; 1928) about 1902. He had been working on digestive
secretion—in fact he received in 1904 the Nobel Prize for this research—and
he arranged to observe the secretion of these digestive glands by turning their
ducts around to open on the surface of the experimental animal's body. Thus
he observed that the secretions begin when the animal perceives food. Why?
Because the secretory reflex, which is an inherited response to ingested food,
has now become "conditioned" to the sight of food, for the reason that the
sight has been so often associated with the ingestion. This is association by
frequency of contiguity. Pavlov called it *conditioning* because he wanted no
truck with the vocabulary of the psychologist-mentalists. He was a thorough-
going materialist, getting his view specifically from Sechenov's objective psychology of 1863 (Boring, 1949), but presumably more generally from the
Russian Ortgeist.

At first this work on conditioning did not become very quantitative. You
found the salivary reflex conditioned upon the sight of food, and then you
found that by accompanying the sight with a tone you could get the tone by
itself to make the saliva flow. You found that, when the normal stimulus to
the reflex is eliminated, the conditioned response becomes less frequent and
finally disappears, is *extinguished* as the phrase is. Nor was this work extensive until the Americans learned about it in 1914 (Morgulis, 1914), just after
John B. Watson, founding behaviorism (1913b), adopted Pavlov's method
as a behavioristic substitute for the introspectionists' association. Presently,
however, there were being established learning curves, plotted against repetitions of the contiguity, and extinction curves, and then curves of generalization which showed how specific is the response to a stimulus (if the dog is
conditioned to 1012 cps will he also respond to 1000 cps or does he discriminate between the two tones, or can he be taught to discriminate?)
(Hilgard & Marquis, 1940).

There is another development in the psychology of learning which has resulted today in a great quantity of measurement. It began in 1898 with Thorndike's work on learning in animals. He found that cats can learn to perform a
fixed series of acts in order to escape confinement in a "puzzle box," a box
with trick catches and buttons that have to be operated in a given order to open
the door. Thorndike (1898) concluded that the pleasantness of escape for the
animal fixed, in the process of learning, the movements that had just preceded
it. Later it was discovered that rats in learning a maze learned first the move-

ments that lead directly to the food-goal. Learning is slower the more remote it is from the goal. That is the *goal gradient*. It is a measurement. You can plot it.

This retroactive effect of success upon learning was named by Thorndike (1911) the *Law of Effect*, but nowadays it is simply called *reinforcement*. In the current scene the work of B. F. Skinner and his students measures, with modern electric recording-apparatus, the operant responses of rats, pigeons and other subjects. The *operant response* (Skinner's word, 1938) is a response that is reinforced after its occurrence by reward (success). The recent book by Skinner and Ferster (1957) is a huge manual of 912 sets of curves which measure the conditions and variation of operant responses. Actually this research moves over toward the measurement of motivation, for the learning curves that depend on schedules of reinforcement are really descriptions of how certain different kinds of motivation work for a pigeon.

Individual Differences and Statistical Method

In the excitement occasioned by the publication of Darwin's *Origin* (1859) there stand out the contributions of Darwin's cousin, Francis Galton, on mental inheritance and the measurement of human faculties. Darwin himself did not at first have much to say about the origin of man, and, even before he had published *The Descent of Man* (1871) and *The Expression of Emotions in Man and Animals* (1872), Galton (1869) had brought out *Hereditary Genius*, his elaborate study of the degree in which human ability, as indicated by public reputation, runs in the same English families.

Galton noted that it is apparent that idiots and men of genius occur with comparative rarity in a population, whereas average ability is quite common. For this reason he took over from Quetelet (1835) the normal law of error, which Quetelet regarded as the law of the distribution of the natural magnitudes that vary by chance—as if Nature were shooting at a target and missed the bull's eye, often a little to one side or the other, but only seldom by a great amount. Quetelet supported this application of the law to human dimensions by showing that it held approximately for the girths of chest of 5738 Scotch soldiers and for the heights of 100,000 French conscripts. Galton assumed that it would hold for genius too and posited a scale of seven grades of superior ability (A, B, C, . . . G) and seven of inferior ability (a, b, c, . . . g) with the average the most frequent, lying between A and a. Using Quetelet's form of the probability table, Galton could assert that natural ability A would occur in one man among four, whereas ability G would be found only once among 79,000 men, and an ability greater than G only one time in a million. He had, of course, no direct scale for the measurement of ability, but he hoped that the frequencies, interpreted in accordance with the probability function, would give him a scale of equal intervals of genius. It was a good attempt at measurement and it was a long time before it came to be generally realized that you can not assume a priori that the normal law applies to nature's magnitudes. You have to measure first and then see whether it applies. Those who sided a little with Quetelet and Galton have called it a "law of insufficient reason" (*Princip des mangelnden Grundes*), a law that holds in spite of there being insufficient reason for it (von Kries, 1886), whereas others have ridiculed it as a law of "the equal distribution of ignorance" (Boole, 1854) which is just what it is until empirical evidence for its application has been found (Boring, 1920*b*; 1941). And there was another slip in Galton's measurement of ability: reputation is not a good index of genius, not when genius is equated to natural ability.

Galton was an indefatigable measurer. His classical *Inquiries into Human Faculty and Its Development* (1883) is packed full of measurements and attempts at measurement of the phenomena that he met as he lived his life. He used to carry a paper cross and a little needlepoint, arranged so that he could punch holes in the paper to keep count of whatever he was at that time observing. A hole on the head of the cross meant *greater,* on the arm *equal,* and on the bottom *less.* He "measured" individual differences in imagery in all the sense departments. He carried a "Galton" whistle on a cane to poke through the bars at the zoo to see how high a pitch the different animals can perceive. He measured many abilities in sensory discrimination and motor precision and proposed to inventory the English nation for their capacities as tested in this manner. Thus he was really the inventor of the mental test, although that term was coined in America by Cattell (1890) in an article to which Galton appended an approving note (Boring, 1950*a*, 476–488).

Galton's studies of *Natural Inheritance* (1889)—the book by that title came out in 1889—showed that it is often necessary to measure the "co-relation," as he called it, between two variables, as between the statures of fathers and sons. He went far enough to see that this relationship involves two "regressions toward mediocrity"—the fathers of the sons are nearer the average than their sons, just as the sons of the fathers must also be nearer the average than their fathers. But Galton was no mathematician. He had to have help and presently turned over the problem to Edgeworth (1892), who renamed the "index of co-relation" or "Galton function," as it was being called, the "coefficient of correlation," with the symbol *r* for *regression.* After that Karl Pearson took over, developing the products-moments method of linear correlation (1896) and founding with Galton and Weldon *Biometrika* in 1901.

From this point on the development of statistical methods and their use in psychology is too huge a topic to consider here. Let me nevertheless make four comments.

(1) The early work in biometrics was largely the study of relationships by

methods of correlation. The problem of the significances of differences, and thus of experimental control, did not emerge until Gosset (1908)—for so many years known only under his pseudonym, "Student"—raised it in 1908 and provided the first mathematics for what is now, since R. A. Fisher revolutionized modern statistics, a *must* in nearly every statistical investigation.

(2) The a priori assumption that the normal law applies to biological and psychological variables, and thereby provides a device for changing ordinal scales into equal intervals, has continued well into the present century. The scaling of mental tests in terms of standard deviations or some fraction thereof (standard scores, T-scales, stanines) in some ways preserves this ancient fallacy.

(3) Although Fechner in 1860 made use of the normal law of error in his method of right and wrong cases, and Galton in 1869 used the same tradition for measuring human ability, the development of psychophysics and of statistics remained quite separated until the two were brought together in the same handbook in England by Brown and Thomson (1921) and later in America by Guilford (1936).

(4) The great current interest in psychological scaling developed independently in psychophysics and in mental testing. In psychophysics it was held back by the preoccupation with Fechner's Law and the dubious assumption that the jnd provides a unit of subjective magnitude. Progress had to wait for the increase of interest in the "direct" methods for producing, first, equal-interval scales, and then, ratio scales (Stevens, 1946; 1958). In mental testing, progress has been slower, for standard scores—the use of variability (discriminal dispersion) to determine equal intervals—are still quite generally employed, although Thurstone (1925, 1927, 1928) has shown that alternative procedures are possible for the tests. Both histories exhibit the persistence of an ancient habit of thought that, in spite of demonstrated error, continues by its acceptance to hinder progress.

How Measurement Begins and Progresses

The foregoing pages have been given over to showing how measurement began and progressed in psychology's four major quantitative efforts. Let us now see if we can extract from these histories any generalities about the kinds of emergence and advance that normally occur in scientific progress.

There are, it may be said, five kinds of progressive change in scientific quantification. These categories are neither rigid nor mutually exclusive, but consideration of them serves, nevertheless, to make clear the general nature of the history of quantification in science.

(1) *Quantification is adopted because it is more adequate to the description*

of phenomena. Qualitative accounts are cumbersome, usually limited to verbal distinctions and thus to discrete states rather than to continuous functions. The scientist often moves over into quantification in order to avail himself of a language more adequate to what he would report. Galileo's measurement of the relative frequency of pitches (1638) is such an instance, as is Bouguer's determination of the relative jnd for illumination (1760). Here belong Pavlov's devices for measuring amounts and rates of glandular secretion, the work that led later to the discovery of the conditioned reflex.

(2) *Quantification is favored by the desire of investigators to claim the prestige of science for their research.* Especially has this motivation operated among the psychologists, insecure because of their unscientific heritage from philosophy, and thus repeatedly insisting on the scientific validity of their new experimental psychology. Both Fechner and Helmholtz asserted the scientific status of psychology, and Wundt and Titchener devoted their lives to this demonstration. Fechner's triumph was that he had shown that sensation can be measured. Ebbinghaus, stimulated by his reading of Fechner, noted that although sensation had been measured, no higher mental process had; so he set about the task of measuring learning and memory. Galton's attempted measurement of genius by use of the normal law of error was a case of his wanting to make genius amenable to scientific rigor, though he was not then being a propagandist for the new psychology. The furor about mental chronometry in the late nineteenth century, after Donders had established the subtractive procedure for reaction times, was due to the excitement of bringing apperception, cognition, discrimination, choice, association, and judgment under scientific measurement. Science was conceived as having captured one of nature's last hold-outs, the human mind.

(3) *Sometimes progress in quantification is quick because of a sudden insight into a new possibility.* In general, scientific progress is continuous and gradual and even the crucial insights have had usually to wait upon the changing Zeitgeist before they can occur. Nevertheless there have been some quick changes. What were some of them in psychology? Weber's establishment of the law of the jnd. Fechner's measurement of sensation. Bessel and the personal equation. Ebbinghaus' measurement of learning and forgetting. Pavlov's seeing that conditioned secretion would measure perception and cognition. Thorndike and the law of effect. Gosset and the significance of a difference. Skinner and operant conditioning. Stevens and the ratio scales. Most of these insights are not brand new. They had their backgrounds and anticipations. Nevertheless they represented a time of rapid change of interest and of subsequent scientific activity, stimulated by a new insight or method or fact, whichever it was.

(4) *Quantification may depend on historical preparation.* Fechner's originality depended upon Weber, Herbart, and even to some small extent on Gauss, just as the subsequent excitement about Weber's and Fechner's Laws

depended on Fechner. Stevens and the others who work now with equal-interval scales have their roots in the investigations of Plateau, Delboeuf, and Titchener. Quetelet prepared the way for Galton to measure genius, and Galton the way for Pearson and the new statistics, and that for Gosset and Fisher and the significance of differences. Skinner needed Thorndike's law of effect as his anticipation.

(5) And then, of course, there is ordinary progress. A *new line of investigation is established and everyone joins in the new pursuit*. Mental chronometry after Donders. Psychophysics after Fechner. Learning and memory after Ebbinghaus. Conditioning after Pavlov. Scaling and operant conditioning nowadays.

Scientific progress is not, however, solely the consequence of facilitating situations and events. Progress has its deterrents and inhibitors. Here are a few that have been noted in this paper.

(*a*) Sometimes *progress seems to be checked by a failure of what might be considered a normal incidence of insight*. Some trends are so obvious to the historian looking back; why was the next step not seen at the time? It is impossible, however, to separate these cases from those in which a positive inhibitor can be specified or at least indicated, the cases which we consider next. Why, for instance, did not Wundt's active Institute at Leipzig take up the measurement of learning? Why was that advance left for Ebbinghaus? Was the failure at Leipzig merely because no one thought of how to do it, or was it because the Leipzig Ortgeist favored the measurement of sensation and tended to shut everything else out?

(*b*) Certainly the *Zeitgeister and Ortgeister work both as facilitators and inhibitors*. It is hard to go about measuring the velocity of the nerve impulse when all your colleagues of distinction are so sure it can not be done. Yet Helmholtz did. Why was any considerable effort to measure equal sensory intervals by direct comparison instead of indirectly by reference to the counting of just noticeable differences, why was this productive undertaking deferred, in general, until seventy years after Fechner's *Psychophysik*? Why was the acceptance of the normal law of distribution as something given in nature, a natural law of randomness or of human ignorance, why has it persisted to confuse statistical measurement so long? Both these instances are of the Zeitgeist. The climate of opinion was set for a long time against what seems at the present moment to be inevitable progress.

These cases are ones in which the Zeitgeist worked pretty much unconsciously. What was really resistance to progress remained inarticulate, imperceptible in currently accepted habits of thinking. The Zeitgeist can, however, become articulate, and here follow three such cases.

(*c*) The *quantity objection* to the measurement of sensation grew out of psychology's philosophical heritage, which supported introspectionism, the study of consciousness, as the proper business of psychology. Now actually the observation of equal sense-intervals is not inconsistent with introspection-ism, but the quantity objectors asserted that introspection does not reveal sensory magnitudes. They were less wrong in their introspection than in their conception of what a psychological or physical magnitude is, but their Teutonic contentiousness must have held psychophysics back during the latter part of the nineteenth century.

The same kind of objection was raised against the mental chronometry of the reaction times, but in this case the Zeitgeist helped to shut off a development that was already doomed to failure.

(*d*) The same Geist that objected to psychology's measuring sensation and the times of mental processes *opposed the mental tests* because they were behavioral and not made dependent on the control of conscious processes. Since the tests in company with statistical measurement moved along fairly rapidly, it is impossible to say how much effect this explicit opposition had; but the opprobrium in which the "mental testers" were long held by the "orthodox" psychologists was strong, and it seems that it must have had some deterrent effect.

(*e*) Against Galton and the measurement of mental inheritance, and thus ultimately against the tests, was the *opposition to the new theory of evolution,* an opposition stronger in Great Britain than in functionally minded America. It too was a conscious phase of the Zeitgeist acting as inhibitor.

So opinion—sometimes within scientific awareness, sometimes in spite of scientific unawareness, operates to aid or hinder progress, and you may not know which it is, any more than you know at the moment whether progress has got itself into a blind alley or is going straight with a clear course ahead.

And that is the way quantification in science comes about, is pushed ahead or held back—at least it is the way these things seem to me to have happened in psychology.

The Influence of Evolutionary Theory
upon American Psychological Thought

卍卍 1950

S UPERFICIALLY regarded, the origin of American psychology presents us with a paradox. The men who got what Scripture later
called "the new psychology" [1] under way in America in the 1880's and early
1890's—James, Ladd, Cattell, and Baldwin—these men and the others who
came on the scene before 1900 were all looking to Germany for the pattern of
the new psychology.[2] There the new psychology was called *physiologische
Psychologie* or *experimentelle Psychologie* and its founders had been Fechner
and Helmholtz and Wundt who set the stage for the new movement in the
1850's and 1860's.[3] Up to the end of the century America was consciously
copying Germany, determined to make psychology physiological and experimental, energetically concerned with the founding of laboratories and the ac-
cumulation of psychological apparatus, crossing the ocean to get its doctor's
degrees—mostly from Wundt's *psychologisches Institut* at Leipzig. Consciously America was copying Germany, but unconsciously America was doing
something quite different. It was building up its own particular brand of functional psychology which, under many names and in many forms, has dominated the American scene for more than half a century and, since the first
World War, has become in turn something for Europe to copy. Therein lies
the paradox. In seeking to import the new German movement, America unwittingly imposed upon it the special properties of the American *Zeitgeist*,
altering the German model even in the act of accepting it.

We must examine first the history of these crucial events in the psychology
of the latter half of the nineteenth century. We must see how American psychology got its start, and how it was, in a sense, the child of German psychology and British biology.

(1) *The new German psychology* of the later nineteenth century, one

Reprinted with permission from S. Persons (Ed.), *Evolutionary Thought in America*,
New Haven: Yale University Press, 1950, 267–298.

of the parents of the still newer American psychology, was itself the offspring of a marriage between the German physiology of sensation and the British philosophy of empiricism and associationism.

Sense physiology of the first half of the nineteenth century thus furnished many of the origins of the new experimental psychology. There were first the independent discoveries by the Englishman Bell in 1811 and the Frenchman Magendie in 1822 that sensory nerves are different from motor nerves and that the nerves are not simply the passive conductors of a *vis nervosa.* There was Johannes Müller's promulgation in 1826 of the doctrine of specific nerve energies, the rule that sensory quality depends upon the particular nerves excited and not upon the transmission of the qualities of the stimuli. There was Ernst Heinrich Weber who in 1834 presented the evidence for what Fechner later named Weber's Law. There was Purkinje, the phenomenologist observer of visual phenomena, who was stimulated by Goethe in his study of color and whose name is now attached to some of the facts of night vision. There was Lotze, at heart a philosopher, who wrote a physiological psychology in 1852 and started the later controversy about the relation of space perception to learning. That, all in all, indicates the quality of the setting for the new psychology within physiology.

The philosophical setting was British *empiricism,* which later became *associationism.* It began with John Locke's insistence in 1690 that the mind is a piece of white paper on which experience writes, that understanding thus arises only by way of sensation. Bishop Berkeley came next in that tradition with his subjective idealism, his emphasis upon the idea as the immediate datum of experience. There followed the famous Hume, the less famous David Hartley, the Scottish philosophers, and then James Mill and his son, John Stuart Mill. With these men associationism grew up, the mental chemistry in which it is assumed that elementary ideas combine to form complex ideas and that perception, thought, and understanding are to be explained as due to the compounding of mental elements.[4]

The new experimental psychology was born about 1860. It was in that year that Fechner published his psychophysics, the book that showed how sensation can be measured and that laid down the principal methods which still are used.[5] At the same time Helmholtz was interesting himself in psychological principles and in writing the basic handbooks on visual and auditory sensation.[6] Wundt was putting these results of Fechner's and Helmholtz' and other investigators' together into systematic form, naming the new field *physiological psychology,* and issuing the first general handbook and systematic text in 1874.[7]

All that is the movement which William James heard about in America. It is what turned him to physiology and psychology and made him the first medium of the introduction of the new psychology into America.

(2) Meanwhile in *England* there was Darwin. The philosophical psy-

chologists—Bain, Spencer, Ward, and Stout—did not have much effect upon American psychology except indirectly, but Darwin did. The *Origin of Species* and the *Descent of Man* raised the problem of continuity between men and animals, and Darwin's *Expression of Emotion in Men and Animals* translated this problem to the level of mind. The brilliant and versatile Francis Galton, Darwin's cousin, took up the problem of mental inheritance in his *Hereditary Genius* of 1869, and then in his *Inquiries into Human Faculty* launched the study of individual differences in human capacity, a subject matter and an interest which affected American psychology profoundly. Galton was the originator of mental tests and of the statistical methods for dealing with the measurement of individual differences.[8]

England was also the scene of the beginnings of animal psychology. Romanes, stimulated by Darwin, undertook to study animal inheritance. He built up careful criteria for the evaluation of anecdotal material, but he was criticized by Lloyd Morgan who believed that Romanes credited the animals with too much intelligence, and who laid down his canon of parsimony, the rule that the attribution of mental capacity must be minimal for the behavior observed. It was these English beginnings that were taken over in the late 1890's by American animal psychology.

(3) American psychology really began with William James's interest in the new German movement, for it did not derive from the older American psychological interests.[9]

The year 1867 saw James in Berlin struggling with the decision as to whether to make a physiologist or a philosopher of himself. He finally chose physiology—because he preferred philosophy. He mistrusted his own adequacy to so broad and difficult a field as philosophy. He might get, he thought, a safer corner within it if he chose the easier physiology and then cultivated physiological psychology as a scientific side door to philosophy. James had been training himself in science, aiming eventually at an M.D. The year before he had spent with Louis Agassiz on the Amazon and had learned to hate descriptive science. His mind was impatient of the isolated fact. He wanted broader generalizations. So in 1867 in Berlin he was turning to physiology as something clearly within his intellectual means, something that could lead him through the new physiological psychology toward or even into philosophy.[10]

What actually did James know then about the new physiological psychology? Not much in 1867. He got hold of Lotze's *Medicinische Psychologie* of 1852 and read it. It is not clear that he knew Wundt's *Beiträge zur Theorie der Sinneswahrnehmung* of 1862, but he certainly knew Helmholtz's *Tonempfindungen* of 1863 and his *Physiologische Optik*, which had been coming out in parts since 1856. In the autumn of 1867 James wrote in a letter:

> I have begun going to the physiological lectures [at the university of Berlin] . . . There is a bully physiological laboratory, the sight of which, inaccessible

as it is to me in my present condition [his poor health], gave me a sharp pang. I have blocked out some reading in physiology and psychology which I hope to execute this winter. . . . It seems to me that perhaps the time has come for psychology to begin to be a science—some measurements have already been made in the region lying between the physical changes in the nerves and the appearance of consciousness-at (in the shape of sense perceptions), and more may come of it. Helmholtz and a man named Wundt at Heidelberg are working at it, and I hope I live through the winter to go to them in the summer.[11]

James did not, however, get to study at Heidelberg with Helmholtz and the man named Wundt. Instead he went home to nurse his health, to get his M.D. at Harvard in 1869, to be ill again, and then to accept appointment as instructor in anatomy and physiology at Harvard in 1872. He kept working the facts of physiological psychology into his lectures on physiology, and in 1875, when he first offered his course on physiological psychology, he actually had a two-room demonstrational laboratory set up, where his students performed some of the psychological experiments that were regarded as basic. James really started the new experimental movement in America, as Stanley Hall himself remarked in 1890 (although he took it back later on).[12]

All this is not to say that James was either the necessary or a sufficient cause for the appearance of the new psychology in America. He is more nearly a symptom of what was about to happen, the first measle that makes sense only later when the disease has been recognized. To find the idea of the importance of the new psychology growing in James's mind for reasons that lie deep in his own needs and personality is not to say that experimental psychology would not have come to America without James. It would. James shows merely how these infections start. The spread of interest in the 1880's was much too rapid to have been entirely dependent on promotion by James, who was by temperament anything but a promoter and who did not even get his all-important *Principles of Psychology* published until 1890. Without James that start would have been different, but it would have been made. The thesis of the present exegesis is that America took what it was ready for, that it took up with evolution and the new psychology for similar reasons and that the theory of evolution, as the more basic principle, affected American psychology.

In 1878 Stanley Hall got his Ph.D. in psychology from Harvard, the first Ph.D. in this field in America. James was, of course, on Hall's committee. The thesis work was done in the physiological laboratory of H. P. Bowditch. Hall "founded" the psychological laboratory at Johns Hopkins in 1883. Now let us see what happened in American psychology in the next decade, 1883–1892.

Of books there was Dewey's *Psychology* in 1886, Ladd's *Elements of Physiological Psychology* in 1887, Baldwin's *Senses and Intellect* in 1889, James's *Principles* in 1890, and Baldwin's *Feeling and Will* in 1891.

Hall founded the *American Journal of Psychology* in 1887, the *Pedagogical Seminary* in 1891. Cattell and Baldwin started the *Psychological Review* in 1894, the *Psychological Monographs* and the *Psychological Index* a year later.

As to laboratories—there were a dozen of them by 1892: Harvard, Hopkins, Indiana, Wisconsin, Clark, Nebraska, Michigan, Iowa, Pennsylvania, Columbia, Cornell, Wellesley, in that order.[13]

What Americans had gone to Leipzig to study with Wundt? G. S. Hall, J. McK. Cattell, H. K. Wolfe, E. A. Pace, E. W. Scripture, Frank Angell, Lightner Witmer, Howard C. Warren, Harlow Gale, G. T. W. Patrick—all before 1894.[14] Titchener went from his native England to study with Wundt and then came to live in America and to influence it toward the fuller acceptance of the German model. James never studied with Wundt.

My point is that all this excitement of getting the new psychology under way in America in the 1880's and 1890's is not to be accounted for by any personal acts of James, nor by the older American tradition in psychology, nor even by the wave of interest in evolution, which helped indeed but was not alone a sufficient cause. America was ready for what the times had for it, and out of those materials, with the efforts of many men, it created something which was, in its emergent totality, unique—as unique as anything with causes and a history and a respectable number of anticipations ever is.

The adjectives that best apply to American psychology are *functional* and *practical*. James had a functional psychology. Dewey started the Chicago school of functional psychology. Columbia under Cattell went in for practical psychology, the mental tests, and what has been called a psychology of capacity. Baldwin and Stanley Hall were influenced directly by the theory of evolution, which is in itself a practical theory since it stresses individual differences and for the most part regards usefulness as a reason for development. This psychology, which had already emerged before the end of the nineteenth century, was not the psychology of Germany which the Americans had gone abroad to get.

It is almost true that American psychology was personified in the person of Cattell. His pattern was the American pattern. Cattell caught the spark of the new psychology from Lotze at Göttingen and Wundt at Leipzig in 1880–1882. Then he came back to Hopkins to study psychology and had brief contact with Stanley Hall, newly arrived there to take charge. After that Cattell returned to Leipzig, brashly offering himself to Wundt as his assistant in what Wundt styled "ganz Amerikanisch" fashion. He took the Ph.D. with Wundt in 1886, presenting a thesis on reaction times in which he stressed the matter of individual differences. That is significant. Wundt did not approve of this innovation, but Cattell persisted and succeeded, as he often did later in life, in achieving a modified success in rebellion against authority. He returned to America, went to England to lecture at Cambridge where he got acquainted with Galton, coined the name *mental test* and wrote an article about the tests, sent Wundt a typewriter which may, indeed, have enhanced the already stupendous volume of his productivity, founded two psychological laboratories, the first at the University of Pennsylvania and the second, in 1891, at Columbia. At Columbia he got a testing program for the mental capacities of college students under way, and from there on his life proceeded along the same pattern of the practical hardheaded promotion of psychology with all its pedantries left out. He did not make American psychology what it is any more than James did. The forces that account for American psychology account for Cattell, as they account for James.[15]

What were these forces? That is difficult to say. The dynamics of historical causation are seldom sure. Concomitance so often looks like a cause. There can, however, be no doubt that the American character was direct, forceful, frank, democratic, and practical, assessing values in terms of usefulness. F. J. Turner suggested in 1893 that such a character has been generated by the fact that for three centuries America has had a movable western frontier with free land beyond it.[16] Every man is a king when he can own his own land, moving westward again when his domain becomes too circumscribed by the advent of other settlers. Thus democracy and equality of opportunity get themselves worked into the basic structure of the value system of the frontiersman, who, it is argued, furnished America with its creed. Equality of opportunity belongs, however, only to the strong, the resourceful, the practical, those men who can stand up in the struggle with nature for existence. The "hither edge of free land" was just disappearing, with the frontier completely gone, when American psychology was getting itself established. Is it absurd to perceive a connection? Was not Cattell really a frontiersman? Was not Stanley Hall a perpetual settler, clearing the land, building a cabin, and then moving on when the region got congested? Was not the American wave of laboratory foundings essentially a pioneer movement? [17]

John Dewey has noted that the psychology of individual differences flourishes in democracies.[18] That is right because the findings of a psychology of individual differences never support inherited class distinctions. America for seventy years has wanted a simple direct psychology, removed from the subtleties of metaphysics and epistemology and from the mystery of inner experience. It is a shirt-sleeve psychology that it has desired—and that it has, for the most part, had.[19]

Has all this anything to do with evolution? The pioneer's struggle for existence has certainly something to do with Darwinian theory. America was ready enough to fall in with the excitement about evolution in the final quarter of the nineteenth century, and psychology, developing in the American pattern, was quick to use the facts and principles of evolution. It was not merely that Baldwin and Hall could take the concept of mental evolution as a central theme in some of their most important work, for there were also more covert relations. Without evolutionary doctrine in the forefront of discussion, could James have appealed to *use* as an explanation of psychological functions? Can we possibly imagine a doctrine of special creation working just as well for him? And what would have become of Dewey's contribution, and the Chicago school, and eventually of pragmatism, without evolution? At the very least I think we can say that American psychology, in so far as it was functional and practical and pragmatic, used evolutionary principles to make itself work, and that all these values, belonging with the American character, helped conversely to make that character what it was—and is.[20]

William James

There is really not so much more to be said about James and evolution and his functional psychology. James, the physiologist, read Darwin. He admired him greatly as a pattern for a scientist. He accepted the Darwinian theory in part, as his treatment of instinct and emotion shows, but he was also critical of Darwin and did not go the whole way with him. As an evolutionist James was, nevertheless, more of a Darwinian than a Lamarckian. He thought naturally in terms of the use of mental functions as having survival value.

James was even better acquainted with Herbert Spencer. In 1875 he offered his course that was called "Physiological Psychology—Herbert Spencer's Principles of Psychology," and he continued it for many years. In 1879 and half a dozen times thereafter he offered "The Philosophy of Evolution," which used Spencer's *First Principles of Philosophy* as a text.[21]

Is James truly a functional psychologist? There is some room for argument about that matter. He thought of mind as useful to the person who owns it. Someone who analyzed his employment of the word function in his *Principles* found that he almost always meant *use* by it.[22] James was closely associated with Dewey in many ways, including the promotion of pragmatism, which is, one may say, "functional philosophy" in that it deals with truth in terms of consequences. James Angell picked up his functionalism from both James and Dewey. In any broad use of the term, James ought to count as the anticipator, or with Dewey the cofounder of American functional psychology.

Functional Psychology

John Dewey's great influence has been due to the fact that he has been, for fifty years of effective propaganda, the philosopher of social change. Thinking men usually think about change, for the *status quo*, being already present, does not need thought. Thus Dewey has come to have great importance in the thoughts of many thinking men. He has been against laissez faire and things as they are. He has been for that progress which can be gained through the struggle of intelligence with reality. He has been against complacence, and pedantry, and formality, and for experiment, and use, and innovation. That value pattern shows clearly throughout his life. "Philosophy," he wrote, "recovers itself when it ceases to be a device for dealing with the problems of philosophers and becomes a method, cultivated by philosophers, for dealing with the problems of men." [23]

Was Dewey, we ask, influenced by the theory of evolution? Emphatically Yes. He lectured in 1909 on "The Influence of Darwin on Philosophy," showing how very great the influence had been and, in general, approving of it. There are, however, two different ways of being influenced by Darwinism. You can be impressed by the role of nature in natural selection, by the importance of chance, by the inability of acquired characteristics to effect permanent biological progress. Then you become a biological aristocrat and you are not John Dewey. Or you can see how the survival of the fittest means that use and functional practicality are basic to all progress, that struggle is fundamental in the nature of human life, that kings have no divine right because individual differences exist at random and nature rules by selection among them, and that in the end the aristocracy of chance which nature establishes can be overthrown by the effectiveness of social inheritance and social evolution. There you have a tempered Darwinism that is John Dewey.[24]

To his thinking about psychology Dewey brought the concept of functional use for the events of the mind, and thus, closely related to functional use, the notion of functional activity. The way to express this matter is to say that both consciousness and activity function *for* the organism—the use of consciousness is to produce activity which "saves" the organism. That is the essential tenet of the Chicago school of functional psychology which Dewey started, and which Angell carried on. In the doctrine of this school behavior and physiology and conscious states are mixed in with each other because they are unified, not by their essential natures, but by their common aim for the survival and use of the organism.

The Chicago school may be said to have been started by Dewey's paper, "The Reflex Arc Concept in Psychology," which he published in 1896.[25] Dewey argued that what we are interested in is coordinations, total reactions that are not properly reducible to a sum of reflex arcs, none of which in turn is properly reduced to a stimulus (as a first event), followed by a response (a later event), with perhaps a sensation intermediate between them. The stimulus immediately involves the response, and the response the stimulus, so the argument ran. A function is thus a coordination, an organism achieving an end. Purpose gives it unity, and functional psychology becomes the study of the organism in use. Functional psychology is thus practical through and through, in the way that Darwin's theory was the greatest practical theory of living that has ever been put forth.

After ten years at Chicago with Angell, Dewey went to Columbia in 1904, leaving Angell behind as the chief representative of the functional school. Angell did little more than explicate Dewey. He favored "the psychology of mental operations"—Dewey's coordinations. Thus, he said, psychology passes beyond the question "What?" (description) and finds itself answering the questions "How?" and "Why?" (function and use). For the most part, he said, functional psychology is "the psychology of the fundamental utilities of consciousness"—utilities in which mind is "primarily engaged in mediating between the environment and the needs of the organism." The function of the psychological act is "accommodatory service"; the function of consciousness is "accommodation to the novel," since consciousness tends to disappear in the presence of what is habitual.[26]

We must not, however, exaggerate the importance of evolutionary theory. It was not Darwin who discovered that the body's organs are useful to it, nor was Darwin the originator of the thought that the mind is an organ. Functional psychology has back of it, besides evolutionary theory, all of faculty psychology and also all of the specific analysis of mind into functions, faculties, capacities, and propensities by the phrenologists early in the nineteenth century.[27]

Mental Evolution

The immediate effect of the doctrine of evolution upon psychology was in England. Galton, as we have noted, published *Hereditary Genius* in 1869, and it was followed shortly by Darwin's *Descent of Man* and *Expression of the Emotions in Man and Animals*. The doctrine of the evolution of mind was being put forward seriously and vigorously. Galton's book was impressive. He showed that men of great reputation and public distinction in Great Britain tend to be related, to come from the same families. His view that genius becomes recognized through reputation whatever the economic conditions to which it is born was not effectively criticized until much later.

Galton, as we have observed, found himself promoting the study of individual differences in human abilities, proposing to inventory the psychological capacities of the members of the British nation, inventing and advocating eugenics, and in general showing how to apply the consequences of the inheritance of mental abilities to practical affairs. Romanes' books on animal intelligence and mental evolution came out in 1882–1888, and Lloyd Morgan expressed his interest in the problem in *Animal Life and Intelligence* and in other books. These were the three prominent men in England who were furthering interest in the psychological problems of evolution.[28]

Now who were the men who played the complementary role in America? Interest in evolution was spread broadly. James gave a course in the subject.

Dewey founded a school that depended on it. James Mark Baldwin and Stanley Hall may, however, be singled out as the most vocal proponents of the application of the theory of evolution to mental capacities. Both men were prolific writers. Neither was a scientist in the sense that he spent his own time in the observation of natural phenomena. Each read what others had done, synthetized his reading and published the results in books. Hall was more the encylopedist, Baldwin more the egoistic theorizer.

It is difficult to estimate Baldwin's actual importance. He had a brilliant mind, a facile but not a stimulating pen, and a persistent drive. He was a very prominent man in the affairs of American psychology, and he also gained attention by his polemical vigor. Such things operated to get him considered and quoted while he was on the scene, but they did not gain for him any posthumous effect that is recognizable as important.

Baldwin published three books on evolution. The first was *Mental Development in the Child and the Race* (1895). The second appeared as *Social and Ethical Interpretations in Mental Development* (1897). Later there was *Development and Evolution* (1902). The second of these books may be regarded as an early social psychology which gave such importance to imitation as a principle of organic selection in social evolution that Baldwin is usually the standard reference for that now unpopular theory of social interaction.[29]

In general Baldwin, in common with H. F. Osborn and C. Lloyd Morgan, defended the theory which Baldwin named *organic selection*. That theory was psychological in that it brought consciousness and volition into the picture, for it held that organisms adapt themselves voluntarily to the needs that the environment lays upon them, and that these adaptive habits can be maintained through many generations until such time as chance variation gets the habits established as naturally inheritable characters, thus finally relieving the organism from responsibility for their maintenance. In this manner organic selection becomes a kind of social inheritance pro tempore, a social regenerator which preserves the Lamarckian principle through enough generations until the Darwinian principle can take over. It is clear that we are seeing here how the theory of evolution was to effect social psychology.

Baldwin advocated and expounded the theory of evolution. Stanley Hall assumed it and used it, somewhat speculatively, to give content and pattern to his broad theories. Hall sometimes said that his brand of psychology was "psychogenesis," and sometimes that it was "synthetic psychology." The synthetic method for Hall consisted of the encyclopedic marshaling of facts in the support of a single hypothesis. You see the result in Hall's books and articles and also in the papers published from his famous seminary. Hall was past master at guiding his students in ransacking the library for relevant facts that had never met each other before and in stimulating the students into the publication of their papers and also into a personal discipleship which lasted for many years. Underneath this use of the synthetic encyclopedic method there runs, however, the constant reiteration of the genetic theme. Mind comes from matter and man from his protozoic ancestors, and the life of man consists in the perpetual unfolding of his potential characteristics which turn out again and again to be the reverberations of the development of the race.[30]

Of himself Hall wrote:

As soon as I first heard it in my youth I think I must have been hypnotized by the word "evolution," which was music to my ear and seemed to fit my mouth better than any other. I cannot conceive why I seemed thus predisposed to an interest in everything that could be brought under that term. . . . I think my curiosity somehow got an early tilt toward origins, and even in college [1863–67] I brought much censure upon myself by advocating the view that man had sprung from apehood.

"I was bat-eyed," Hall added,

to the difficulties and impatient at objections, and had a blind spot in my mind for every break in the developmental order and implicit faith that if anywhere there seemed to be gaps it was only because we lacked adequate knowledge. Somehow, sometime it would be proved to the silencing of all doubters that all worlds and all in them developed very gradually and by an inner and unremitting impulsion from cosmic mist and nebulae—and perhaps even this would be resolved into something more primitive—while all religions, gods, heavens, immortalities, were made by mansoul, of which a perfect God was perhaps the noblest creation; that man sprang from primeval amoeba of which chemistry would sometime tell us the origin and perhaps be able to reproduce; that every human institution, organization, and even science itself were but the unfoldment of infantile impulses in man, the courses of which could be traced back to the very dawn of the psyche in the lowest forms of animal life; that spontaneous generation, although not proved, must somehow be true; that life had a chemical basis; and that even atoms, like Haeckel's plastidules, had souls of which the human psyche was only an aggregation.

It was that broad, bold, untechnical enthusiasm that made Hall so stimulating and that spread his influence so far. Evolution was basic in his concern, which embraced, nevertheless, many other fields. "There is a sense," he said, "in which all my active conscious life has been made up of a series of fads or crazes." The fads overlapped one another, lapsed and recurred, but Hall's own list of them is as follows: (1) evolution, (2) experimental psychology, (3) animal life, habits, and instincts, (4) child study, (5) pedagogy, (6) sex psychology, (7) food, appetite, and motivation, and (8) religious psychology. Only his excursion into experimental psychology and the founding of two laboratories took him away from his main interest in genetic psychology. It remained persistently the common bond. Someone once introduced him to an audience as "the Darwin of the mind," and he took great pleasure in a characterization which so nearly expressed his aspirations.

One gets, perhaps, the spirit of this evolutionary psychology best from Hall's seminary. There the doctrine of recapitulation, as developed by Haeckel and Spencer, was common gospel, and the psychic life of man was considered as containing constant reverberations of his phylogenesis.[31]

Thus Quantz, writing from Hall's seminary in 1898 under the title "Dendro-psychoses," went into the matter of the effect of trees on man and the reverberations of the arboreal life of his ancestors that are still to be observed. "The climbing power of infants," he wrote,

> often surpasses that of adults, and goes to show that our ancestors were tree-dwellers and that the children clung to their mother whose hands were occupied in climbing from branch to branch. Young apes, as a rule, hang beneath their mothers, holding on by the long hair of their shoulders and sides. Those that failed to do this would tumble to the ground or be left behind and fall a prey to enemies from which the mothers were fleeing. Hence, natural selection would bring about a high degree of this climbing power. . . . Even the reflex act of grasping an object which touches the palm can be of no value to the child now, except to point to a former period when life itself depended on it. . . . In the use of its hands the baby shows a kinship to tree-climbers. In grasping an object it does not put the thumb on the opposite side, but takes the object between the fingers and the palm. Arboreal ancestors in going from bough to bough would strike the branches palm first from above downward, grasping with the fingers. . . . Putting babies to sleep by rocking is probably taking advantage of a rhythm which has become ingrained through long ages of swaying in the branches of trees. . . . The fear of falling is instinctive, as it is found in children who have had no individual experience to justify it. . . . Such fears of falling (barophobia), as well as the child's "monkey-like propensity to climb everything everywhere," may be reverberations from different stages of a life in which climbing and falling were daily experiences.

And so on through many pages.[32]

Similarly F. E. Bolton from the same seminary reported on "Hydro-psychoses," showing how man recapitulates some of the aquatic phases of the evolutionary series and that there are to be found pelagic reverberations in his mental life.[33]

There is thus no question about the profound effect of the theories of evolution upon the psychology of the Clark school. How influential was the school? Hall himself made disciples who remained loyal throughout their lives. On the other hand, Hall's loose speculation, his dictum "Build the top of the mountain first," antagonized the experimentalists. He influenced pedagogy more than he influenced the new psychology. Nevertheless, both he and Baldwin were symptoms of what was new in the new psychology, and functionalism was favored by the fact that the irrepressible Hall and the irrepressible Baldwin were both for it.

Individual Differences

There is no doubt that the theory of evolution furnished support and re-enforcement for a psychology of individual differences. There is also no doubt that the interest in evolution was not a necessary condition for the growth of a psychology of individual differences. One finds the roots of this development in the faculty psychology of the Scottish philosophers. They influenced the thinking of the French psychologists, and thus share some responsibility for the way in which Binet and Henri and others, like Ribot, found themselves concerned with individual capacities. The Scottish school also influenced Gall and his phrenology, which was another movement for assessing individual differences, one that originally centered in France.[34] Long before evolution was a popular theory or Darwin had written the *Origin of Species*, phrenology was spreading to England and America because of its personal appeal. If you can really know something personal about each of your fellows by merely observing his appearance, then you will have suddenly gained a certain security against the adventitious complexities of the social world which is so full of personal surprises.[35]

On the other hand, it is quite clear that it was a belief in Darwinian theory which led Galton to his interest in individual differences in human capacity. Beginning with the inheritance of genius, he came presently to his attempts to assess and inventory human abilities. He invented various anthropometric tests, tests of sensory capacity, of reaction time, of memory span, and of imagery, and he actually arranged to have a laboratory where the public could take these tests for threepence and learn what their capacities were. Nine thousand three hundred thirty-seven persons took the tests, but if Galton had not thought that these individual differences are inherited, he would not have bothered with them.[36]

Galton's concern with individual differences dates from the early 1870's. Cattell's dates from the early 1880's, for by 1886 he had managed to recast his doctoral thesis with Wundt, the thesis on reaction times, into a study of individual differences. In 1890 Cattell wrote an article, "Mental Tests and Measurements," the article in which he coined the term *mental test*. Galton added an approving note to the article, which gave the specifications for ten tests of abilities and made suggestions for about fifty more. By 1893 Cattell was advocating the giving of these tests in schools. By 1896 he was publishing results on the mental testing of Columbia students. Cattell more than any one other person was in this fashion responsible for getting mental testing under way in America, and it is plain that his motivation was similar to Galton's and that he was also influenced, or at least re-enforced, by Galton.[37]

Presumably the theory of evolution determined Cattell less than did the spirit of hardheaded American common sense, but all these things are wrapped up together. Later it was the existence of the tests that raised again the nature-nurture problem which Galton had posed.

Meanwhile in France Binet and Henri were developing tests of a more intellectual character and argued in 1896 for an individual psychology.[38] Galton's and Cattell's tests had measured simple sensory or motor capacities, or else other simple faculties like memory span and imaginal type. Binet and Henri turned to the more intellectual and verbal capacities. It was for a while a question as to which kind of test was going to differentiate people better in respect of scholastic capacities and the achievements of genius. Stella Sharp, an American, reviewed the situation in 1899 and decided in favor of the tests of the "complex" or "higher" capacities, and she was right.[39] We all know how after 1900 the Binet tests supplanted Galton's and Cattell's tests, how the Binet scale came into use as a measure of what Binet called "intelligence." [40]

The choice of the intellectual and verbal skills over the sensory and motor capacities was in no conscious sense related to beliefs about evolution. The choice was made because it worked better, but, once made, it was found that the Binet scale of "intelligence" had significance for the problem of mental inheritance. Thus the question came back into association with the interest in evolution. The nature-nurture problem is, however, a matter which we must defer for later consideration.

Although Cattell did not establish intelligence tests, he did put firmly into the American scene a psychology of capacity, as it may be called. The tests tested human *faculties, capacities, abilities.* Nowadays we say they test *abilities* and *aptitudes.* A capacity, as tested, turns out to be pretty much the ability to compete in the civilized struggle for existence—the kind of personal characteristics which Americans seemed to find especially interesting. There is thus, via Cattell, a Columbia tradition which can not be separated from the main American faith.

Animal Psychology

It was the Darwinian theory that gave animal psychology its start. Before Darwin common sense tended to accept a view that was not unlike Descartes' and that actually owed a great deal to him. Descartes had held that the animals are automata, that their bodies are machines, whereas man has a rational soul which interacts with his body at a specified point in his brain. That is the Cartesian dualism of mind and body. Body is extended substance, but mind is unextended, not occupying space. The two are discrete and there are no intermediates between them, no substances that are as much like mind as they are like matter.

Actually this dualism represents the influence of seventeenth-century theology upon Descartes, an influence abetted by language. *L'âme* in French means both *mind* and *soul*, as does *Seele* in German. That confusion and the Cartesian dictum together made it impossible clearly to distinguish the properties of the mind from the properties of the soul. When people thought of the soul as immortal, they thought actually of mind or consciousness which continued after death without a body. Theology, asserting the truth of immortality for man and denying it for animals, was declaring that men have souls and that animals have none. We have to go only one step farther and identify man's soul with his conscious mind, in order to follow Descartes in denying a conscious mind to animals.

The Darwinian theory, on the contrary, asserted the existence of continuity between man and animals, continuity in all respects, mental as well as physical, since man is believed to be derived from animals by continuous change. We have already noted how Darwin and Romanes and Lloyd Morgan attacked the problem of the mental evolution of animals to man.[41]

G. J. Romanes wrote three important books, intended to support the thesis that intelligence is continuous between the animals and man. The first, which displayed the data, he called a *comparative psychology*, using that term for the first time. For collecting evidence, he adopted a carefully safeguarded anecdotal method, protecting himself against the exaggerations of anecdote by an application of rigorous criteria of evidence. He was anxious, of course, to find as much manlike intelligence in animals as possible, and he had to beware of his own bias. Romanes lacked for his descriptions, however, a good classification of mental states, but he concluded that all animals and man can have "simple ideas," that "complex ideas" are limited to the higher animals and man, and that abstract or "notional ideas" are "the unique prerogative of man." This was a conclusion that furthered the concept of continuity while leaving man the foremost of God's creatures.[42]

It was Lloyd Morgan who in 1894 applied to Romanes' interpretations a principle of parsimony, which afterward came to be called Lloyd Morgan's Canon. "In no case," he said, "may we interpret an action as the outcome of a higher psychical faculty, if it can be interpreted as the exercise of one which stands lower in the psychological scale." Romanes, anxious to prove the Darwinian theory, attributed to animals as much intelligence as their acts would justify. Lloyd Morgan was holding that one should, in such a situation, attribute as little intelligence as their acts would justify.[43] After Lloyd Morgan, caution in anthropomorphizing the animal consciousness became standard in comparative psychology.

Lloyd Morgan's caution was re-enforced by Loeb's theory of the tropism, which was offered to the world at the same time. Loeb had little difficulty in convincing the readers of his paper that plants and protozoa are virtually Cartesian automata in their responses to stimulation. If tropistic action is determined entirely by physicochemical forces, it may therefore be supposed to be independent of volition or reason. No more than Descartes did Loeb think, however, that men are mere automata, governed only by unconscious tropisms. He sought, rather, to establish the point in the evolutionary scale at which consciousness emerges, and concluded that the existence of associative memory, the ability of an organism to profit by experience, demonstrates the emergence of mind.[44] Since the higher vertebrates obviously possess associative memory, the effect of Loeb's argument was to preserve a dualism, but to shift the critical point of separation lower down in the evolutionary scale. Men and dogs are conscious, protozoa and plants are not.[45] Such a view supports the Darwinian theory because it fills in the "missing link" between man and the animals.

About the time that Loeb's theory of tropisms was becoming well known, Jennings in America published a monograph describing the psychic life of the protozoa. Ignoring Lloyd Morgan's Canon but confining himself to the careful experimental observation of the behavior of protozoa, he was able to build up a convincing case for protozoic consciousness.[46] Later, when it was found that Paramecium could be taught to modify his behavior, it looked as if even Loeb's criterion of consciousness had been met at the very bottom of the animal scale.[47]

The result of this argument about the point of emergence of mind in the evolutionary series, an argument beginning with Romanes in 1882 and culminating with Jennings in 1904, was to make it appear that, if you start with man and work down, you will still be observing consciousness in the protozoa when you get to them, but that, if you start with the micro-organisms and work up, then you will find tropistic considerations adequate and fit, and there will be no point in the series at which there will be any such change as will lead you to assert that man himself is not governed entirely by physicochemical laws. This sort of dualism is not Cartesian. It is a Leibnitzian parallelism. You can regard everything as conscious or as unconscious, as you choose.

Now it was this controversy about Darwinian continuity that got comparative psychology started. Comparative psychology could have begun without the theory of evolution, for there have always been persons interested in animal behavior. Mere interest in animal abilities would not, however, have led to the systematic comparison that was required in the search for breaks in the continuity of the scale, nor would it easily have resulted in the cautious kind of observation that Morgan's Canon and Loeb's tropistic hypothesis entailed. It seems quite likely that, without the exitement over the theory of evolution, animal psychology would not have gotten so good a start so soon.

Once the comparative description of animal behavior was established as proper scientific procedure, it tended to perpetuate itself. Most of the comparative work in animal psychology has consisted of sampling abilities at successive levels of the evolutionary scale. Yerkes, for instance, worked on the worm, the crab, the turtle, the frog, the mouse, the rat, the crow, the dove, the pig, the monkey, the chimpanzee, and man. It was the scheme of evolution, not mere catholicity of interest, that determined him.[48]

Objective Psychology

The tendency to regard the human body as a machine, affected by and affecting the external world, but independent of mind, consciousness, and will, is very old. The French psychologists liked to think in such terms. La Mettrie in 1748 wrote *L'Homme machine* to demonstrate that point of view. If Descartes could argue that animals are automata, others could certainly extend the principle to man.

Psychological objectivism was also promoted in the eighteenth century by the scientific study of reflex action. The term reflex was itself invented to indicate that action in response to stimulation may occur because the incoming animal spirits are "reflected" by the columns of the spinal cord out along certain motor paths. Robert Whytt showed in 1751 that some purposive action depends only on the functioning of a segment of the spinal cord and occurs in a decapitated animal without a brain. Since the brain has generally been supposed to be the organ of mind, reflex action is usually regarded as unconscious and therefore automatic. In the middle of the nineteenth century, however, there arose an interesting argument between the physiologist Pflüger and the philosopher-psychologist Lotze. Pflüger argued that consciousness is associated with the action of nervous tissue and that the reflexes must therefore be conscious, as indeed appears from their purposive nature. Lotze held that consciousness depends upon the brain and that the reflexes, being incapable of modification to fit special situations, are obviously unconscious. In this argument Lotze was playing the role of Loeb, and Pflüger the role of Jennings, for the reflex like the tropism can be regarded either as physiological mechanics or as evidence of conscious purposiveness.[49]

The Loeb-Jennings argument prepared the way for J. B. Watson's behaviorism of 1913. Watson, concerned primarily with the psychology of animals and of children, realized that the primary data of observation are always items of behavior—movements or secretions—and that these responses are in themselves evidences of the abilities of an organism to react discriminatively to its environment. Why bother, Watson asked, to reason out what consciousness is like, when the organism's capacity to accommodate itself to its environment is the principle point of interest? So Watson boldly proposed that psychology ignore consciousness and deal directly with human capacity as indicated by accommodatory behavior. That was behaviorism, a psychology of stimulus and response.[50]

Was Watson influenced by the theory of evolution? Not directly. He could, however, gain acceptance for his view because it was consistent with the American faith. Behaviorism (Watson to the contrary notwithstanding) was a form of Dewey's functional psychology and of Cattell's capacity psychology, the American psychology of the abilities of men as measured by their adaptive or discriminatory performances. Watson's view was essentially American, a psychology consistent with the belief in necessity of struggle for survival.

Behaviorism was itself too unsophisticated to last. It has now given place to positivism or operationism or whatever one prefers to call the newest psychological objectivism. The operationist argues that all the data of psychology, including the data of consciousness, are to be defined by the operations which are used to observe them. You can know nothing more about mind than you can find in the evidence for the existence of mind. This movement gets its sophistication from the logical positivism of the Vienna Circle and from the operational physics of P. W. Bridgman, but this is not the place for its full consideration. It is sufficient here to point out that the epistemology of operationism was already implicit in the faiths of behaviorism, functional psychology, and capacity psychology, the basic American psychological faith.[51]

Nature versus Nurture

Nowhere is the contrast between the once new psychology of Germany and the still newer version in America more striking than in respect of the importance assigned to the problem of mental inheritance. The Germans in the days of German greatness in psychology were attempting the complete description of the generalized normal human mind. They were concerned with its immediate physiological basis, but not at all with its biological origin. The Americans, on the other hand, were led by their interest in individual differences to consider seriously the origins of the differences, whether they lay in ancestry or in education. The theory of evolution posed for them one of their most important problems.

This interest began, as we have already seen, with Galton's *Hereditary Genius* of 1869 and his other books during the next two decades. He coined the catch phrase "nature and nurture" in 1874. He published his study of the psychological resemblances of twins in 1876. In 1877 Dugdale described the Jukes, a family in which mental deficiency predominated through several generations. By the end of the century it was pretty generally accepted that genius and imbecility are both inherited and that heredity works for mediocrity too.

At the beginning of the present century the study of biological inheritance was greatly stimulated by the finding of Mendel's laws of inheritance which had been overlooked for almost forty years. The study of genetics then became exceedingly active among the biologists, and everyone was looking for inheritable unit characters.[52] When Goddard published in 1912 his account of the Kallikak family, showing the inheritance of feeble-mindedness through six generations after it had once been introduced into a "normal" strain, it seemed for the time being as if Galton's case had been proved.[53] There were various books on eugenics in the second decade of the century, all published with the intention that the human stock should be biologically improved by selective parenthood.[54]

At the same time the intelligence tests were getting established. Binet's first scale of intelligence came out in 1905, a scale which implies the growth of intelligence with age, thus assuming that intelligence is biologically determined. It was possible to figure a mental age, and in 1911 Stern suggested that the effect of maturation be eliminated by taking the intelligence quotient, the ratio of the mental age to the chronological age. After the Stanford revision of the Binet scale in 1916, it was customary to expect the IQ to remain approximately constant during the growth of a child. That approximation was taken to mean that the IQ is unalterable, congenital, and therefore inherited.[55]

During the next two decades the role of learning in human abilities was recognized more and more. From the outside there was social pressure, for persons with a liberal political philosophy did not like a doctrine that established an aristocracy, even an aristocracy of brains. Democracy required that nurture should be able to prevail over nature. The IQ turned out to be not so constant as had been at first supposed. Intelligence continued to be indefinable, and no one succeeded in making up international and intercultural intelligence tests that would really test out national or racial differences, without dependence on cultural difference. It became increasingly clear that economic status affects intelligence as the tests test it, perhaps because it affects educational status which is in turn reflected in the types of skills required in the tests. At any rate intelligence tests were suspect of being dependent more upon verbal ability than upon a general factor common to all abilities.[56] The new methods of factor analysis favored the reduction of human abilities to many rather than a few factors. By the time of the second World War psychologists were ready to deal with learned abilities and with the aptitudes for learning the abilities. The aptitudes might be native but they too might have been learned. All in all intelligence from 1920 to 1945 might be said to have been on the way out; yet intelligence had furnished the strongest argument for native mental ability.

On the other hand, the role of nature was becoming clearer. Comparative psychology showed that instinctual behavior occurs in many animals without learning, even though practice may improve its adaptive character. The startle reflex for sudden loud sounds was analyzed in man and found to be fixed and involuntary.[57] Mental Mendelian characters did not turn up, except perhaps color blindness which is said to be inheritable and sex linked. The study of twins began to show how both nature and nurture perpetually operate concurrently. Are identical twins, when brought up in different socioeconomic circumstances, more or less alike than fraternal twins brought up under the same circumstances? Whether nature or nurture appears stronger in a given case depends on what the tests are, but no other two people are likely to be so similar as identical twins brought up under the same circumstances.[58]

The logic of the situation, moreover, required a belief in the concurrent action of nature and nurture. A child can learn to walk provided he has inherited legs to walk on. He can learn to multiply provided he has inherited the brain to do it with, as indeed some feeble-minded children have not.[59] Heredity works mostly, however, at the level of aptitudes and not at the level of finished abilities. That is because maturation is working. Aptitudes are forming as a consequence of general development of the child or young animal, and practice, while necessary, becomes more and more effective as the aptitude develops. One twin, as he develops, is given climbing apparatus, while the other is deprived of it. When the two are put together with the same opportunities to climb, the practiced twin does better at first. Soon, however, the other twin catches up. His aptitude had matured without practice and he learns quickly because he is now old enough.[60]

The nature-nurture literature is large, and the details of how much of human ability comes from heredity through the chromosomes and how much through cultural influence, education, and practice do not concern us. The fact is that the original problem which evolutionary theory set—the problem as to whether mind is inherited—is answered. In part, mind is inherited. There are few complex abilities of social importance that do not depend both upon adaptive learning and upon the inheritance of the organs or aptitudes that are essential for the learning. Mental inheritance does not, however, seem so strange as it did a hundred years ago, for nowadays everyone realizes that the mind is for the most part the way the nervous system functions, and not an unextended Cartesian substance that may prove to be immortal after it has lost its body. The growth of objectivism and the decline of mentalism in psychology has in itself been an answer to the question of biological and psychological continuity between animals and man. Evolution favors continuity and unity, just as objectivism favors the unity of the sciences.

The Case

We can now review the case for the importance of the influence of evolutionary thought on the development of American psychology. Such historical causation is not easy to validate or to assess.

The adult character of American psychology was formed in its youth, in the last quarter of the nineteenth century, when James and Hall and Baldwin and Cattell were building something new, based on what was going on in Germany and in England. The paternal ancestry of American psychology is German psychology, but the maternal ancestors are the biology and psychology of England. The child was, moreover, greatly influenced by the environment in which it grew up. Its nurture determined how its nature should realize itself.

The formative environment was the American temperament of the late nineteenth century. A rough, crude, frank, aggressive, practical, boastful nation America was. The Europeans found us ambitious, self-assured, direct, and unpolished. Our diplomacy had only just passed the shirt-sleeve stage. A psychologist can see in American boastfulness some ambivalence, a self-assertion based on insecurity, like whistling in the dark. Certainly the psychologists of that period had no thought that a new insight resided in them. They were looking to Germany for the best and newest, and trying to see that America did as well or better. They seemed scarcely aware of the fact that, in taking over German psychology, they were remaking it along American lines. To read Cattell's early propaganda for the mental tests, you would think that the mental tests were just a product of experimental psychology, and that America was supporting the Leipzig tradition in finding a use for its devices of mental measurement.[61] In a sense Cattell was right on this matter and Germany did contribute what America applied. There is a clear inheritance here. But America presently did much more than apply experimental psychology to human problems. It changed the whole German intent as to the purpose and significance of psychology.

This view of the American temperament is consistent with the various delineations that have been made since Turner, the historian, first undertook to explain the American character as appropriate to the pioneer, the pioneer who understands that there is ahead of him a perpetually retreating frontier beyond which there is opportunity for those strong enough to take it.[62]

The pioneer struggles to wrest from nature first his living and then his comforts. Natural selection and the survival of the fittest color his daily thoughts. It is no surprise, then, that America should have taken readily to evolutionary theory, nor that it should mold its thinking on many topics with respect to survival and success by means of the concepts of accommodation and adaptation.

When we find that American psychology has been predominantly the *functional* psychology of Dewey and the Chicago school and also the *capacity psychology* of Cattell and the mental tests, are we then to say that American psychology is founded upon the practicality of the American temperament or the adaptative principle of the theory of evolution? Plainly it is founded on both. Seemingly neither was a necessary condition. Conceivably either alone might be a sufficient reason for American psychology, but we can never tell since neither of the two occurred alone. Certainly the two forces were summative, and an American psychology of practical adjustment of the organism to the requirements of living was the necessary consequence.

The explicitly *evolutionary psychology* of Baldwin and of Stanley Hall must be regarded as contributory to the basic trend rather than essential in it. These prolific writers were constantly advertising the importance of evolution. Basic effective motivation generally lies deep, in a man or in a historical movement, but basic motivation can nevertheless be re-enforced by superficial conscious resolve. Baldwin and Hall were like the voice of consciousness, reiterating the importance of evolutionary theory for American psychology, which was already quietly taking account of the fundamental principles of biological adaptation for reasons less obvious than Baldwin and Hall brought forth.

Comparative psychology was a separate trend. It got under way definitely in an attempt to answer the question about the continuity of mind from animals to man, a question that Darwinian theory posed. Even for it, evolution can hardly be supposed to have been a necessary condition, for comparative interest in animal behavior occurs independently of concern with the theory of evolution. Nevertheless the fact is that animal psychology got its start in answering this Darwinian question, and that animal psychology got away from the question to stand on its own feet only later when the question had, in a sense, been answered.

In terms of the Hegelian dialectic the thesis had been that men have souls (hence consciousness, hence minds) and animals have not. The antithesis was that mind is continuous from animals to man. The synthesis was that mind and mechanism represent but different points of view toward the same material, that from above downward you see mind extending indefinitely into the animal scale, that from below upward you see that mechanism is essential to mind in man.[63] This solution of the evolutionary problem in comparative psychology, therefore, opened the way for the *objective psychologies* of behaviorism and operationism, which in turn found themselves re-enforced by the prevailing American psychology of function and capacity. Operationism, moreover, has turned out to be essentially a form of pragmatism,[64] which through Dewey and James is closely related to functional psychology and to the American pioneer temperament. Thus it appears that at least three different lines of development (through the tropism, through functionalism, through pragmatism) converge upon modern American objectivism, and that evolution can thus be shown to hold an important position in the development of this system, although it is not a *sine qua non* of operationism.

In brief, then, it can be said that there is an American psychology. Individual psychologists in America hold to the central core with greater or less deviation. In the land of the free, personal predilections count. The central core is, however, the thesis that mind is of use to the organism, or, in more general and modern terms, that it is with the adaptations of the organism to the exigencies of living that psychology is concerned. The proven value of psychology to national survival in the second World War is evidence as to how much American psychology involves use of the Darwinian principle.

NOTES

Antecedents and Beginnings

1. Scripture (1897).
2. On the nature of American psychology see Boring (1950a, 505–583, 620–663, 643–734). To cite the 1950 edition of this book is an anachronism, for the present paper was written in 1946, and the revision of the book profited greatly by being able to draw upon the paper, whereas the paper had only the first edition of the book to which it could go. See also Woodworth (1948, especially 11–36); Murphy (1949, 192–224, 234–283).
3. On the nature of German psychology see Boring (1950a, 275–456); Murphy (1949, 79–102, 146–187); Flugel (1933, 144–214).
4. On British empiricism and associationism see Boring (1950a, 168–202, 219–245).
5. On Fechner see Boring (1950a, 275–296).
6. On Helmholtz see Boring (1950a, 297–315).
7. On Wundt see Boring (1950a, 316–347).
8. On modern British psychology in general see Boring (1950a, 459–502); also Murphy (1949, 99–126).
9. Fay (1939), complains that these early American psychologists are as important as the more recent ones and that their neglect is unjustified. They were not, however, functionally important, not if their importance is properly measured by their posthumous effects.
10. On James in 1867–1890 see Perry (1935, II, 3–50).
11. H. James (1920, I, 118 f.); also Perry (1935, II, 3).
12. On the controversy between James and Hall as to their professional priorities see Perry (1935, II, 6–10, 22 f.). On James's early laboratory see Harper (1949). Wundt also had a demonstrational laboratory at Leipzig as early as 1875; see Boring (1950a, 323 f.).
13. On the wave of laboratory founding in the United States see Ruckmick (1912), esp. 520.
14. On Wundt's American students see Boring (1950a, 347); Flugel (1933), 206–214.
15. On Cattell see Boring (1950a, 532–540, 548 f.).
16. On the effect of the free frontier on American character, see Turner (1920), which reprints the famous original paper of 1893 (pp. 1–38) and other later essays on related topics. This general topic has now received discussion in Boring (1950a, 8 f., 506–508).
17. On the American Creed and an analysis of it that differs from Turner's see Myrdal (1944, 3–25).

18. On the way in which a democratic society favors a psychology of individual differences see Dewey (1899, 21 f.); cf. also (1917, esp. 273).
19. On the way in which the American character has led to psychologies of capacity, behavior, and physicalistic operations see Allport (1945, esp. 117–119); Boring (1950a, 641–658).
20. It has been said that English science tends to be practical, like American, and that Newton and Maxwell (a Scot) were exceptions in their having theoretical breadth: Bernal (1939, 197). That view makes Darwin appropriate to England, but implies that Darwin plus the practicality of a democracy are not alone a sufficient cause for the sudden growth of an applied psychology—for the reason that applied psychology thrived in America while it was starving in England. America had what England had not, a pioneer spirit and a readiness for shirt-sleeve science.

James

21. On James and Darwin and on James and Spencer see Perry (1935, I, 468–470, 482); Harper (1949).
22. On James's use of the word *function* see Ruckmick (1913, esp. 111).

Functional Psychology

23. On Dewey and functional psychology see Boring (1950a, 552–556, 578 f.); Heidbreder (1933, 201–233). On Dewey's philosophy and functional orientation see Ratner (1928; 1939).
24. On Dewey and Darwinism see Dewey (1910, esp. 1–10). The conception of special creation is essentially aristocratic because it gives divine rights to species; relative to it the theory of evolution is democratic, even though evolutionary change is slow and difficult.
25. The famous paper that started the ball rolling for the Chicago school is J. Dewey's "The Reflex Arc Concept in Psychology" (1896).
26. On Angell and functional psychology see Boring (1950a, 556–558, 579); Heidbreder (1933). The presidential address is J. R. Angell, "The Province of Functional Psychology" (1907). See also Hunter (1949). The standard textbook of functional psychology is Angell (1904) and later editions; see especially chap. iv on attention. For an analysis of functional systems of psychology in their accommodatory and teleological character see Titchener (1929, 158–193, esp. 177–193).
27. On the relation of functional psychology to phrenology see Dallenbach (1915). On the dependence of phrenology on the faculty psychology of the Scottish school see Spoerl (1936).

Mental Evolution

28. On the effect of the theory of evolution on psychology in England see Murphy (1929, 111–126).
29. On Baldwin see Boring (1950a, 528–532, 547 f.). For negative criticisms of Baldwin's predilection for theorizing in the absence of facts see Bolton (1895, 142–145); M. F. Washburn, necrology of Baldwin (1935).
30. On Hall and his relation to the theory of evolution see Hall (1923, esp. 357–367), from which the quotations in the text are taken. See also Fisher (1925, esp. 20–26); also Hall (1908). In general on Hall see Boring (1950a, 517–524), and the commentaries and biographies cited on 545 f.
31. On recapitulation see Fisher (1925).
32. On the arboreal reverberations see Quantz (1898, esp. 450–467).
33. On the aquatic reverberations see Bolton (1899, esp. 170–186).

Individual Differences

34. On phrenology, Scottish faculties, and functional psychology see Dallenbach (1915); Spoerl (1936); Bentley (1916, 102–115). On phrenology see Boring (1950a, 50–60)
35. The popular appeal of phrenology has recently had its analogue in Sheldon's somatotypy (1940; 1942). Life becomes more interesting than usual if you can quickly assess the temperament of friends and strangers by estimating their constitutional types in respect of endomorphy, mesomorphy, and ectomorphy.
36. On Galton see Boring (1950a, 476–488, 500 f.), and references there cited.
37. On Cattell see Boring (1950a, 532–540, 548 f.), and references there cited. The articles mentioned in the text are: G. Cattell (1890), (1893); with L. Farrand (1896).
38. The important early paper in the French movement toward tests is Binet and Henri (1896). For their other papers see Peterson (1925).
39. The early American reaction against Cattell is Sharp (1899).
40. On the history of mental testing see Peterson (1925), bibliography of 242 titles; Boring (1950a, 570–578, 581–583).

Animal Psychology

41. On the development of animal psychology in general see Boring (1950a, 472–476, 498, 622–631, 659 f.).
42. On Romanes see Boring (1950a, 473 f., 497), and references there cited.
43. Lloyd Morgan's reaction to Romanes (1890–91); (1894) (the Canon of parsimony is in chap. iii); (1900). See also Boring (1950a, 474 f., 497 f.).
44. On tropism see Loeb (1890); (1899, Eng. trans. 1900). See also Boring (1950a, 475, 498).
45. On associative memory as evidence of the existence of consciousness see Washburn (1908 or any later ed., chap. ii).
46. On protozoic consciousness see Jennings (1904), and the series of articles beginning in 1897. See Boring (1950a, 622–626, 659).
47. For the early instance of protozoic learning see Day and Bentley (1911).
48. On R. M. Yerkes see Boring (1950a, 628, 660).

Objective Psychology

49. For details of the history of objective psychology and of reflex action see Fearing (1930); Boring (1950a, 631–641, 660 f.).
50. On behaviorism see Murphy (1929, 251–268); Boring (1950a, 641–653, 661–663).
51. On logical positivism and operationism in relation to psychology see Stevens (1939), and references there cited; Boring (1942, 13 f., 18 f., 33 f., 46 f.); (1950a, 653–659, 663); Boring, *et al.* (1945). There is also a line of development from James and Dewey and C. S. Peirce through pragmatism to operationism, which has been held to be a form of pragmatism. See V. J. McGill, "Pragmatism," in Runes (1942, 245–247).

Nature versus Nurture

52. On mental inheritance see Murphy (1949, 366–371).
53. On the supposed inheritance of feeble-mindedness see Goddard (1912).
54. A representative book on eugenics is Davenport (1911).
55. On the growth of intelligence testing see Murphy (1949, 351–372); Peterson (1925, 117–242).
56. On the relation of intelligence-test scores to social, economic, and cultural factors see Klineberg (1940, 223–264, 282–316; 1935, 152–199).
57. On the startle reflex see Landis and Hunt (1939, esp. 20–51).
58. On nature, nurture, and twins see Woodworth (1941).

59. On the inevitably concurrent contribution of heredity and environment to specific abilities see Woodworth (1941); Carmichael (1925).
60. On maturation of aptitudes see C. P. Stone (1934). See also L. Carmichael (1926, 51–58; 1927a, 34–47).

Case for Evolution

61. On Cattell's belief that Wundt's experimental psychology was the material on which to build mental tests see the references in n. 37 *supra*.
62. On the pioneer nature of American character see the references in nn. 16, 17 *supra*.
63. The synthesis in the Hegelian dialectic shows that consciousness in animals is relative to the point of view that you take up over against observable behavior. An analogous case appears in cosmology. Thesis: the Ptolemaic view—the sun goes around the earth. Antithesis: the Copernican view—the earth goes around the sun. Synthesis: Einstein's view—all motion is relative, and Ptolemy is right from one point of view and Copernicus from another.
64. On operationism as a form of pragmatism see n. 51 *supra*.

The Scientific Method

⟦⟦

*B*ORING'S contributions to scientific method are, in fact, to be found in all sections of this volume. For example, in the History section the paper on the "Experimental Control" (pp. 111–125) is not only a history, but one of the best analyses in psychology of the relation of experimental design to more general principles of induction.

The present section begins with a series of papers on operationism. These represent Boring's most enthusiastic advocacy of a position on scientific methodology. His early recognition of the value of this doctrine may be traced in part to the fact that he had independently invented it. His 1922 paper on "The Stimulus-Error" (pp. 255–273) implies such a position. More explicitly, in a popular piece in 1923, "Intelligence as the Tests Test it," he offers what is probably the first operational definition of intelligence. For its historical interest, we have reproduced the relevant sections of that paper.

E.G.B. is unique among the advocates of operationism in applying it to constructs about conscious contents. Two papers illustrate his approach: "Temporal Perception and Operationism," and "An Operational Restatement of G. E. Müller's Psychophysical Axioms." These papers also supplement the treatment of the mind-body problem as represented in that section of this book. Following this, we get his mature perspective as he answers the questions which he posed for himself and others on "The Use of Operational Definitions in Science."

The paper, "The Role of Theory in Experimental Psychology," has a broader topic, but includes also some of his wisest comments on operationism,

as on pages 222–223, where he states that when a construct "gets two alternative operational definitions, it is beginning to be validated. When the defining
operations, because of proven correlations, are many, it has become reified.
. . . A thing or a relation is real in as far as it has many alternative defining
operations." "Statistical Frequencies as Dynamic Equilibria" illustrates Boring's long-standing concern and dissent over the use of probability theory as
a scientific theory, a concern first shown in his classic paper of 1920, "The
Logic of the Normal Law of Error in Mental Measurement" (reprinted in
Boring, 1962). The section closes with consideration of "The Validation of
Scientific Belief." E.G.B. uses the occasion of the examination of a border-
line case, that is, extrasensory perception, to analyze general features of the
validation of scientific theory. Such validation turns out to center around such
psychological and sociological factors as unconscious bias and social consensus,
rather than around logical principles.

Intelligence as the
Tests Test It

▨▨▨▨▨▨▨▨▨▨▨▨▨   1923

IF you take one of the ready-made tests of intelligence and try it on a very large number of persons, you will find that they succeed with it in very different degrees. Repeat the test, and you will find that they cannot, with the best will in the world to do well, alter their scores very greatly. Then give the same group another intelligence test, and you will discover that the differences among individuals are approximately, although not exactly, the same. And you can go on. You will find that an adult, after continued exposure to his social and educational environment, does not greatly alter his score on a given test; that children, however, do steadily improve their performances until somewhere between ten and twenty years old; that the average age at which improvement stops is about fourteen years; but that children while improving tend to maintain the same individual differences, so that in a given group every child would keep about the same rank within the group. These are basic observational facts of the psychology of intelligence. What do they mean?

What the Tests Test. They mean in the first place that intelligence as a measurable capacity must at the start be defined as the capacity to do well in an intelligence test. Intelligence is what the tests test. This is a narrow definition, but it is the only point of departure for a rigorous discussion of the tests. It would be better if the psychologists could have used some other and more technical term, since the ordinary connotation of intelligence is much broader. The damage is done, however, and no harm need result if we but remember that measurable intelligence is simply what the tests of intelligence test, until further scientific observation allows us to extend the definition.

An observational method for extending knowledge of intelligence as the tests test it is the method of statistical correlation. The relation to intelligence

Reprinted with permission from *The New Republic*, 1923, **34**, 35–36.

of any measurable capacity at all can be determined by comparing the relative performances of a large number of persons in an intelligence test with their achievement in the measure of capacity in question. If the correlation is considerable, yet not perfect, say 60 percent, we say that the particular capacity is partly dependent upon intelligence and partly independent of it. We shall not be far wrong if we think of such a capacity as complex, involving 60 per cent of intelligence and 40 per cent of some special ability that is not intelligence.

The method of correlation gives us at once some insight into the nature of intelligence as the tests test it. No satisfactory intelligence test exists at present which employs a single type of mental operation. Most tests for intelligence, like the army tests, consist of batteries of single tests, every one of which appears, on inspection, to test some special ability, like arithmetical ability, or an appreciation of verbal relations or of logical relations. When one obtains the correlations among the different tests that make up the battery called an intelligence test, one finds that the separate tests do not correlate with one another so very highly—not so highly as a rule as does one combined intelligence test with another. These results are explained by saying that the separate tests are really tests of separate abilities, and that each of these abilities involves, in part, intelligence, which is a factor common to all the tests, and in part a special ability, which is not intelligence and which therefore explains the failure of the tests to correlate very highly. When the separate tests are combined in a total score, the special abilities, being unrelated, are supposed to cancel out, leaving the score to represent the "common factor," intelligence.

Thus we see that there is no such thing as a test for pure intelligence. Intelligence is not demonstrable except in connection with some special ability. It would never have been thought of as a separate entity had it not seemed that very different mental abilities had something in common, a "common factor."

A Confusion of Meanings. One of the most frequent reasons for the misunderstanding of the tests is the fact that the existence and importance of these special abilities are usually lost sight of. The psychologists themselves are very apt to forget them and it is no wonder that their lay audiences are scarcely aware of them. Yet it is not even possible to understand the nature of tested intelligence without considering them. They are forgotten in part because the "common factor" has seemed especially important and the interest of the testers in the last decade has centered in it. Words, however, have also helped to obscure their existence. The tested intelligence of an individual is often called his "mental age"; the increase of intelligence in childhood is generally called "mental growth." In this way psychologists have inadvertently equated the "intelligent" to the "mental," overlooking in their terminology the vast number of special abilities that help to make up the "mind." It is high time for a change of words here. The present usage requires us to say that the average adult has a "mental age" of about fourteen and that "mental growth" on the average stops at fourteen. Nothing could be more untrue. The statement can be true only of intelligence as the tests test it. The special abilities, which make up skill and knowledge, continue to cumulate presumably throughout all adult life.

A very useful conception of intelligence, and one that is approximately correct in the light of our present knowledge, is that intelligence is like "power" as the physicist uses the word: the amount of work that can be done in a given time. All intelligence tests involve the maintenance of time-limits to some extent, and most tests are "speed" tests where all the work is performed against time. We may think, then, of intelligence as power and of a special ability as a machine that utilizes the power for a particular purpose. No machine can operate without power, and power is actually demonstrable only when it has a machine through which to operate. It is idle to speculate as to which is the more important, the power or the adaptive device for the utilization of the power; and it is folly to bet one's fortune on the power, forgetting the machine.

Temporal Perception
and Operationism

🔲🔲🔲🔲🔲🔲🔲🔲🔲🔲🔲🔲🔲🔲🔲   1936

IT is the purpose of this note to show how the classical problem of temporal perception turns out to be specious when it is considered with respect to the operational procedures by which perception is known, and thus how it forms a striking instance of the failure of immediate experience successfully to play the rôle of the content of consciousness.

The fundamental problem of temporal perception appears in the question: Can *duration* be an *immediate experience?* In general the answer, from the Wundtian to the Gestalt school, seems to have been Yes. An observer reports that a short duration is quite as "immediately given" as a short extension (Curtis, 1916). A pattern of successive metronome clicks has unity, and thus, if immediately given at all, must be immediately given as a whole.[1] If an observer can recognize, without counting, thirty-two successive clicks as distinct from thirty-one or thirty-three, then in a sense these clicks form a "unitary whole" within the "range of consciousness" and are "immediately given." [2] The conception of a conscious present is founded on similar facts. The present, though logically specious, nevertheless has "sensible duration"; a conscious event comes set in a "block" of duration (James, 1890, I, 608–610). A considerable monograph could be written on the history of the notion that a temporal perception is unitary, and in general this unity has been taken to imply immediacy of experience.

The more recent history of the problem is somewhat as follows. There was implicit in the experimental psychology of the nineteenth century a punctiform elementism. The stimulation of two different retinal points was thought of as giving rise to two distinct sensations, each with its given quality and intensity. This view implies that a perceived line would be a row of sensations. Although Külpe and Titchener added extension and duration to the list of sensory attributes, it is doubtful whether this punctiform analysis, so con-

Reprinted with permission from *The American Journal of Psychology*, 1936, **48**, 519–522.

sistent with physiological analysis into receptors and their insulated fibers, was ever fully surrendered until Gestalt psychology attacked it. Then Külpe's point became evident: an extension is as simple, as unitary and as immediate in perception as is a quality or an intensity. It is natural to try to endow duration with all the virtues of extension, for ever since Kant it has been hard for anyone to believe that space can have any properties, except multi-dimensionality, that are not possessed by time. Moreover, we have all the evidence cited in the preceding paragraph that duration is introspectively as unitary and immediate as extension. Temporal patterns are a perceptual fact; are they not to be treated like spatial patterns? Most psychologists have treated them thus, without noting the paradox that inheres in the notion of the immediacy of a duration.

When the physiology of temporal perception is considered, psychological thinking is apt to become a little more realistic. It may be possible to think of experiential events which succeed one another throughout a second of physical time as coalesced into a unitary conscious present which is immediately given, but in physiology *immediacy* means time, and the end of a process is more immediate than its beginning with respect to whatever follows. Thus the present writer has emphasized the fact that a temporal perception, which acts as a whole, must somehow or other cumulate itself so that it has an adequate surrogate of itself when it ends. It can not be effective as a whole until it is completed, and then there must be some trace of the beginning still extant if all of the perception is to act (Boring, 1933, 136–146). Similarly Koffka (1935, esp. 452) has pointed out that a temporal perception requires cumulation in a neural surrogate at its end, and suggests that the temporal differentiation in the perception becomes spatial in the neural surrogate, presumably because spatial differentiation is about the only kind of differentiation that the brain is known to be able to provide.

These latter views reflect the operational envisagement of the matter. Operationism directs attention away from the fixed entities to the processes of knowing, and in the case of consciousness these processes are, in the first phases of their occurrence, the physiological processes of introspective report. In other words the problem as to whether a perceived duration must be cumulated in order to be perceived as a whole evaporates from the operational point of view. Instead we note that there is no meaning to the assertion of the existence of a temporal perception, except that certain physiological events exist prior to the report and that their differentiation is such as the report can adequately indicate. The paradox is gone because there is no longer any requirement of immediacy. For immediacy we substitute physiological *continuity*, which is probably all there is to this ancient psychological concept in any context.

This conclusion follows so simply that it may be hard for the reader to see that anything important has been said. I make bold, therefore, to suggest specifically that operationism leads to the following three conclusions, which are positive and univocal and which may be substituted for the equivocal paradox of the immediately experienced duration.

(1) A perceived duration or temporal pattern is a psychological entity that is inferred from and defined by certain operations of introspective report, which adequately imply the differentiation of the perception. This "behavioral" inversion of the point of view toward experience makes the perception, not a private immediate experience, but a psychological *construct* which (in a rat or a person or myself) is just as public as is any other convincing inference from data.

(2) The term *immediate* as applied to temporal experience turns out to be meaningless. If *immediacy* means *without lapse of time*, then the word cannot be applied to the perception of an enduring event. If it means *without intermediate processes between the event and the knowledge of it*, then it can not apply to any event. In any case the beginning and the end of a unitary temporal whole would have to be differently immediate. Instead of *immediate* we may say *continuous*, meaning that the process between the event and its manifestation in report is uninterrupted. This is obviously the proper meaning of the old term *immediate*. On the other hand, observational processes that are interrupted, as when a second knowing organism observes a first, or as when data are kept to be combined later with other data to yield a general function—such discontinuous processes are plainly what were said to be *mediate* in the old-fashioned sense.

(3) What is thus said of time may be said of everything else. If we could argue that the immediate perception of extension points toward the immediate perception of duration, then we can argue that the conclusion that duration can not be immediately perceived points toward a conclusion that extension can not be immediately perceived. Besides, the perceptions of extension and intensity and quality are all just as much processes as the perception of duration, and just as much involved in mediacy. Like duration they may be thought of as constructs based upon the operations which yield them.

Thus we get altogether rid of the troublesome notion of the immediacy of experience. If it applied to extension it had to apply to duration, and, applied to duration, it was both an impossible paradox and an obvious introspective fact. The trouble seems to be that what is introspectively obvious is not necessarily true.

NOTES

1. *Cf.* W. Wundt (1911*a*), Eng. trans., 1912, for the persistent assertion that temporal patterns are unitary wholes. Nowadays, when Gestalt psychology has set Wundt off as an elementist, we are apt to forget how much he asserted the unity of wholes.
2. This is Wundt's view developed in relation to Dietze's experiments. *Cf.* Wundt (1911*b*, 330–337) where the unity of conscious wholes is considered for temporal perception.

An Operational Restatement of
G. E. Müller's Psychophysical Axioms

𐂷𐂷𐂷𐂷𐂷𐂷𐂷𐂷𐂷𐂷𐂷𐂷𐂷𐂷𐂷𐂷𐂷𐂷𐂷𐂷𐂷𐂷𐂷𐂷𐂷𐂷𐂷𐂷𐂷𐂷   1941

PSYCHOPHYSICAL parallelism was basic to so much of the conceptual thinking of the experimental psychologists of the later nineteenth century that the principle then seemed almost axiomatically valid, like the laws of the conservation of energy and the conservation of mass. "No psychosis without neurosis" was good scientific sense in psychology, and the interactionist was necessarily suspect because the general acceptance of the physical world as a closed system made it appear impossible for an immaterial (mental) event to become the cause of a material (physical) one. At any rate there was no great opposition when Fechner, Helmholtz, Mach, Wundt and Hering assumed that every mental process must be correlated with a process in the brain, and that the nature of one must imply something about the nature of the other—at the very least that change in one must mean change in the other.

Thus one can say that the new physiological psychology was actually based upon the principle of psychophysical parallelism or, in more modern phrase, psychoneural isomorphism. This note is not concerned, however, with the history of this concept, which has been presented elsewhere, but with its apparent axiomatic nature and with the question of what happens to a dualistic axiom when it has to be restated by a monistic positivist. When G. E. Müller (1896) brought his thorough analytical mind to bear upon the problem of the physiology of color vision, he felt the need for a definite formulation of these fundamental psychophysical (he meant, *psychophysiological*) axioms.[1] He formulated five, of which the first three, the more general ones, are reproduced below.[2] These axioms lay down the general principle that a change in sensation is correlated with a change in neural process, that a difference in the kind or direction of sensory change implies a difference in the kind or direction of neural change, and conversely.[3] Köhler's (1929, 58–67)

Reprinted with permission from *Psychological Review*, 1941, **48**, 457–464.

postulate of isomorphism, according to his own statement, arose out of his desire to modernize Müller's axioms, just as this note is motivated by my faith that it is now possible and wise to try to modernize Köhler by going back to Müller and beginning again.

The point about Müller's axioms is that they still seem sensible to a positivist [4] like myself, and that fact must mean either that there has been a failure of integrity of thinking at some point or that what was good parallelism in 1896 is subject to operational translation into good physiology in 1941. There is, of course, no need for everyone to make this translation. Positivists have too often taken the police role, asking to see the operational licenses of all concepts. The burden of translation, if there be any burden at all, lies with those positivists who feel insecure without operational reductions. Whether their modes of thought represent a step in the 'modernization' of science the future will decide. In the meantime, let us see whether the seeming validity of Müller's axioms means that they can be given this physiological translation, and whether any criticism of them arises in the undertaking.

Müller's first axiom and my translation of it are as follows:

Müller's Axiom	*Operational Reduction*
1. The ground of every state of consciousness is a material process, a psychophysical process so called, to whose occurrence the presence of the conscious state is joined.	1. A subject who asserts the occurrence of a specific 'experience' actually is indicating the occurrence of a specific neural event antecedent to the assertion.

There is, of course, a basic difference underlying Müller's and my axioms. Müller is speaking of a symmetrical correlation of coördinate terms. I am considering a temporal disjunction. An 'assertion' is an effector-event, a statement, a public report, and is thus a consequent of the neural processes which its nature implies. There can be, says this axiom, no assertion of differentiation except there has been prior neural differentiation, though the converse is not true, since there may be neural differentiation which cannot lead to a report of difference (Boring, 1936; 1937). I have to assume veracity and fidelity in introspection, but then Müller too had to make those assumptions. I am also, like Müller, omitting consideration of the *Aufgabe* in order to simplify the discussion, but it might be noted here that a common case of unreportable neural differentiation occurs when the *Aufgabe* is directed to some other kind of report, as when a subject cannot report intensive differences because he was prepared observationally to indicate only differences of quality. Nevertheless my statement still matches closely one of Köhler's.[5]

One has to choose, of course, his own operational definition of consciousness, and I have chosen 'assertion' for the reason that I think it matches most nearly the introspective operation that Müller had in mind, and that the Gestalt psychologists have in mind when they are speaking of isomorphism.

It would be just as easy to write an alternative set of definitions based upon discrimination as the operation for getting at consciousness. Fundamentally there is no difference between the two sets, for an assertion is discriminative in so far as it is specific or adequate.

The second axiom, split in half, with Müller on the left and me on the right, is as follows:

2*a*. To an equality, similarity or difference in the constitution of sensations . . . there corresponds an equality, similarity or difference in the constitution of the psychophysical process, and conversely.

2*a*. A subject cannot assert that there is a difference between 'sensations' unless there has been a difference in neural events antecedent to the assertion, nor a similarity of 'sensations' unless there has been some degree of functional equivalence among the antecedent neural events; but the converse is not true, because not all neural differences can give rise to an assertion of difference.

2*b*. Moreover, to a greater or lesser similarity of sensations there also corresponds respectively a greater or lesser similarity of the psychophysical processes, and conversely.

2*b*. Moreover, an assertion of greater or lesser similarity indicates a greater or lesser functional equivalence among antecedent neural events, and an assertion of identity of 'sensations' indicates the equivalence of the neural events in giving rise to that assertion; and conversely.

The reason that the operational 2*a* is not reversible, like Müller's 2*a*, lies in the fact that there can be no differentiation in report without antecedent differentiation in the neural processes upon which report is dependent, although not all neural differentiation can be sustained in the report. If it be argued that the situation is really symmetrical in that both the antecedent neural process and the consequent report have features irrelevant to the total process of reporting, no harm is done, provided the essentially directional nature of reporting is kept clear; but I have chosen *assertion* as a co-relative term which excludes all that is irrelevant to its antecedents. For instance, the assertion remains the same whether it be written or spoken.

Similarity I have translated as *functional equivalence* because I cannot conceive of any other good meaning for similarity in this context. Two neural processes would be similar in their relation to report to the degree in which they are interchangeable with respect to the same report, but I should offer no objection to a translation in terms of differentiation: "differentiation between reports is not greater than the differentiation between the neural events upon which they depend."

The third axiom becomes, with Müller on the left and me on the right:

3*a*. If the changes through which a sensation passes have the same direction, or if the differences which exist between series of given sensations are of like direction, then the changes through which the psychophysical process passes or the differences of the given psychophysical processes have like direction.

3*a*. If the direction of two 'sensory' changes is asserted to have been the same, then the two changes in the antecedent neural events must have been alike in some respect, since they are equivalent in giving rise to the assertion.

3*b*. Moreover, if a sensation is variable in *n* directions, then the psychophysical process lying at the basis of it must also be variable in *n* directions, and conversely.

3*b*. Moreover, if a 'sensation' is reported as variable at different times in *n* different ways, then there must have been *n* different modes of variation of the antecedent neural events; but the converse is not true, for different modes of neural variation may be equivalent in giving rise to the same assertion.

Axiom 3*a* applies to the single attributive dimension, like the pitch of tones. Such a dimension is continuous because different distances on it can be equated: one pitch difference can be made equal to another pitch difference in another part of the scale. In other words, two neural differentiations are equivalent for the same report, but there is no necessity for their being alike in any other way. It is not impossible, as some of Wever's (Wever, 1933, 422–424; Wever & Bray, 1937, 108–110) work seems to suggest, that difference in neural frequency should be the condition for a report of the difference between low pitches, and a difference in particular fibers excited the condition for a report of difference between high pitches; yet, if such a situation were to exist, it would mean that a frequency difference had become equivalent to a place difference since the two differences would be functionally equivalent for report. Ordinarily, of course, we expect neural similarity for identical reports; we expect that the antecedents of visual extension must have a great deal in common with the antecedents of tonal volume, because the observer, knowing first about visual size, can immediately begin to pass judgment upon tonal size. There is, however, no necessity for such an inference, and an equivalence could be learned.

Axiom 3*b* takes care of different attributes, like the pitch, loudness, volume and density of tones (Stevens & Davis, 1938, 70–75, 123–127, 160–166). Since these four attributes are distinct, there must, at the very least, be four modes of neural variation to account for them. You could not get Stevens' isophonic contours for them unless there were at least four neural continua in each of which different distances are functionally equivalent for report, and in no two of which differences equivalent for report are to be found. (This statement has nothing to do with the question as to whether an attributive continuum depends upon the innate properties of the nervous system or is acquired by learning,[6] as some have thought tonal volume might be, nor with the fact that the four continua are interrelated so that any values of two ought to predict the values of the other two.) Axiom 3*b* is not reversible for the reason discussed under axiom 3*a*.

That is all. Is there a moral? Perhaps. One sees here why psychoneural isomorphism as an axiom is so convincing. The principle is based on the simple assumption that one can not talk (or make an assertion) without a nervous system whose functioning is antecedent to the talking. One sees too, I suggest, that no great pother need be stirred up because of the rejection of positivism by the Gestalt psychologists. They do not have to be positivistic if they do not want to be, and they can be translated when there is need. The process is bound, nevertheless, to be clarifying and is sometimes corrective, as when a *conversely* of Müller's turns out not to be true, but in general any clear dualistic statement implies the operations upon which it depends, and he who reads may work the operations out and then rest secure with whatever degree of specification he has thus achieved.

NOTES

1. Müller (1896, 5) also gives the relevant references to some of the other pioneers in the 'new' psychology who had expressed themselves on this matter: Lotze, Fechner, Mach and Hering. Mach (1865) laid down a 'heuristic principle' like Müller's axioms: "To every psychical there corresponds a physical and conversely. To like psychical processes there correspond like physical, and to unlike unlike."
2. The fourth axiom laid down the distinction between intensive attributive series (with zero at one end of the scale) and qualitative attributive series (with no zero at either end of the scale). The fifth axiom was concerned with the production of intermediates by the mixture of two extreme processes.
3. *Cortical gray* is a familiar example of Müller's use of the axioms. Having established the system of colors without an absolute zero but with every color being some degree of black or white, blue or yellow, and green or red added to a constant gray, he inferred the existence of some constant cortical process which would account for the constant gray.

   An early example of the same kind of a priori logic is to be found in Grassmann's establishment of Newton's law of complementaries in 1853. Newton had formulated the law in 1704, but he was not sure that it held so exactly that only two complementaries, mixed in the right proportion, would give gray. They seemed in practice to yield 'a faint anonymous color' near gray, and Newton wondered whether a 'pure' gray might not require more than two colors in the mixture. Helmholtz in 1852 tried superposing two square spectra at right angles, thus giving an illuminated square in which every possible paired mixture of monochromatic lights was represented at some point. The locus of complementaries in such a diagram ought to appear as two curves of gray, but Helmholtz could be certain only of the two blue-and-yellow points. Then Grassmann (1853), a mathematician, laid down the principle that a continuous change of stimulus must give rise to a continuous change of sensation, that stimulus intermediates must give rise to sensory intermediates, and thus that there must be for every color one other color which, when mixed with the first in the right proportions, will give gray, because poorly saturated colors on all sides of gray can be got by paired mixtures, and this axiom of correlated continuities thus fixes the locus of an intermediate mixture which will give an exact gray. This is a case where logic was accepted by everyone, including Helmholtz when observation had proved inadequate. Of course Grassmann's isomorphism lay between sensation and stimulus, Müller's between sensation and physiological process.

4. I am using the words *positivism* and *operationism* (and their derivatives) in the sense that I understand the *positivism* to which Köhler and Koffka object in psychology, as signifying an operational reduction of phenomenal data to other data which are not distinguishable from what have been called physical data. *Cf.* K. Koffka (1935, esp. 684 f.); Köhler (1938, esp. vii). In this sense I am by temperament a positivist, a reductionist. Carnap's logical positivism is something more specific.

5. Köhler (1929, 67), "*If to me, my language is an adequate 'symbol' for my own direct experience, it is an objective symbol for those physiological processes at the same time.* . . . It does not matter very much whether I take it as a symbol for one or the other, since in the respects in which they correspond, there is no difference between them."

6. On the contention that there is theoretically no limit to the possible number of attributes and that the existence of an attributive dimension does not indicate whether it is native to the organism or acquired by learning, see E. G. Boring, The relation of the attributes of sensation to the dimensions of the stimulus (1935).

The Use of Operational

Definitions in Science

𝔊𝔊𝔊𝔊𝔊𝔊𝔊𝔊𝔊𝔊𝔊𝔊𝔊𝔊𝔊𝔊𝔊𝔊𝔊𝔊𝔊 1945

1. (a) *What is the purpose of operational definitions? When are they called for?*

Since it is obviously impossible to explicate an operational definition for every construct-term used in scientific discussion, there must be some principle which determines when operational definitions are useful.

Ans. The primary advantage of operational definitions lies in the unification of science and the resolution of controversy. The purpose of science is the simplification of our knowledge of nature under a set of broad generalizations, and the simplification is greatest when laws are stated in a single language, which inevitably turns out to be "physicalistic." Scientific controversy seldom involves disagreement about the observed primary data. It occurs usually in connection with the interpretation of the data, arising on the occasion of the validation of concepts or because of the ambiguity of meaning of conceptual entities. Positivistic procedures force such concepts and entities back to their observational bases and thus out of the realm of disagreement.

1. (b) *Logically, operational definitions could form an infinite regress, since the construct-terms used in describing an operation are themselves in need of definition.*

How is this regress limited in scientific practice?

Ans. When a speaker's statement is not clear to a hearer, it is always fair for the hearer to ask the speaker for an operational definition of the terms he has used. Since the operational definition introduces new conceptual terms,

Reprinted with permission from *The Psychological Review*, 1945, **52**, No. 5. This paper represents Boring's answers to a series of questions which he himself proposed in organizing *The Psychological Review*'s 1945, "Symposium on Operationism." The other participants were P. W. Bridgman, Herbert Feigl, Harold Israel, C. C. Pratt, and B. F. Skinner.

a regress is begun, one which may be infinite. This regress is not, however, embarrassing, for it can be terminated as soon as there is mutual understanding between the speaker and the hearer, as soon as there is no further demand for definition. Such closure may, however, always be opened again when a new hearer enters the discussion.

2. *When the same construct is defined by two independent operations, should it be said that there are really two constructs? For instance, it has been said that tape-measured distance and triangulated distance are really two kinds of distance and should perhaps have different names.*

Against this view it can be argued that these are operations for showing the equivalence of operations, e.g., for demonstrating the identity of taped and surveyed short distances.

Ans. A concept like *distance* requires operational definition, but it is possible to identify two operations in terms of further operations. There are operations which establish the equivalence of triangulated and tape-measured distances when they are of terrestial magnitudes, so that one can for short distances speak of *distance* and mean either or both operations. Such equivalences are, however, valid only within the probable error and limits of the operations involved, and are subject to the dubiety of interpolation, extrapolation and inferential inadequacy. Nevertheless, it is only by such processes that one passes from the particulars of specific operations to the most useful larger generalizations.

3. *(a) Are hypothetical operations which are physically impossible with present available techniques of scientific use? Is the other side of the moon what you would see if you went there?*

It is arguable that an unperformable operation has value in stating the conditions by which a construct could be validated. Such a statement shows that the construct is not at the moment valid.

Ans. Bridgman has shown that the concept of absolute quality for hue is a pseudoproblem, since one hue can be defined only in its relations to others. It is, however, possible to define the principal hues relativistically by discrimination. Principal green is the hue that is greener than any other hue, greener than any yellow-green, greener than any blue-green. One could conceivably find out whether certain animals perceive principal hues and how many. It is not certain, however, whether these techniques of discrimination are practicable with animals. They have never been developed. Still principal hues for an animal can be given such an operational meaning. They are defined by the system of discriminations which would be found *if* such experiments proved practicable.

3. *(b) Is there a use for hypothetical operations that would define constructs which are actually at the moment nonexistent?*

Red and green are supposed to be derived from yellow in the course of evolution. The discriminatory operations which would establish the existence of two new colors, derived similarly from blue, could be stated, although they could not be performed at the present stage of evolutionary development. The operations which would define a new invisible planet are similar.

Ans. Similarly there is statable and operational definition for principal hues in respect of an animal that turns out eventually not to perceive principal hues—unattainable operations which define a nonexistent entity. The operations can also be laid down that would define the next pairs of hues to develop in human evolution, the pair that would have the relation to blue that red and green have to yellow.

3. (c) *Is there a use for hypothetical operations which could never be performed?*

The definition of infinity depends on operations which can never be completed.

Ans. Such statements of hypothetical operations tend to clarify the understanding of analogous operations that can be performed with positive results and also to suggest research.

4. *Is* experience *a proper construct for operational definition?*

It has been held that experience is ultimate, subject to immediate intuition but not to operational definition.

Ans. *Experience* and all the "subjective" entities are as much in need of operational definition as are any other scientific concepts, or are more so because of their equivocality. To say that *experience* reduces operationally to *discrimination,* meaning that discrimination is itself differential reaction, statable, when not private, in physical terms, is to bring experience within the universe of scientific experimentation and psychology within the unity of the sciences.

5. *Are there scientifically good and bad operations, and how are operations evaluated if they differ in value?*

Objectivists hold that the data of experience can always be operationally defined if the data become public, because the operations of publication define the datum. It is, however, argued further that the operations of verbal report are "poorer" than the operations of discriminatory choice (C.R.; jumping stand) because the verbal response itself involves terms that are less rigorously defined.

Ans. Operations can be good or poor. Operations that bring scientific concepts into relations with larger systems of generalization tend toward the unification of science, are the most productive definitions, and as such are better than more isolated operations. Thus operations that depend on the distinction between the meaning of the words *verbal* and *non-verbal* are poor, because one wants at once the definition of a *word*. If one defines a word as a symbolic or vicarious entity to which a subject reacts as he would to the equivalent referent which the word symbolizes, then one has a better, less mystic definition, even though it then be found that animals and even inamimate objects 'understand words.' The test of goodness of an operation is its univocality.

6. *Is operationism more than a renewed and refined emphasis upon the experimental method (as understood already by Galileo, if not even by Archimedes)—i.e., a formulation of modern scientific empiricism and pragmatism (especially of the Peirce-Dewey variety), mainly of criteria of factual meaningfulness and empirical validity?*

Ans. All positivism from Mach to Bridgman has stressed the advantage for clarity of reducing dubious concepts to empirical ultimates—either to the data of observation (Mach) or to the processes of observation (Bridgman). Operationism is, however, something more than experimentation because it aims, not at the pluralism of particular experiments, but at the unification of science in the most general system of terms available. The effort to lay down operational definitions has the effect of influencing experimentation toward the attack upon the more significant problems.

7. *Must operationists in psychology relegate theorizing of all sorts to the limbo of metaphysics? Bridgman in physics is perfectly aware of the value of theories as long as they are in keeping with his operational requirements. The Gestaltists, particularly Köhler and Koffka, have repeatedly attacked positivism (an identical twin of operationism), reproaching it for its (alleged) opposition to theoretical construction. C. C. Pratt (1948, 147–154) on the basis of his operationism maintains that all theoretical explanation is circular or tautological. Köhler (1940, 107–125) holds a strictly opposite view. Which position is the most adequate for psychological research?*

Ans. Every scientific datum is public. Science does not consider private data. If a datum is public, the operation of its publication is statable. There can be no scientific data that can not be operationally defined. On the other hand, the meeting of the demand for clarification by operational definition takes time and thought. Not all scientists wish to spend their energies in this way. Gestalt psychologists prefer to depend on the adequacy of a free use of language to establish satisfactory communication. They should not be coerced into greater precision of language. Let the operationists state their operations for them or puzzle them out, while the Gestaltists are left free to discover what their trust in less rigorous language will achieve scientifically.

There can, of course, be private operational definitions. A deaf and dumb man on an uninhabited atoll might make them and use them. They would still be likely to have the form of self-communication, but their terms might not always be "physicalistic."

8. *Some radical operationists assert that the meaning of a quantitative concept lies exclusively in the set of measuring operations which determine the application of the concept. (E.g.: "Intelligence is what the intelligence test tests.") But how can we then know what it is that we are after in constructing tests; and what possible meaning is there in talking about improving or revising tests and measurements if there are no criteria outside the chosen test methods?*

Ans. Operationism is not opposed to the validation or extension of a concept. If intelligence is what the tests test, it is still possible to ask whether what the tests test is neural speed or normal education or something else. If it should turn out to be normal education, then you have two equated operations for the same entity. (See my answer to question 2 supra.)

9. *Are all scientifically legitimate definitions operational in character? This is (at least in part) a terminological question, but certainly one that it would pay to settle (not only) among psychologists.*

Ans. Since science is empirical and excludes private data, all of its concepts must be capable of operational definition. *Mental energy* is an example of a concept that usually lacks operational definition, although of course it could be given one in each context in which the term is used. *General ability* has a clear operational definition in terms of the correlational matrix from which it is derived. The *supernormal phenomena* of psychic research have many particular operational definitions, but the general definition is poor because it is negative, because it defines *supernormal* as ignorance of the relation of the phenomenon to other known systems.

10. *What is a definition, operational or otherwise? It is important to know whether one is presupposing a logical apparatus for dealing with the language of science or intending through a psychological analysis to justify such an apparatus.*

Ans. A definition is a statement of equivalence. A term is defined when it is pronounced the equivalent of other terms or events. Not all definitions are operational, but the most rigorous definitions are. Non-operational definitions are apt to be statements of synonyms. See any dictionary.

11. *For the purpose of operational definition, what class or classes of events may be used properly as defining-operations? Specifically, can a phenomenon be identified or its properties be defined in terms of the events (operations) which are effective to produce, or occur as results of, the phenomenon?*

Ans. A phenomenon can be identified in terms of its antecedent or consequent phenomena if the correlation is symmetrical and perfect. No operational definition inheres, however, in the mere statement of such equivalence, but the statement cannot be made rigorously unless the operational definitions of both terms are statable. If they can be stated and the correlation is found to exist, then the equivalence of the two operations is established. (See my answer to question 2 supra.) Is *hearing a tone* equivalent to *excitation of the temporal cortex?* You need the operations for hearing a tone and for excitation of the cortex and also the observation to establish the equivalence of the two. On the other hand, is the *super-ego* equivalent to *conscience?* That is a matter of a priori definition, and one may choose to define *conscience* as *super-ego*, furnishing an operational definition of the *super-ego*. Only if one has an independent operational definition for *conscience* can the question of empirical correlation be raised or answered.

Rejoinders and Second Thoughts

Let me first comment on the other five initial contributions to this symposium.

Feigl (1945) seems to me to be the expert as well as the clear simple expositor. With him I can go along with no serious dissent. Several times my notes on his paragraphs remark: "Better than I could have said it." Twice he seems to contradict one of my statements (regress of operations vs. ultimate ostensive definitions; limitation of scientific definitions to empirical ones), but the ground for the difference is either practical (concerned with what actually happens) or semantic (turning on what the term *science* should include).

Bridgman (1945) I am also able to follow with approval except in part of what he has to remark about discrimination. On certain other matters he has said exactly what I hoped he would say in answer to some of these questions. I believe, however, that a few of my colleagues will think that he has in his present thought modified his more extreme position about the pluralism of constructs which he held in *The Logic of Modern Physics*. After all that book is eighteen years old and Bridgman might be expected to develop his thinking in a couple of decades.

Pratt! (1945) I do not know what to say about him. He directs his incisive invective against values that I believe I am prepared to defend, and then he ends up with conclusions that seem perfect to me and beautifully formulated. For instance, he does not want operational definitions of *experience* because they are impossible, whereas I have been arguing that psychology needs operational definitions of *experience* more than of anything else, because *experience* is such a vague and perpetually misunderstood term in psychological nomenclature. But then it seems to turn out that Pratt and I are in agreement, for it is only *immutably private experience* for which he refuses an operational definition, and even I am not asking for means to publicize the immutably private. We must perforce ignore the immutably private, and Pratt is with me in consigning its definition to metaphysics and enjoining science to ignore experience which is not publishable.

Skinner (1945) is full of his unpublished book and that makes difficulty. He can not get away from the complexities in which his thought is now at home, nor present them fully in the space at his disposal. Again and again I want the referents for his terms. Can many of us be sure what is meant by the sentence: "A verbal community which has no access to a private stimulus may generate verbal behavior in response to it"? In general, I think I follow Skinner, who has limited himself to a discussion of how operationally privacy may be invaded, and agree with him. But he scares me. He has probably implied something that I missed.

Israel (1945) would seem to be the only one of the six of us who is, if one dare put it so clumsily, against operationism. He was, of course, the *casus belli* of this symposium. The rest of us may not like the word operation*ism* or want to be called operation*ists*, but we all agree that operational analysis and definition are scientifically important and that psychology needs them. I shall, therefore, return presently to Israel on equivalence of operations and on purposive behavior.

1. *Empirical Operations.* Feigl (1945) makes the valid point that there are practical reasons for considering in science only the empirical operations, even while admitting that logic and mathematics may also have their defining operations. On the other hand, Skinner (1945) is certainly correct in noting that to the basic observations must be added the manipulative and calculational procedures and the logical and mathematical steps that intervene between statements (and, as he says, "*nothing else*").

2. *Ostensive Definitions.* To what I have said about the regression of operations until social agreement is reached should be added Feigl's point that the regress tends to converge upon simpler as well as more generally understood terms, and that the ostensive definition thus in practice provides a limit to the regress, just as it also provides the beginning of meaning in the genesis of the acquisition of language.

3. *Equivalence of Operations and the Singularity of Constructs.* Israel (1945) objects to operationism because it breeds a plurality of definitions which, being independent, prevent scientific generalization into constructs. He quotes the Bridgman of 1927: "The concept of length involves as much as and nothing more than the set of operations by which length is determined." Israel believes in the need for general constructs and thinks that operationism is against them. He finds operationism inconsistent in the way it slips from particular operations to absolute constructs. Pratt (1945) is dealing with this same point when he discusses the circularity of operational definition and holds that it does not sterilize the construct. Bridgman (1945) himself makes, I think, the correct rejoinder in his reply to *Question* 2 and even better in his reply to *Question* 11. He even says: "Operational definitions . . . are in practice without significance unless the situations to which they are applied are sufficiently developed so that at least two methods are known of getting to the

terminus." Feigl (1945) also seems to me properly to explicate this matter in his reply to *Questions 8, 2,* and *11.* The essence of science lies in generalization and you can not go far in generalization without the use of the generalized abstractions which we call *constructs.* If the operationists had thought that operational analysis would prevent generalization, they would soon have abandoned the sterile pluralistic chaos that would have resulted.

4. *Circularity.* I have the impression that Pratt (1945), in his tilt with Köhler on circularity, does insufficient justice to the equivalence of operations because he does not fully appreciate the symmetry of his astronomical example. Neptune is the observed-and-calculated perturbations of Uranus. Neptune also is the observed speck of light in the telescope. Pratt thinks that the first Neptune was an hypothesis until it was explained by the second Neptune, the speck of light. It seems to me that such logic is reversible, that Neptune is also an hypothesis for the speck of light, one which is explained (re-enforced) by Uranus' perturbations. A planet is a whole lot more than a speck of light. You can not really see a construct like a planet in "direct experience." You can see a speck of light at a given time and place with a telescope to help you. You can see a perturbation (on the paper on your desk) with enough calculations to help you.

5. *Verbal Communication As an Operation.* Both Bridgman (1945) and Pratt (1945) object to the status of ultimacy that Stevens assigns to discrimination when the defining operations for experience are being laid down. Bridgman (1945) says that "the discriminatory response is conditioned by the cultural background of the subject," and that such analysis, involving the use of words, is suspect because not all the terms in the operation are known. Just so. To formulate operations in which some of the terms are words, not the physical data of words but the meanings of words, is a risky business and likely to undo the value of all the operational effort. It is for this reason that Skinner (1945) has tried to give us an operational account of how words work and mean in the sample situation of a response to a private stimulus. Skinner is thus anticipating Bridgman's point by indicating how culture actually can be taken into account.

I myself would press Bridgman's point against Allport's dislike of an operational definition of *similarity.* No psychologist can, of course, talk about similarity without making the similarity public (if it was not already public) and the operation of publication is presumably determinable. To object to an operational definition of *similarity* would seem to be merely that you are relying on the identity of meaning for the word *similar* when different people use it. A better operational definition for *similarity* can be formulated, I think, in terms of equivalence or functional substitutability.

It is for this reason that animal experiments are likely to be more clearly formulated than human experiments. Human subjects so often use words, and words need to be defined. The animals also use words, but they are the words of discriminatory response, the words whose history in conditioning performed within the experimental setting fixes their meaning, to the animal and to the experimenter. Bridgman is skeptical of volume, as an attribute of tone separate from pitch and loudness, because the discriminations that are used to get the experimental uniformities depend on the meaning of *volume* and other related spatial words. To some extent I agree with him. If I could get rats consistently to discriminate tonal volume or anything that is the kind of joint function of frequency and intensity that tonal volume is, then I should be much happier about the status of tonal volume.

No one has ever found out whether any hue-perceiving animal other than man perceives principal colors, but it is invaluable to know how that animal experiment could be performed, as I have indicated in my answer to *Question 3(a)*. To avoid the use of such word-meanings as *pure* and *simple* as applied to colors and to substitute a system of discriminations as defining the meaning of a principal hue is to gain greatly in the precision of the operations employed.

6. *Privacy.* Pratt (1945) argues about the privacy of experience. Of course, any atom of existence in the first moment of its being is private to itself before it has come into relation with other atoms. Similarly any event so long as it affects only a single person is private to that person. There is no question about the possible privacy of ultimately scientific data. The point is that science habitually deals with these published privacies, and a privacy that is inherently unpublishable is unknowable (in any rich cognitive sense of *knowable*) and not material for science. It is the immutably private that has no value for psychology or for any science.

This fact means, incidentally, that any datum that has come into psychology must have inherent in it the potentiality of publication and that in itself often adds to our knowledge of the datum, tells us, for instance, something about the relation of brain events to final efferent paths of publication. No one who has learned this lesson is going to be found correlating a datum of "experience" with an isolated neural event occurring in a particular brain spot at a particular instant.

7. *Purposive Behavior.* Israel's (1945) second objection to operationism is that it will not, he thinks, handle the definition of *purpose*, a construct which he regards as essential in psychology. He seems to think of purpose as somehow connected with wholes, but of course the operations defining wholes are just as statable as the operations defining elements. But purpose—what is the positivistic account of purpose? Years ago a purpose used to be thought of as a final cause, a way in which the future attracts the present into itself, a sort of temporal suction. Nowadays the goal becomes a drive, the future runs around into the past and pushes the present into the future. Purposes no longer pull; they push, like causes. There is, however, no difficulty about setting up operational definitions of vectors, drives and needs; and, unless one

has operational definitions for these dynamic constructs, one is likely to get into trouble with the ambiguity of words. Note what Skinner says about the different meanings of "I am hungry."

It is not impossible that someone may sometime do better with the operational definition of purpose by regarding purpose as the symmetrical opposite of cause, and then noting what purposes correspond in reversed time to the correlations that represent necessary causes and sufficient causes. I throw this out as a suggestion for a positivistic account of purpose, one which does not involve the verbal expression of previously private intuition of intention. The working out of the details turn out, however, to be more involved than one might expect.

In *conclusion* let me say that this symposium has strengthened my faith in operationism immeasurably because of the essential agreements that run through accounts that diverge in detail. I am almost ready to think that operationism is entitled to its *ism* as long as it continues to meet with opposition. An *ism* is a weapon which is always discarded when opposition ceases.

The Role of Theory in
Experimental Psychology

ꕤꕤꕤꕤꕤꕤꕤꕤꕤꕤꕤꕤꕤꕤꕤꕤꕤ   1953

THE dedication of a great new psychological laboratory turns the mind back upon the history of experimental psychology, and how the need for separate laboratories arose, and how the business of laboratory founding prospered and continued in the 1880s and 1890s, first in Germany, begun by Wundt's new Psychologisches Institut at Leipzig in 1879, and then in America—only four years later, mind you—by G. Stanley Hall's new Psychological Laboratory at Hopkins in 1883, exactly seventy years ago.

The early psychological experiments were for the most part sensory. For the first two-thirds of the nineteenth century experimental psychology, such as it was, went on in physiological laboratories. The course of development of interest was: physiology, the nervous system, sensory nerves, sensation. The alternative would have been: nervous system, motor nerves, movement, behavior, conduct, ending up with discriminatory response instead of sensation, but history chose the former, not the latter course by which to reach the present. This early special concern with sensation was promoted by philosophy which in the eighteenth century accepted empiricism, with sensation as the avenue of communication between the mind and the outer world. So it came about that from 1800 to 1850, say, systematic psychology belonged to the philosophers, the empiricists and associationists among them, while experimental psychology was practiced by certain physiologists. After that, ostensibly under Wundt's influence but perhaps more as an inevitable sequence in the *Zeitgeist*, the German philosophers took over the experiments, founded the laboratories, and developed experimental psychology, properly named *physiological psychology* in accordance with its lineage, under the aegis of philosophy.

Reprinted with permission from *The American Journal of Psychology*, 1953, **66**, 169–184. An address delivered at the dedication of Mezes Hall at The University of Texas on April 1, 1953. Professor Boring represented The Society of Experimental Psychologists which held its 1953 meetings, as part of the dedication, at The University of Texas.

It was William James who made America conscious of the new German movement, and very soon America was following close behind Germany in its practice of psychological experimentation, although always at first with its eye on German leadership. By the end of 1892 there were fourteen laboratories of experimental psychology in America, and by 1898 there were twenty-four, the latest being the laboratory at the University of Texas (Ruckmick, 1912, esp. 520).

The Germans continued the liaison of experimental psychology with philosophy, and in 1905, when Emerson Hall was dedicated at Harvard, Wundt wrote Münsterberg (1906, esp. 31) congratulating him that the new laboratory was still to be affiliated with philosophy and not to "migrate to the naturalists." Most of the leaders of the new psychology in America, however—nearly all but James, Münsterberg and Ladd—sought for psychology's emancipation. Cattell and Titchener, poles apart on most matters, were agreed on this, and gradually the departments of philosophy and psychology got separated, though Harvard's psychological laboratory moved out of the philosophers' building only in 1945 and Texas has now built a new laboratory and taken its philosophers in.

While the adolescent new psychology was seeking emancipation from its parent, it was also exhibiting its inheritance. The talk in the new laboratories turned on theories and systems. All the new textbooks followed the pattern of Wundt's systematic *Physiologische Psychologie*. The word *system* then meant two different things: coverage and consistency. The texts tried to treat of every chapter known to be proper to psychology, but they also tried to create a definition of psychology and to remain epistemologically true to it. The later systems of this sort were Titchener's in 1910, Watson's in 1919, and McDougall's in 1923. Withal there was an increasing effort to avoid epistemological discussion and elaborate theorizing and to get down to concrete fact, with the uncontroversial standard textbook of physics as a model. In 1935 two colleagues and I, thinking that the victory of fact over theory was at last ready to be consummated, blithely published a textbook, written by a congeries of experts, and called it *Psychology: A Factual Textbook*, meaning to leave out all controversy and speculative theory and to give the students only the depersonalized facts of psychology as they had been accumulated in the new science. We managed pretty well as to coverage and depersonalization, but the *Zeitgeist* was against us, and I think now, a mere twenty years later, that I was insufficiently aware of the true nature of science, as I shall describe it in the exegesis that follows.

In the 1930s the systems changed. They became set less on coverage and more on consistency. It was Tolman's *Purposive Behavior in Animals and Men* in 1932 which initiated the new trend. Interest shifted to learning and then expanded to include action. Tolman (not unlike Jennings in 1904) was able to see in behavior such new phenomena as purpose, phenomena that thitherto had been regarded as conscious. In 1936 he introduced into systematic thinking the "intervening variables," new concepts to replace the now obsolete mental processes. Hull, with a belief in the power of formal logic, also became interested in learning and behavior. His latest, and, alas, his last contribution is his posthumous *A Behavior System* of 1952. Tolman and Hull did not always agree and they both inspired disciples, some of them now distinguished in their own right. Others came in. Soon the social psychologists were trying to create systems for their special subject matters. At the present time you can find laboratories where concern with theory and systems is so great that the divorce from philosophical heritage seems little greater than it was fifty years ago.[1] Is that wrong? Or, in view of what has happened to theoretical physics since relativity theory took hold of it, may it be good?

There are indeed other laboratories where theorizing with hypothetical concepts and the building of systems is regarded with strong disapproval. The new fury of theories, say these single-minded experimentalists, is a regression, taking us back into the slough from which we have just struggled. Are these critics right? What are we to think?

Because there is this uncertainty, I ask you now to inventory psychological and scientific theories with me. Let us see what kinds there are and what rôles they play in experimental science and especially in psychology; yet first let me lay down a basic dictum which my exposition should eventually justify. It is this. *The hypothetical constructs pervade science. They are the stuff of which it is made. The difference between being theoretical and empirical is mostly a question of how far the process of reification of the constructs has progressed.* Now to our list.

(1) *Theories with no evidence.* Let us begin at one extreme by observing that there are theories that have no empirical basis whatsoever. Any mystic can dream up such a theory, but the pressure of western culture is so great nowadays that he is almost bound to find some rationalizing evidence for it. It then becomes difficult to say whether the evidence produced the theory or the theory the evidence. Thus I may perhaps be forgiven for once again ushering onto the stage those hard-worked stooges of philosophic interpretation, the rustic empiricist and the rustic rationalist, who for the first time saw a real elephant. The empiricist said (as surely everybody now knows): "Gee, I always thought elephants were yellow; what's the use of thinking anyhow?" And the rationalist said: "Hell, there ain't no such animal!" There you have two theories formed without evidence, the theory of yellow elephants, and a general taxonomic theory that precludes the existence of an elephant.

(2) *Theories with rationalized support.* Very close to these unfounded theories are theories which are strongly held but in which the evidence is scanty and seems, at least in part, to have been dug up as rationalization. Voliva supported his theory of the flat earth by a photograph of twelve miles

of the shore line of Lake Winnebago: you could see, he argued, that the shore is horizontal and not bowed. There have been many theories that the earth is hollow, and Teed's view that not only is it hollow but that we live on the inside he supported with evidence as well as invective against the bigoted scientists who would not accept his theory. Animal magnetism grew out of astrology with little empirical basis, but think how much evidence for it was being adduced when it got into Mesmer's hands (Boring, 1950a, 116–123, 130 f.). Anyone who has examined Velikovsky's *Worlds in Collision* knows how packed with evidence and argument that book is. These men qualify as cranks since they show a paranoid strain when their enthusiasm is rejected or ignored by orthodoxy (Gardner, 1952). Does the great Goethe also belong here with his brilliant and preposterous arguing through two decades and two volumes that Newton was wrong on the basic theory of color mixture and that his own inadequate theory should be substituted? (Boring, 1942, 112–116, 123 f.).

(3) *Theories with insufficient evidence.* There are also the theories that are based on insufficient evidence and are entertained with but a low level of confidence. This group contains the plausible suggestions in addition to theories once strongly held but now on the way out. Take the theory of recapitulation, the conception that man in his development recapitulates his phylogenetic history, morphologically in the embryo and also psychologically in the neonate and the child. Haeckel and Spencer originated this theory, but it was Stanley Hall who held most specifically that the child's life echoes his phylogenesis, showing both aquatic and arboreal reverberations. This theory Hall entertained gladly but without too great certainty. There was evidence for it but the evidence was not controlled (Boring, 1950c, 268–298, esp. 279–282). Hering's theory of color vision, vigorously enough defended when it was new in the 1870s, was still held at the beginning of the present century, held in spite of such contradictions as the failure of primary green and primary red to appear to be complementary, held weakly by those who found no better theory to displace it. Here we meet up with J. B. Conant's (1947, 84 et passim) principle of the horror vacui for scientific theories: an established theory is not displaced by contradictory facts but continues in use until there is a better theory to supplant it.

(4) *Hypotheses that cannot be tested.* In the modern design of experiments it is customary to form hypotheses which can be tested by experiment. The hypothesis is derived by intuition or induction from observations or experiments. The tests consist of experiments which verify or fail to verify a particular difference that has been deduced from the hypothesis and is thus predicted by the hypothesis. Such hypotheses are, in the broad sense of our present usage, theories—theories to be confirmed or discarded or kept around for future test.

Now among these hypotheses are those that can be formulated but not tested. Mostly the reason for the inscrutability of such hypotheses lies in the fact that they contain terms for which there are, or seem to be, no available observational operations, terms which therefore lack practicable operational definitions. An example is McDougall's (1908) drainage theory of attention which assumes a limited amount of cortical energy ('neurokyme') that can be displaced in the cerebral cortex as attention moves from one focal object to another. This theory was attempting a physiological explanation of the limited range of attention, of the fact that attention to one thing always requires the drainage of attention from others; but there was, when this theory had its vogue, no operational definition of neurokyme. Bridgman (1927, 3–31) might therefore have called the concept meaningless; nevertheless cortical energy could have been defined as concentration of electrical potential, and the operations for observing the degree and locus of such a concentration could have been specified even though they could not then be applied to the brain. (Similarly it has been argued that the other side of the moon does not exist because it can never be seen.) In the same way, it could have been said that Köhler's psychocerebral theory of isomorphism was meaningless because there was no way of observing electrical concentration of charge on the brain; but now Köhler (1952) has discovered a method. (And similarly some day a human being might see the other side of the moon from a space ship.) It would, in my opinion, be a mistake to exclude from science concepts with operational definitions in which the operations appear to be impossible. Sometimes the operations become possible with new discovery of techniques. Sometimes they can be approximated.

As psychology turns more and more to the use of statistical concepts in its theories, it finds itself relying more and more upon operations which are not literally possible, because the probability concepts of statistics have an infinite dimension which can not be realized in practicable observation. If an event in a series has a probability of p, the theory asserts that the frequency of the occurrence of the event will converge upon p as the number of occasions increases; yet no observed frequency can ever disprove this theory because convergence is asserted only for an infinite number of cases (Boring, 1941). All use of probability theory as scientific model suffers from this disability.

Is the case then different with Bohr's principle of complementarity (which includes Heisenberg's principle of uncertainty), the principle that certain values in quantum mechanics, like the momentum and position of an electron can never be observed for exactly the same moment? Bohr thinks that we must agree that two complementaries that cannot be observed simultaneously also cannot exist simultaneously, and Bridgman should agree with him. Einstein, on the other hand, thinks the two exist simultaneously although they can not be observed together (Hutten, 1943). Modern physics moves toward Bohr's view, but the psychologist, accustomed to meeting up with so many useful unobservable concepts, may find himself inclined to linger with Einstein.[2]

(5) *Hypotheses that can be tested.* When an hypothesis gets confirmed, however, it becomes a fact. These constitute our next class of theories: hypotheses that are confirmed, or are partly confirmed, or can be tested for confirmation if the necessary time and trouble are taken. Seventy-five years ago there was the pretty good theory that the functioning of the occipital lobes of the brain is essential for visual perception in man; now that theory is confirmed and a fact. At present there is another theory that patterns of retinal excitation correspond topologically to patterns of occipital excitation, but that theory still needs more confirmation as to detail. It is not quite yet a fact. W. H. Sheldon (1940; 1942) has a theory that relates tripolar patterns of temperament to tripolar patterns of body type. There seem to have been a number of gross approximations obtained for this theory, although with a good deal of variance and with the publication of much of the observation still lying in the future. Certainly this hypothesis is still just a theory on its way to becoming some kind of a fact. It is these still unconfirmed theories that attract attention and interest, but we shall do well to remember that every established fact is a relation and was a theory if it once existed unconfirmed in a tentative state.

(6) *Generalization as theory.* If a fact is a confirmed theory, then a scientific generalization is a theory. Let us take this matter back to its bare fundamentals. The question is sometimes raised as to when in history science began. Sarton (1952, 3–18) thinks science emerged with primitive man long, long before history was recorded, but in that he is, I think, much too conservative. Surely before man animals had scientific theories, generalizations about variable nature. Here I am suggesting, with the contributions of Gestalt psychology in mind, that an object is a theory about an invariance in ever changing and chaotic experience. Since size-constancy has been found for chickens and apes, it is plain that they know how to make the basic classifications of objects as to size, that they act in accordance with a theory of the invariance of objective size.

It follows, of course, that any Aristotelian classification is a theory and often a fact because it brings the classified item into relation with other items, thus transcending the particulars of observation as all theories must do. The Galileans, of course, are right about the next step in scientific sophistication, but you have to have generalization first. At this level the much snubbed faculty psychologists were right. It used to be said that to account for a memory by referring it to a faculty of memory is a meaningless tautology, but actually what you are doing here is to describe an event as a memory, thus classing it with other events and abstracting it from still others. The modern faculty psychologists who practice factor analysis engage in the same kind of description and claim rightly that a factor analysis is a theory, one which could become a fact (Pratt, 1929).

In brief, a generalized description is a theory. This meaning for the word *theory* is admitted by those who discuss the philosophy of science, although for the most part they prefer to limit the term to the more complex cases, the theories that exhibit the interrelations among abstract concepts. I am insisting on the broader meaning because I am arguing from continuity. I am saying that concepts are created by inductive generalization, that science is made up of confirmed relations among concepts, not among data, that theory is so pervasive that it penetrates even the observational instant, when the observer decides whether to classify his black-white perception as 10.7 or 10.8 on the ammeter scale.

(7) *Systematic classification as theory.* Thus we can pass at once to the theories that use systematic constructs as classificatory concepts for the data of immediate observation. In Titchener's laboratory at Cornell you used to learn to identify sensations in order to note their occurrences in your introspective reports. Later there was doubt whether you were really observing sensations or only their attributes. You would think the observer could tell the nature of what he observes, but, of course, he could not. He had to be trained in classification, which is what introspective training was (Boring, 1942, 22–25, 48 f.). It was the same in the Harvard Psychological Clinic twenty years later when they had invented for classification and communication a special set of terms for needs and other motivational concepts (Murray, 1938, 743–750). When you knew how to use the list, you could spot particular needs in protocols with relative ease, just as the psychoanalyst keeps seeing complexes to which the layman is blind. I remember how a professor of genetics many years ago showed me published drawings of cell nuclei dated both before and after the discovery and description of chromosomes. Chromosomes kept showing up in the later drawings, not in the earlier. In other words, microscopes do not reveal concepts until the concepts have been invented. The shape of a chromosome is as much a theory to the histologist as is the size of a grain of wheat to a chicken.

(8) *Descriptive theories.* Next come the theories that are more than generalizations and the classification of data as concepts and that stop short, nevertheless, of the introduction of new hypothetical concepts. These are descriptive theories, which describe not merely data and simple phenomena, but principally the functional relationships among data, relationships abstracted from phenomenal experience by the experimental method. Here is where Skinner, by his own vehement choice, comes in. His theories of behavior are the generalized functional relations, the curves plotted between time and cumulated responses, when reinforcement and extinction are introduced in accordance with particular experimental designs. Skinner (1950)

asks: "Are learning theories necessary?"; and he means: Is it necessary to go further to intervening variables and hypothetical constructs, after the manners of Tolman and Hull, in order to have a scientific knowledge of the facts of learning, or may one stand firmly on this positivistic base with the facts clear before him and almost no hypothetical superstructure at all? To these questions no categorical "yes" or "no" is possible. Skinner exhibits a great many important relationships in behavior and, standing closer to his data, he enjoys maximal security; yet this is not to say that learning theory could not conceivably advance further from the data. It might gain power by moving in Hull's direction, or, as Skinner himself suggests, rational equations might be discovered for some of these functions. Inevitably the terms of rational equations would require the creation of new theoretical parameters representing them. Otherwise the equations would not be rational. Skinner's position is sound and safe for the time being, yet I cannot imagine psychologists being content not to progress further if they can find stable concepts which eventually gain enough versatility to make them seem real—as electricity and atoms do now.

The preceding three cases, (6)–(8), and some instances of the still earlier ones delineate theories that are, in a sense, self-contained, that do not, in Skinner's phrase, appeal to a second dimensional system for explanation. These are the descriptive theories, the ones that are sometimes not called theories, the theories that Skinner is espousing when he asks "Are theories necessary?" There are also, however, the theories which are often called *explanatory*, in contradistinction to *descriptive*, the ones where the generalized data in one system are explained, as the phrase is, by terms in another system. The next five classes of theories, (9)–(13), are of this kind. It is with them that the current discussion of theoretical psychology is ordinarily concerned.

(9) *Analytical theories*. Of these correlational or parallelistic modes of explanation the best known is undoubtedly the explanation of the molar by reference to the molecular, or elementism, as it has been more often called. Water *is* H_2O. The whole is simply the sum of its parts. Chemistry got far with such theories, and first the associationists and then Wundt tried to do as well for psychology with a mental chemistry. Not so many now can recall the assured faith of the introspective elementists only fifty years ago. "The Elements of the Mental Life." "Sensation and Feeling as the Basic Forms of Psychic Elements." "The Structure of Sensory Ideas." "Intensive Ideational Connections." "Psychic Connections." So run the more atomistic of Wundt's chapter headings in his *Physiologische Psychologie* of 1902–1903. Yet the reflexologists were as elementistic as the introspectionists. John Dewey inveighed against this atomism of reflexes in his early preGestalt paper of 1896, and the Gestalt psychologists rejected Watson's behaviorism, along with Wundt's and Titchener's introspectionism, as not recognizing that the whole

is apt to be more than the sum of its parts; that is to say, to depend not only on the parts but also on the relations amongst them.

Analytical theories are still useful. The analysis of facial vision into component sensory clues most closely resembles old-fashioned mental chemistry (Supra et al., 1944; Worchel & Dallenbach, 1947; Cotzin & Dallenbach, 1950), but you have also in modern phrase the analysis of capacities and skills into primary mental abilities by factor analysis (Cattell, 1946; Thurstone, 1947), the analysis of discriminatory behavior into abstracted parts of the situation by the observation of transfers of training,[3] and the analysis of personality into traits, needs, abilities and factors in ways too numerous to detail. All that has happened to discountenance these analytical theories is the success of Gestalt psychology in impressing on psychologists the importance of field theory and the frequency with which simple disjunctive analysis fails adequately to explain the phenomenon under investigation.

(10) *Physiological theories.* Because psychophysical parallelism dominated nineteenth-century psychology, the more common kind of psychological theory has been the explanation of conscious events in terms of the nervous system. So Titchener (1910, 41) wrote: "The psychologist answers the question 'what' by analysing mental experience into its elements. He answers the question 'how' by formulating the laws of connection of these elements. And he answers the question 'why' by explaining mental processes in terms of their parallel processes in the nervous system." That triad of activities was set up as the goal of the new scientific psychology, which had been on this account called *physiological psychology:* (1) analysis, (2) synthesis, and (3) explanation in terms of the nervous system. Actually Titchener's system would have collapsed if he had had only conscious events to analyze and synthesize without the nervous system and the world of stimulus for underpinning. So we had in those days the Hering theory of vision and the Helmholtz theory of hearing to explain the observed sensory relationships of those two sense departments, and, if the physiology of these explanations seems now so speculative as to place the theories under our next classification, still we have today better physiology from Hecht and Békésy and others to fill this classical need. The establishment of sensory and motor centers in the brain was good psychophysiological theory, though it must be admitted that Lashley's theories of equipotentiality and mass action as cerebral theories for learning have stood up less precisely than he originally hoped. Nevertheless there exists today a great deal of good physiological fact whose correlation with psychological events is well established, and C. T. Morgan, later assisted by Stellar, has found enough of it to fill the greater part of a book (Morgan & Stellar, 1950). So, in spite of unrealized expectations, retracted assertions and great gaps that never were filled, there is actually today a large body of reliable fact that constitutes the physiology of psychology, the body of the physiological explanations of behavioral and conscious events.

(11) *Conceptual theories.* Skinner (1938, 421 f.) has remarked, undoubtedly with a gleam in his eye, that perhaps the term *CNS*, when it is used by psychologists, means Conceptual Nervous System. That is one of Skinner's contributions, his purging the organism of the pseudophysiology which psychophysical parallelism had forced upon psychology in the nineteenth century. Hering (Boring, 1942, 206–209, 218) did not know that there were three color substances in the retinal cones, each capable of undergoing a reversible reaction to provide a photochemical basis for each of six primary colors. His was merely an *als-ob* theory: *if* the eye worked in this fashion, *then* these perceptual laws would hold. The substances still needed to be validated by being discovered in some second way other than by observing the laws of color. G. E. Müller's cortical gray to explain the seventh primary color by molecular motion in the cells of the occiptal cortex (Boring, 1942, 213), and McDougall's (1908) cortical energy to explain the phenomena of the limited range of attention are similar physiological fictions. Perhaps Avenarius's System *C* is the best example of the hypothesization of physiological entities, for the System *C* was merely that part of the nervous system which is necessary for consciousness (Boring, 1950a, 396, 433). Avenarius did not know what part was necessary, yet he was sure that some part was necessary; so he named it, thus making a greater contribution to semantics than to neural anatomy. There have been many physiological theories of psychological events in which the physiological "facts" turned into concepts as a theory lost acceptability and became a description instead of a correlation.

While Skinner was rejecting the Conceptual Nervous System and sticking to honest description, Tolman was rejecting the Nervous System and keeping the Concepts (Tolman, 1936). It was his idea that you can deal with psychology in terms of stimulus and response but that you need to simplify the description of relationships by the use of hypothetical constructs, conceptual entities which are conceived as variables intervening between stimulus and response. Tolman's idea was that between stimulus and response there intervene the effects of physiological drive (P), heredity (H), previous training (T) and age or maturity (A), and that these effects, these intervening variables, I, are functions of P, H, T, and A. Behavior is thus a function of the stimulating conditions and all these variables, and the intervening variables, when they first come into existence, are just as redundant as Avenarius's System *C*. Gravitation was at first a similar redundant hypothetical construct. The justification for such concepts in theory building will lie in their fertility. If by simplifying thinking, they suggest hypotheses that are at first unexpected and then confirmed by experimental test, they will have been fertile. If the same concepts begin to enter into more and more hypotheses about different empirical relationships and the hypotheses stand up, then the concepts will begin to acquire thinghood or reality, as gravitation has.

We cannot here go further with Tolman nor enter into the complicated system of behavior that Hull (1952) has offered psychology, a system that makes wide use of intervening variables and hypothetical concepts. It is enough to say that we are now considering the most active field of psychological theorizing. Although it may seem at times as if Tolman and Hull got but little distance beyond the tautologies of description, as if they had not yet fully escaped from the meshes of philosophy which hindered psychology at the first, this matter is something that only posterity can judge. The systems of both these men have been useful in creating bands of loyal disciples, hardworking scientific in-groups who may, indeed, ultimately contribute more to psychology than do the systems which first captivated their imaginations.

(12) *Physical models.* After the physiological and conceptual explanatory systems come the physical and mathematical models. It is hard to keep the models distinct from the theories, and London (1949) believes that any theory which is explanatory and not merely descriptive is a model. You see, if you set up a physical analogy for some set of psychological events, a model whose physical interrelations appear to constitute an explanation of the events, then there are three positive things that may happen, independently or in combination. You can get interested in the mathematical expression of the physical relationships that are the essence of the model, and then you have either a physico-mathematical model, or, if your interest shifts to the formulae, a wholly mathematical model. Or you can wonder whether your physical model may not, after all, really exist in the nervous system, and presently you find yourself with a physiological theory on your hands, one which could become real if its terms were later to be validated. Or you may change your model over into a conceptual system and hope eventually that its terms will get validated, will acquire thinghood and be counted as real. The main difference between a model and a theory is, in my opinion, that you do not think of a model as actually existing nor do you usually hope that it may eventually acquire thinghood. Thus the model is recognized as an analogy as the theory is not, and you accept small deviations from the model as reasonable, whereas small deviations from a theory should be fatal to it unless they may be counted as errors of observation or sampling. Hering's theory of vision would have fared better had it been thought of as a model rather than as physiological fact. A model tolerates exceptions.

We may consider the physical models first. There was, for instance, McDougall's (1903, esp. 167) hydrostatic analogy for learning and inhibition, a model which tended to move over toward physiological theory as a system of cortical neural plumbing. Before the modern electronic robot came on the scene, there were various simple little mechanical analogies constructed, like Hull's mechanical model of the conditioned reflex (Baernstein & Hull, 1931). Perhaps the most influential physical model in the history of experimental psychology was Köhler's (1920) model of the distribution of electrostatic charges, which he used to explain the organization of perception in his

Physische Gestalten of 1920, the book addressed primarily to physicists and biologists, the one that is said to have got him his chair at Berlin. This model, however, came to move over toward physiology under pressure from Gestalt theory's doctrine of psychocerebral isomorphism, and now the model is actually acquiring thinghood as Köhler (et al., 1952) measures the movement of electrical potentials in the occipital cortex when the stimulus-object moves in the visual field. This is the kind of future that every modelist would like to see his model eventually achieve.

Of course, the physical models that everyone is discussing nowadays are the calculating machines, the servo-mechanisms, and the other robots of cybernetics (Wiener, 1949, esp. 137–155). Only seventy-five years ago psychologists were rejecting Helmholtz's notion of unconscious inference as a paradox, as a contradiction of terms. Nowadays, if you want quick reliable complicated inference, you get a machine and not a man. Whether the machine is, therefore, conscious does not bother the twentieth century positivist as it did the nineteenth century idealist.

Probability theory and statistics still sometimes appeal to urns that contain black and white balls to be drawn out and their frequencies noted, but these urns are conceptual nowadays. No modern probability theorist would dare use real urns with less than an infinity of balls, and infinity simply is not a physical dimension.

(13) *Mathematical models.* As mathematics is the powerful chief tool of physics, so the mathematical models are more suitable for adaptation and inference than the concrete physical models. They are not so dramatic, nor so clear to those who do not think readily in mathematical terms, nor is the promise of attaining status as reality so plainly written on them. On the other hand, they are easily manipulated by those trained to think mathematically, and the assertions derived from the initial assumptions can often be tested by comparison with known fact.

Some time ago Rashevsky announced that he thought that the time had come for "a purely theoretical biophysical psychology," and he proceeded to show what should be done. He assumed nervous conduction, connections between neurones, the convergence and divergence of connections, the principles of excitation and inhibition, the all-or-none principle of conduction, and two kinds of transmission between neurones. All these principles he put over into mathematical terms and proceeded to work out relationships that would constitute the lawful principles to be found in the nervous system by virtue of these first assumptions (Rashevsky, 1936). Earlier he had done the same sort of thing for the brain (Rashevsky, 1935). There are also some mathematically minded psychologists who have worked on mathematical models of learning, like Pitts (1943) and Bush and Mosteller (1951). Nevertheless, for all the work that has been done in this field, there does not seem as yet to be much new fact in the form of confirmed deductions. Examine the *Handbook of*

Experimental Psychology or the volumes of the *Annual Reviews of Psychology* for new facts derived from the use of mathematical modeling to see how little there is.

Perhaps a comment is in order here about mathematiphilia and mathematiphobia. There has always been a great deal of research in experimental psychology that could be successfully attacked without the use of much mathematics. Psychologists were not, therefore, forced to use mathematics in order to succeed professionally. Thus there have been some who eschewed mathematics and some who delighted in its use. The 'phobes have believed that the 'philes are trapped by the sheer pleasure of mathematical manipulations, and certainly there have been instances where precise and elaborate deductions have been drawn from unreliable and scanty data. On the other hand, there can be little doubt that the 'phobes include many persons who suffer, when they face mathematical argument, from mental dazzle, as David Katz (1950, 115 f., 125–127) has named the way in which efficiency is diminished by the irrelevant appearance of difficulty or complications. If you find it easier to add 22 and 43 cents than 22 and 43 *Clostridii pastoriani*, the difference would be due to the dazzle that the formidable name of these bacteria induces.

(14) *Reification of concepts.* We come finally to the question of how concepts become real, how they gain thinghood, as Bergmann (1943) puts it. In the first place we must note that none of the material that enters into science and stays there is a phenomenal particular. Science considers only generalities or constructs. Many of these constructs have attained the status of real relations or objects by the versatility and consistency with which they enter into scientific theories and facts. In the equation for the falling body, *g*, the acceleration due to gravity, is a construct and quite real. So is gravitation real, and an atom, and a star, and the red color of that book. They are all constructs which fit into so many factual formulae that they have lost their dubiety. It is Bergmann who reminds us that a star and a microscopic object are just as much constructs as an atom. So is the atom just as much an object as the star. In this way we discover how to measure the success of the theorizing that is going on in psychology. Do the intervening variables and the other hypothetical constructs stand up, get involved in more and more relations, find themselves used by many persons, appear to be gaining the status of something real? They will not have succeeded until they get in some degree that sort of thinghood.

Another way of saying this same thing is to note that, as long as a new construct has only the single operational definition that it received at birth, it is just a construct. When it gets two alternative operational definitions, it is beginning to be validated. When the defining operations, because of proven correlations, are many, then it has become reified. For the most part the factors that factor analysis yields stand tautologically at the first level. They merely describe the data that are included in a correlational matrix. Naming them, by examining their relations to the tests that generated them, adds no whit of reality to their existence. On the other hand, an empirical correlation does. When Halstead (1947, esp. 147–149) sought to relate the factors that came out of the analysis of a test battery to his observation of brain lesions, he was actually making one of the rare attempts at this kind of validation. Unfortunately his correlations are not sharp and the best he could do was to relate to gross lesions in the brain an impairment index, based on all four of the factors of biological intelligence. I once hoped that Spearman's general factor would turn out to be speed of reaction; that would have been a validation, but of course my hypothesis was wrong (Peak & Boring, 1926). Still the basic fact remains. A thing or a relation is real in as far as it has many alternative defining operations.[4] That is why an object is really a theory about experience.

There lies psychology's array of theories, and the question of the rôle of theory in experimental psychology is answered. Psychology *is* theory, just as science is theory—descriptive theory sometimes, and explanatory theory at other times, yet theory, because it is concerned with constructs that are things and their relations. Psychology and science are theory empirically based. You check constantly against phenomenal particulars but you are after the generalities that the particulars yield. So I might stop here, but there is still the question of the relation of psychology to philosophy. Did experimental psychology once break away from philosophy and is the modern interest in theory and system bringing it back? And is this trend, if it is trend, progressive or regressive? Do we encourage it or discourage it?

In general, science has always been philosophy—natural philosophy, mental philosophy; but historically there have been two schisms, one between the rational and the empirical, and the other between idealism and freedom, on the one hand, and materialism and determinism, on the other. The Greeks and the Scholastics, from Plato to St. Thomas, felt a certain scorn for the empirical as work for artisans, and deep respect for rationally given ideas. It was in these days that the circle, a perfect form, was accepted a priori for the orbits of the planets which, because of their divine origin, could not conceivably have been provided with inferior orbits. When the observed data did not agree with this superior knowledge, the theory of epicycles (a circular motion of a circular motion) was found to lessen the discrepancy. In the same manner the modern fanatic holds to his theory while exerting his ingenuity to find rationalization to support it.

The Middle Ages gave place to the new learning with the weakening of aristocracy and the beginnings of democracy. The acceptance of the Copernican theory was, in a sense, a sign that scientific empiricism comes in as the divine right of kings goes out. By the time you get to Descartes, Newton, and Leibnitz, there is no discernible line between natural philosophy and the other kinds. It was then that empiricism, with Locke, Berkeley, and Hume, took over philosophy, establishing the ground for what later became empirical or scientific psychology. Empiricism runs to positivism, and it was Hume's positivistic skepticism that created a crisis for the empiricistic trend. First the Scottish philosophers rose against Hume, and then Kant, being wakened from his dogmatic slumbers, accomplished the restoration of the a priori ideas which Hume had condemned. Kant did not, however, destroy empiricism; he simply led the German idealists away from determinism to freedom and moral responsibility, while the scientists, the physicists and physiologists, stayed behind. Thus the nineteenth century became the period of the greatest schism between philosophy and psychology, and the reaction of many of the new scientific psychologists—not all, not Wundt or Stumpf or Münsterberg—against philosophy was but part of this general movement.[5]

Now in the twentieth century relativity theory has again obliterated the line between theoretical physics and philosophy, and it may be that psychology should profit by physics' example. Certainly, if the line between philosophy and science was never more than a Kantian artifact, we need not worry when it wavers and disappears. The main matter for the theoretical psychologists to keep in mind is, as I said before: Are the new concepts, the new hypothetical constructs, the new intervening variables, getting thinghood fast enough? A healthy concept grows up, is weaned, and eventually goes out from the home where it was conceived to make new friends and to play a lasting rôle in the real world, that is to say, the world of constructs. Experimental psychology in the United States is healthy and growing rapidly. Mezes Hall with its splendid facilities is a symptom of national vigor in psychological research. All this great and expanding body of investigation ends, moreover, in theory, because theory is whither it is directed and the only goal in which it can end. The difference about which we are inquiring is actually not qualitative but quantitative. Should theory be kept simple and near description, we are asking, or should we generate hypothetical constructs and intervening variables freely for use in conceptual structures, in the hope that they may in due course harden into the stable realities of science and thus promote more progress than timorous description alone would yield? It would not be enough to examine the handbooks to see what the new conceptualism has contributed to firm fact, for that would be like attempting to divide college Freshmen into able and dull by looking them up in Who's Who. The new concepts are not yet old enough to have produced or to have become reified. We must perforce wait and posterity will make the judgment.

Meanwhile it is proper to advocate a modified tolerance. Let us try to get rid of lazy persons and of those who use rationalization to support pet theories that are contradicted by many facts, but among the tough-minded hardworkers let us bless both the factualists, congratulating them on their sanity, and the conceptualists, saluting them for their courage. It will take many different motives and personalities working synchronously, though perhaps not together, to maneuver psychology ahead to that understanding of human nature of which the world now stands in such great need.[6]

NOTES

1. An especially wise, mature, and effective discussion of recent contributions to psychological theory is given by Gustav Bergmann (1953).
2. Thus Einstein thinks of an ultimate truth as lying behind the limitations of man's techniques of observation. He is quoted as having said on probabalistic concepts' being due to man's restricted observation: "Der Herr Gott würfelt nicht!" ("The Lord God does not play games of chance.")
3. Woodworth, Transfer of training (1938, 176–207), bears on this kind of analysis in the sense of Woodworth's statement that "the theory about which most of the experiments on transfer revolve . . . is called 'the theory of identical elements' " (p. 177).
4. Bridgman (1927, 3–25) opposes this view holding to the pluralism that different defining operations always yield different constructs. I think Bridgman is wrong. See Bridgman (1945), Boring (1945 and this volume, 200–209). Did Bridgman partially yield the point? (Note particularly Boring, 1945, 241, 243, 279; Bridgman, 1945, 247)
5. A not inconsiderable portion of the thought of the last two paragraphs I owe to the enlightening article by Philipp Frank (1952).
6. Since this paper was written, K. M. Dallenbach has published his address of 1951 on the same topic (1953). Here Dallenbach writes in favor of accepting Titchener's advice to "carry your theories lightly," although he does not underestimate the importance of theory in the choice and formulation of experimental problems. The chief difference between us—and it is a big difference—is that he distinguishes fact from theory, whereas I, appealing to continuity, do not; and I distinguish fact from the phenomenal particulars of data, whereas I suspect from reading this paper that Dallenbach does not.

The current activity in making and criticizing theories is illustrated by the fact that this same number of the *Psychological Review* (January, 1953) contains five other important articles on theory (Bakan, 1953; Davis, 1953; George, 1953; Kattshoff, 1953; MacCorquodale and Meehl, 1953).

Statistical Frequencies
as Dynamic Equilibria

🧩🧩🧩🧩🧩🧩🧩🧩🧩🧩🧩🧩🧩🧩   1941

Introduction

THE growing importance of statistical methods in both physics and the social sciences makes a complete understanding of their implications and use imperative, and the large controversial literature on the meaning and use of the theory of probabilities in science shows that this need for clarification is not being overlooked. The social sciences use statistics when they are—perhaps only temporarily—ignorant of the nature of determinants which would, if known, adequately account for conduct; but it is the principle of indeterminacy, of *necessary* ignorance, that has forced statistics into physics. The present paper is a plea for more determinism in statistics, for a causal interpretation of probabilities in science and a resort to indeterminacy only when determinacy is known, at least for the time being, to be impossible.

The paper is concerned with the saying of three things. (1) First, it reminds the reader that the Principle of Indifference is not a pseudo-empirical means for getting knowledge out of ignorance, but at best a property of a particular form of model which may or may not be applicable to specific data. (2) Secondly, it notes that the Principle of Independence, the supposed mutual independence of the events in a satistical series or collective, can exist, if the series converges upon a given frequency, only if the number of cases is indeterminate or infinite, and it argues that the number of cases in the law of large numbers must be finite and determinate if the statistical model is to be of scientific use, since a model must have definite dimensions. It follows that, when models, representing convergence within a finite, specific number of cases, are known to apply to a given statistical series, then the investigator is faced with the problem of discovering the nature of the mutual interaction among the events which causes the series to converge. (3) Finally, the paper selects seven classical instances of actual supposed convergence,

Reprinted with permission from the *Psychological Review*, 1941, 48, 279–301.

and points out how they imply the existence of interaction among the events and, in as far as possible, it indicates the general nature of the equilibrating forces which would make the events tend toward a limiting frequency. In this manner the paper deplores a complacency with statistical indeterminacy and suggests that the unknown determinants would often be discerned if the investigator would realize that their existence is implied by the convergence of a collective.

The Principle of Indifference

The Principle of Indifference, as Keynes (1921, 41–64) formulated it, requires that the probabilities of different events should be equal when the evidences for the occurrence of each are equal. The use of the Principle depends, however, upon the definition that is accepted for probability, upon whether probability is regarded as axiomatic, or subjective, or a frequency (Fréchet, 1939). The Principle runs, moreover, into difficulty when the evidences for events are equal to one another and also to zero, for then equal probabilities appear to be derived from equal ignorances.[1]

(1) The *aprioristic* view works at the formal level of the model. The mutually exclusive possibilities are laid down, and, since there is no reason for weighting them differently, they are assumed to be equally likely, so that their consequences can be worked out by theory of probabilities. The discussion of the probabilities in games of chance is generally on this formal *if-then* level: *If* the elementary events are equally likely, *then* the probability of specified compound events would be so and so.

Nevertheless, even at the formal level, difficulty with the Principle of Indifference sometimes develops because some other formal rule relates two terms in such a way that they cannot both be distributed in accordance with the Principle. For instance, if x is normally distributed, then x^3 and $1/x$ cannot be, although the application of the Principle of Indifference to any one of the three variables alone might give a normal distribution. The linear heights and the weights of symmetrical homogeneous objects cannot both be normally distributed, since the weight would vary with the cube of the height. Bertrand's paradox arises because the Principle of Indifference gives different results for the ratio of water to wine in a mixture, and to its reciprocal, the ratio of wine to water in the same mixture.[2] In short, the principle of indifference cannot be applied simultaneously to quantities that are non-linearly related.

It is quite usual for empiricists, defining probability as frequency, to take over the Principle of Indifference and its consequences as a formal model, and to determine the goodness of the model's fit in a particular case or even sometimes to assume that it fits without bothering to test it. That is, after all, the history of the theory of probabilities, which was in part developed by savants in the interests of princes' games of chance. In such games experience with cards and dice and coins indicates that the conditions under which the model will fit "well enough" can be roughly intuited, although this intuition of necessary conditions, as we shall see later, is rarely explicated. It is very important for us, however, to keep the rules of the formal model distinct from its empirical relations. At the formal aprioristic level the Principle of Indifference is only a property of the model and means nothing whatsoever about empirical facts.

Common sense habitually errs by confusing the model with the data. Both the casual scientist and the man of the street will say that, if there are two possibilities, A and not-A, and that is all one knows, then A and not-A are equally likely (which is correct on the aprioristic view of the model) and will happen equally often (which is quite wrong when there is no empirical ground for establishing the fit of the model). Suppose A is *Six* on an ordinary die thrown in the "ordinary" manner (whatever that is!). *Six* and not-*Six* may be equally likely on aprioristic grounds, yet they do not turn up equally often.

(2) The *subjective* view is that probability varies with the weight of the evidence, so that the same events may be differently probable to different persons for whom the evidence has different weights. Although there has been much discussion with the contrary intent (Keynes, 1921, 41–64), it seems to me that at this simple level there need here be no appeal to Indifference. The relative weights are whatever they are. Perhaps they are determined by the betting odds which the subject will accept or perhaps by some other subjective method. Equal likelihood becomes then just a special case of all other relative likelihoods.

A difficulty arising here occurs because such probabilities have in turn their own probabilities. Evidence may be much or little as well as equal or unequal. A slight preponderance of slight evidence is not the same as a slight preponderance within a great mass of evidence. In the limiting case, where the evidences are equal because all the evidence is zero, one has minimal assurance for consequent action, even though action may be required. My point here, however, is that one does not return to a Principle of Indifference merely because evidence is insufficient. Nor does one get assurance out of ignorance, any more than he gets knowledge out of ignorance. The problem of assurance is subjective, and one "gets" only whatever is there to get.

(3) The *frequency* theory of probability simply identifies probability with relative frequency. This is the view that appeals to the scientist and to the positivist, the view that has been so adequately expounded by von Mises.[3] Scientifically it provides the "best" operational definition of probability because it is the most precise. Always it can be given numerical meaning. It is true that subjective assurance can also be quantified, as by betting odds, but

never so precisely. Frequency is, therefore, the only empirical definition to make full use of the precision of the mathematics of probabilities employed in the construction of models. At any rate this definition of probability is the one that is most germane to the argument of the present paper about convergent statistical frequencies.

The Principle of Indifference belongs no more to the frequency theory of probability than to the subjective theory. One simply does not get the knowledge of a frequency out of ignorance about a frequency. What one does is to conclude from known conditions to observed frequencies by the process of induction, and then, according to an appropriate model furnished by theory of probabilities, to conclude further to other frequencies, perhaps testing the fit of the model by subsequent observation. This view is essentially the one so clearly presented by von Mises.

In summary, we can say that the Principle of Indifference is a postulate that is applied axiomatically in the mathematics of probability and thus belongs in the mathematical models available for use in connection with the other two theories. Only in this manner is it validly employed in connection with empirical data. Of course, the fit of these models to observed subjective probabilities or to observed frequencies can be tested, but there is no other way in which the "correctness" of the Principle can become subject to validation. In other words, there is no way in which equal likelihoods can be got into the universe of discourse except by (a) postulating them or (b) observing them. If the equal likelihoods are observed, then they must be (b_1) subjective assurances or (b_2) relative frequencies. To determine empirically whether postulated likelihoods lead to certain predicted assurances or frequencies is simply to determine the fit of a model in a particular case: Thus the Principle of Indifference gains no special interest among all the other relative likelihoods. There is, it is true, the special empirical problem as to how subjective assurance is correlated with consequent frequency, but that is an empirical problem and not a case of testing the Principle of Indifference. Hence it appears that empirical science can get along very well without special attention to the Principle, except as it is postulated in the mathematical logic of the theory of probabilities which furnishes formal models for observed correlations.

Since this is no new doctrine, it seems fatuous to spend so many words in dismissing the unimportant, but the insidiousness of the Principle of Indifference justifies insistence. Let us get ourselves quite clear, therefore, before we proceed, about that major instrument of the probability theory, the tossed coin. It has *Heads* and *Tails* only, and *Heads = not-Tails* and conversely, the two being the mutually exclusive terms of a disjunction. Are *Heads* and *Tails* equally likely? No! Not on the basis of any information already printed in this paper. If the coin is homogeneous as to specific gravity and symmetrical as to weight, are they equally likely? No! These are negative conditions, statements that weight and shape will not effect the separate throws of which the series are composed. What then can we do about such a series? (*a*) We can postulate equal likelihood for *Heads* and *Tails,* and work out, for instance, the probability of seventeen iterations of *Heads* on the basis of the postulation. (*b*) We can assume that this model applies to subjective assurances and see whether it fits, whether a man would give odds of 131,072 to 1 against a run of exactly seventeen *Heads,* no more, no less. Probably he will not, unless he is a confirmed mathematician who settles his feelings of assurance by mathematics. If he will not, we can find out what odds he will give, and how they differ from the odds another man will give. (*c*) We can assume that the model applies to objective frequencies, and see whether it fits there. It may or it may not. It is easy to fix the conditions of tossing so that *Heads* will never turn up, or will always turn up (*vide infra*). And that is a fair proposal in this argument, because the exact mechanics of tossing is so rarely expressed in these statements of conditions, that I am free to introduce any system of tossing that I want. It is not fair to specify that the tossing shall be "without bias" because *without bias* is either another negative condition that determines nothing, or else it prejudges the case, assuming the rejection of all cases that do not fit the model, when the fit of the model is the point at issue.

If all the statements of the preceding paragraph were at the start self-evident to the reader, then indeed, from his point of view at least, the preceding discussion has been fatuous. I think, however, that most persons who work with statistical methods would not have found them self-evident, although I hope they may by now have accepted my logic.

The Law of Large Numbers

It is a property of a statistical series, a collective, that, as the number of cases is increased, the relative frequency of a particular event approaches a specific value as a limit. If this condition is not satisfied, then the event cannot be treated under the theory of probabilities, and it has not, to use von Mises' terms, the properties of a collective. Now it seems a valid scientific generalization that such collectives do exist, that relative frequencies are predictable when the individual occurrence remains unpredictable. We know —or we think we know—from experience (and not from the Principle of Indifference) that the coin comes *Heads* about half the time if it is thrown often enough, and we know that more than one throw is required, since it cannot come half *Heads* in a single throw. Experience teaches us, moreover, that under many conditions which can be set up, a run of two or three

Heads is not unusual, whereas a run of twenty or even ten *Heads* is exceptional. If one points out that coin tossing can be so controlled as to defeat this expectation, then common sense appeals to the records of roulette, to the mortality tables, or to some similar situation where commercial solvency attests the validity of the law of large numbers.

Now I have no quarrel at all with the thesis that frequencies in a statistical series are convergent and that they come under the rule of induction, being predictable without undue error on the basis of past experience. It is, indeed, the purpose of this paper to ask what is implied by the fact that such predictions can be made. The law of large numbers does not, however, express any such simple principle. It states only that the probability, that the relative frequency will not deviate more than a specified amount from some specified frequency, increases as the number of cases increases. Hence under this law the ultimate frequency is determinate only for an infinite number of cases. Every exception to it fits in under the infinitely inclusive rule. If I were to throw 36 *Heads* in succession with an "unbiased" penny and do it on the 50-billionth attempt, then everyone who knew the mathematics of the situation would say, "Well, it's about time!" But, if I were to do it on the first attempt, then everyone would look for bias, and, if bias could not be positively established, only then would they admit, "But it ought to happen once in 68,719,476,736 times." If in the second 36 throws I again got 36 *Heads*, there would still be a statable frequency with which I "ought" to get two such events in succession. It does not seem to me to be a good model which fits every conceivable set of occurrences.

The law of large numbers is especially important because it has a close relation to the Principle of Independence. Statisticians usually suppose that the events of a collective occur in complete independence of one another. Thus the expectation of any event is not affected, so they say, by the outcome of preceding events. A run of *Heads* does not increase the probability of *Tails*. At first thought it seems quite impossible to reconcile this Principle of Independence with the notion that relative frequency approaches a limit, for, if there have been "too" many *Heads*, then there must be a subsequent increase in *Tails* if the limit is to be approached. The Law of Large Numbers, however, takes care of that difficulty. No finite iteration of any event is large when compared with a "sufficiently" large number. The word *sufficient* turns the trick. So long as it remains a word of indefinite specification, however, just so long will the concept of a probability series, a collective, remain vague and half-way meaningless, simply because there is no conclusive test of the existence of such a series.

Von Mises, whose strict operationism led him to champion the frequency conception of probability, is here not so rigorous. He makes his conviction plain that the properties of a collective are realized only for a "sufficient" number of cases, and *sufficient* does not mean a definite finite quantity. While he has not directly espoused the Principle of Independence, nevertheless he has specified it indirectly in his requirement that there be no change in the probabilities of a collective when there has been a selection of its elements in respect of their places within the probability series. In consequence of his holding to both of these principles, he is forced also to espouse the principle of indeterminacy, and then ultimately to deplore the inertia which leads scientists to hold so tenaciously to causal determinism. To those who cannot take time to read von Mises (1939, 243–307) in order to see why the properties of a collective and the law of large numbers lead to the principle of indeterminacy, I can recommend only that they read the rest of this paper where the converse relationship is exhibited: that determinism is gained by an abandonment of the law.

Certainly there is a deterministic statistics! It surrenders the Principle of Independence along with the Principle of Indifference. It goes back to observation and builds upon it inductively. Thus it accepts the frequency theory of probabilities in the sense that the theory of probabilities provides the models which the observed frequencies are to fit. For a law of "sufficiently" large numbers, this conception substitutes a law of relative frequencies converging upon a limit within a determinate number of occasions. In other words, we set up statistical models in which the relative frequency of specific events varies between 1.0 and 0, converging in a specific number of cases upon a specific relative frequency. Such a model is subject to test as to its goodness of fit to the observed frequencies. Both the limiting frequency and the number of cases are thus observed data. That a coin when tossed by a given machine should yield from 48 to 52 *Heads* in 100 throws is an example of specifications which constitute a model; and, if the model does not fit well enough, we can change it, either as to the limiting frequency or as to the number of cases. In many instances we shall find that increasing the number of cases will make the model adequate where it was inadequate before, but that will not always be true. Observation is the arbiter of the fit of a model, and repeated observation under the principles of induction is the only way to determine the reliability of the fit.

The Frequency Matrix

Figure 1 is a frequency matrix for the first 36 occasions of the occurrence of the simple disjunction A or not-A. It gives, as dots on the diagram, all possible relative frequencies, from 0 to 1.0, of the occurrences of A. On the

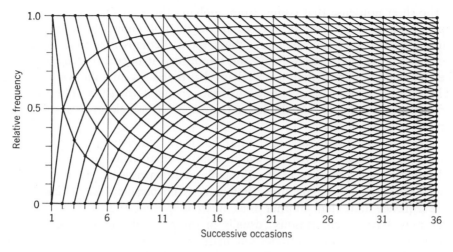

Fig. 1. Frequency matrix for a simple disjunction when successive events are independent. There are in this matrix 68,719,476,736 sequences of relative frequencies (paths through the diagram) from the 1st to the 36th occasion.

first occasion A can occur only "never" (0) or "always" (1). On the second occasion the frequencies can be 0, 1/2 or 1; on the third occasion, 0, 1/3, 2/3, or 1; on the fourth, 0, 1/4, 1/2, 3/4, or 1; on the 36th, 0, 1/36, 2/36, 3/36 . . . , 35/36, 1. Thus one can trace the sequence of relative frequencies of A through the matrix from left to right for the first 36 occasions. For any frequency at any occasion, there are only two paths leading to the next occasion: one leads up and applies when A occurs on the next occasion; the other leads down and applies when A does not occur. Every possible sequence lies in the matrix.

There are 68,719,476,736 sequences through this matrix. No one, in the present state of our ignorance about A, can be known to be more frequent than another, but that is not at all to say that they are equally frequent. Lacking cogent reasons we just do not know about the relative frequencies. Of these many paths 9,075,135,300 end at 0.5 at the right of the diagram, and only one path ends at 1.0 and another one at 0. The number of paths that lead to the 37 frequencies represented on the ordinate for occasion 36 are the numbers of the coefficients of the binomial expansion for the 36th power, a "normal" distribution of frequencies. Because there is only one sequence leading to 1.0 at the right and nine billion ways of getting to 0.5, most persons would say that we shall more often end up at 0.5 than at 1.0. That, however, is the sheer nonsense that comes from applying the Principle of Indifference aprioristically to an empirical case. If we do not know about actual occurrences, we simply do not know about them. Perhaps A is that the President of the United States will not die tomorrow. At once 1.0 at occasion 36 becomes more frequent than 0.5. Perhaps A is that a *Six* on a die will turn up. Then 0.17 is under certain conditions more frequent than 0.5. The number of sequences leading to a final relative frequency has no relevance at all to the problem in hand.

The frequency matrix of Fig. 1 must be clearly understood as representing the occurrence of an attribute whose relative frequencies are unknown in advance and are quite free of the Principle of Independence. In interpreting the diagram we must remember that there is no presumption which favors one sequence more than another or as much as another or as little as another. We must have cogent reasons (usually in the form of past experience with frequencies) before we can prefer one path to another or not prefer it. It may be remarked, moreover, that the matrix, being finite, represents the beginning of a collective, or it includes all collectives in which 36 is a "sufficiently large number."

It should be observed that the free situation represented in Fig. 1 gives a delusory convergence. Frequency changes less and less rapidly as the number of occasions increases. The most that the frequency can change on the fourth occasion is 0.25; on the tenth occasion, 0.10; on the 100th occasion, 0.01. A great deal of the common belief in the law of large numbers must be founded on nothing more than this simple fact that relative frequencies have to change more and more slowly as the number of cases increases, whether a limit is being approached or not.

Finally we may note that Fig. 1 represents the case of drawing balls from an urn and counting the white balls drawn, when there are both white and black balls in the urn and the ball drawn is put back after being recorded. Such a system, so far as my description of it goes, is completely indeterminate as to whether it converges on a frequency or not and as to what, if it does converge, that frequency would be—and this statement holds without regard to the relative numbers of white and black balls in the urn. If the drawings approach any relative frequency as a limit, then that approach is due to those conditions which determine whether a white or black ball is drawn, to the differential determiners which are so often unknown. For instance, in an urn containing 8 black balls and 2 white balls, one could get 100 per cent of white balls by the simple expedient of looking at the balls before they were drawn and choosing always a white. If, without looking, one were to get only 20 per cent of white balls, why then that would be a mystery until one learned why.

The confusion that arises at this point is due to an asymmetry of scientific curiosity. If the distribution of a variable turns out to be "normal," we say that it is "homogeneous" with the variability due to "chance," and relax at once into complacency. If the distribution turns out to be, let us say, bimodal, then we say it must be "heterogeneous," requiring an "explanation." Why do we hunt for causes in the one case and not in the other? (And did anyone ever discover a bimodal distribution of a homogeneous variable and rest content with the finding?) The bridge hand of 13 spades seems to call for explanation as if it were "improbable" and must have been caused by special conditions, whereas any bridge hand at all that ever was dealt is just as "improbable," just as reasonable a ground for wonder, reminiscence and anecdote.[4] Science could get along very well, I think, without the use of the words *chance* and *homogeneous*, and especially without that phrase, that potent anesthetic for curiosity, *due to chance*.[5]

Equilibrated Frequencies

If a frequency series approaches a limit in a specific number of cases, then the events cannot be independent, but are interrelated, so that the occurrence of one makes "more probable" the occurrence of another. Figure 2 is a matrix for the convergence of the frequency of one alternative A upon a relative frequency of 1/2 in 36 occasions. If initially A turns up 18 times in succession, then it must be inhibited from turning up again if the frequency is to be 1/2 at the 36th trial. This is the case of the urn with 18 white balls and 18 black balls, where the drawing of white balls is recorded and the balls are *not* put back after being drawn. The diagram might be taken tentatively as a set of models for the frequency of *Heads* in coin tossing, a set to be revised if the method of tossing were not such as to give this variation within these limits. The conditions of tossing like other scientific conditions ought to be kept constant. If they are kept quite constant, as they easily could be, the model could be made to fit perfectly. We should have only to toss the coin with a machine and to decide whether to turn the coin over or not when returning it to the machine for another throw. Let us suppose that the machine is accurate and that it always turns up the side of the coin that was down in the machine before the toss, and that the coin is not turned over when replaced in the machine. Then the model for the frequencies of *Heads*, if the coin be first put in the machine as *Heads*, is the sequence 0, 1/2, 1/3, 1/2, 2/5, 1/2, 3/7, 1/2, 4/9, 1/2, . . . converging in this fashion upon 1/2.

If we know nothing about the differential determinants between the alternative events, then all we can do is to experiment until we know whether the series converges and what model fits it within the allowable limits of tolerance.

Figure 3 is the matrix for the sequences which end in 1/6 after 36 occasions, as, for example, the frequency of *Sixes* in the throws of a die, when the die is thrown so that the series does thus converge upon 1/6. Of course, a die can be thrown so that the frequency of *Sixes* will approach 1/2, and then the model for it may lie in the matrix of Fig. 2. It all depends upon the differential determiners of its faces.

It should now be plain that, if frequencies approach a limit, they are striking some sort of dynamic equilibrium as the result of the forces which operate

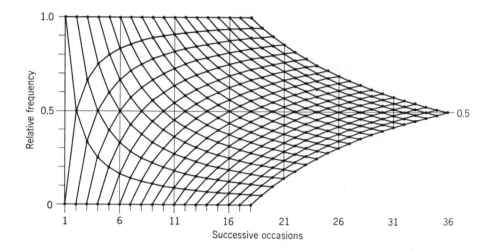

Fig. 2. Frequency matrix converging upon one-half. The diagram is for interdependent events with the limiting frequency of one-half reached on the 36th occasion. There are 9,075,135,300 sequences in this matrix.

between the successive events. In the following paragraphs we get some idea of the kinds of equilibrating systems that operate or might operate to fix statistical frequencies at definite amounts.

Coins and Dice. There are three possibilities: (1) we can be wholly ignorant of the determiners of the particular events; (2) we can know from past experience that the relative frequencies converge upon a constant relative frequency in a specific total of occasions, although we do not know "why" they converge; or (3) we can know wholly or in part about the determiners of the particular events which cause the convergence.

(1) The case of complete ignorance about the properties of the series can have no scientific interest. We can appeal only to the Principle of Indif-

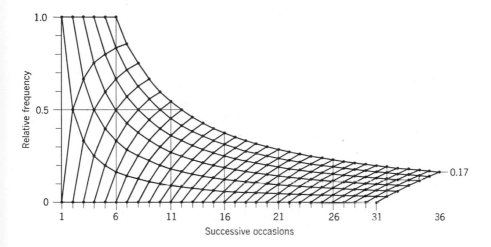

Fig. 3. *Frequency matrix converging upon one-sixth. The diagram is for interdependent events with a limiting frequency of one-sixth. There are only 1,947,792 sequences in this matrix.*

ference, and knowledge conditioned upon ignorance is a delusion. We have already seen that coins can be thrown so that the relative frequencies will converge upon any desired frequency, depending on the dynamics and rules of tossing.

(2) It is very generally believed that there is good empirical evidence that a coin will in the long run come up equally often *Heads* and *Tails*. If this law of the coin is true—in spite of the fact that we can specify conditions of throwing under which it would not be true—then it follows that persons can by intuition recognize the conditions under which equal frequencies of *Heads*

and *Tails* would be approached. We must exclude the completely circular case where "right" results are accepted and "wrong" results are scrutinized with the hope of finding a reason for their exclusion. The *aprioristic* intuition means, then, that we can choose certain situations in which our prediction of 50 per cent *Heads* in a certain number of trials is verified approximately. We can have such a situation, but, when we have it, what can we do with it? We cannot test the "laws of chance," for there are no empirical laws of chance except correlations between conditions and consequent frequencies, and here the conditions are intuited and not specifically generalized. We can, of course, try to analyze the situation in hope of gaining a more precise specification of the determiners of the limiting frequency, but this attempt is seldom made because of the general belief in the indeterminacy of the events in a statistical series. If we make the attempt and succeed, we pass almost certainly into the next case.

(3) When the determiners of the specific events are known, as they would be with a carefully constructed tossing machine, then we know everything and have nothing to learn.

The general problem becomes clear if we consider the case of a biologist who wishes to examine the laws of Mendelian inheritance as to whether the genes combine "by chance," and to parallel these matings of cells by the throwing of coins or dice. The simplest case would be the relation of a Dominant to a Recessive character, with Dominance equated to *Heads* and Recessiveness equated to *Tails*. A homozygous cell would, therefore, be represented by a coin with two *Heads* or two *Tails* and a heterozygous cell by an ordinary coin with one *Head* and one *Tail*. There is no need to enter into details, but, supposing that the results of mating experiments match the results of double throws of these coins, what has been gained? We have fitted a coin model to the biological situation, but we know nothing much about the coin model. We have to observe the frequencies of both the matings and the throwings, and the mathematical model of frequencies was all that we ever needed. Tossing coins has done us no good at all.

It is the same with randomness. No dice box ever gave randomness with certainty. You have to know first what randomness is in order to be sure that the dice give it. If you know what it is, you do not need to throw the dice. The safe way to get randomness with a die is to make out a table (model) for random throws, repeatedly pick up the die, and every time put it down in accordance with the table!

Cards. The same logic applies to the use of cards. Shuffling is certainly not necessarily "random" merely because it keeps the shuffler ignorant of what he is doing. If a shuffler aims at dividing the pack in two and at alternating the cards from the two halves, then he aims at a method which would bring a pack of 52 cards back into its original order every eighth shuffle! This is to me an astonishing discovery. A pack of 64 cards, divided in half, with the cards alternated and with the same side always providing the first card, will return to its original order in six shuffles; 16 cards return in four shuffles, 12 cards in ten shuffles.[6] In other words, "good" shuffling depends upon the failure of the shuffler to realize his intention, since it seems certain that most shufflers try to divide the pack evenly and to alternate the cards. Thus it comes about that, to understand any scientific situation involving shuffled cards, we need to understand the nature of those determiners that make the shuffler deviate from his intention. It is meaningless to say that shuffling—when the system determining the order of the cards is left indeterminate—gives a "chance" distribution of the cards. Unless we know the rules that determine the order of the shuffling, we remain ignorant of essential conditions.

The barrenness of recent research on extrasensory perception has thus been due, I think, to the failure of Rhine and his associates to become interested in the nature of shuffling.[7] These investigators have tended to apply the Principle of Indifference to frequencies, to assert, when a pack consists of five kinds of cards in equal numbers, that guesses about particular cards must be right one-fifth of the time. Thus, when the guesses are right two-fifths of the time, they are amazed and feel constrained to call for explanation upon an hypostatized principle named *extrasensory perception* or ESP. If ESP makes the cards come right two-fifths of the time, what made them come right one-fifth of the time? By what right are these men complacent about this mysterious entity which they call *chance*, while they demand our concern about the other mysterious entity which they have christened ESP? ESP is a mystery because chance is a mystery, and, if we are going to boast about our ignorance of the one, we had better begin boasting about our ignorance of the other. What expectation is there that they will really discover the conditions which make a frequency 1/5 change to 2/5, when they know nothing (and care nothing) about what makes the frequency 1/5? Here is indeed a situation where the use of statistical method leads to an assured complacency and blindness to the basic problem.

Galton Board. Von Mises (1939, 327 f.) has noted that the Galton board shows the properties of a collective, and he describes a Galton board in which the successive events would seem to be entirely independent. Pins are arranged in rows in an inclined plane. The distance between adjacent pins equals the distance between adjacent rows, and the pins are staggered so that the pins of odd rows come half way between the pins of even rows, and conversely. A steel ball of diameter equal to the horizontal distance between pins is started at the top in the middle and allowed to roll down to the bottom. At each pin it makes a choice between left and right. The process is repeated many times. If the Principle of Indifference governed, then the frequencies of the places where the ball arrives at the bottom of the plane in a large number of trials should show a normal distribution.

Some Galton boards are arranged so that a charge of shot, falling through a hopper, strike against each other and produce a symmetrical unimodal distribution because of equilibrating interaction among the shot. Of von Mises' case it can only be said that the conditions which he specifies are insufficient conditions for any kind of a distribution. The simplest Galton board would have a single pin, with the shot, dropped one at a time, turning up in equal numbers to the right and the left of the pin. Here the sufficient condition lies, not at all in the construction of the board, but in those factors which determine whether the shot shall strike to the right or left of the center of the pin (or remain balanced upon the pin!). The case of the shot is like the case of the coin. It is the operation of this approximate ignorance that Galton (1889, 63–66) called "the wonderful form of cosmic order expressed by the 'Law of Frequency of Error.'" The board proves that a shot's falling to the left increases the tendency of subsequent shot to fall to the right, and conversely. Just what is the nature of this equilibration?

Gas. The kinetic theory of gases is often said to be founded upon statistical theory. For the most part, however, the development of the theory is indubitable mathematics and does not involve the theory of probabilities. On the other hand, there is a hint of the Principle of Indifference when it is said that, since the direction of motion of the molecules is unknown, we must regard them as moving equally in all directions, or, for the purposes of mathematical treatment, one-third of them moving in each of the three dimensions.

It would seem, however, that we have to do here with a case of dynamic equilibrium and not of the Principle of Indifference. Suppose, for example, that all the molecules were at some instant moving in only one direction. We should not expect them to continue without the collisions which would tend to alter their directions. Any alteration would diminish the uniformity of direction. Let us imagine the molecules free to move in two dimensions only, NS and EW, and let us imagine that they are all moving NS. Any deviation must be in the direction of increasing the total EW components, since the NS components, being already 100 per cent, cannot be increased. As long as the NS components are greater than the EW components, we should expect the latter to increase, with equilibrium established at equality. Gas pressure is equal in all directions because only thus is the gas in dynamic equilibrium.

Radioactivity. Lindsay and Margenau (1936, esp. 190) discuss the common view that the autocatalytic law of atomic disintegration is a statistical law with the particular events independent and thus indeterminate. "The number of atoms disintegrating is proportional to the number of atoms present," so that the process slows down as it proceeds. Yet they say: "On the *average* each atom is transformed after it has existed for a perfectly definite length of time, e.g., many millions of years in the case of uranium; . . . the explosion of one atom, which occurs with a violence having no analogue on a macroscopic scale, leaves its neighbor undisturbed until perhaps after millions of years the neighbor succumbs to the same fate. The life of an atom appears to be regulated only by chance." It has "an isolated fate."

It is hard to see why an atom, dying because of atomic over-population, as it were, suffers "an isolated fate," even though its neighbors, making up in the formula the N which required that this atom and so many others had to die, may live on undisturbed for a few million years. I should suppose we had evidence here, either for some kind of dynamic interdependence among the atoms, or else for such an interdependence in formation of the radioactive substance as would be necessary to preestablish the atomic life-spans in accordance with the autocatalytic law. Lindsay and Margenau seem to appeal here to "chance" because this atomic action is "isolated" in the sense that it is at a distance. On that principle the operation of gravitation would be statistical.

Mortality. While it is not possible to suggest what dynamic principle controls the deaths of atoms, it is quite clear that there are many such principles determining the deaths of human beings. The mortality tables—the argument of the man of the street that the commercial solvency of the insurance companies proves the lawfulness of chance—are certainly the result of equilibration. Everyone who dies makes life a little safer for those who live on. Everyone who lives jeopardizes his neighbors an infinitesimal amount. If there is an epidemic, social forces are brought into play to diminish deaths and to keep the mortality tables right. If there are "too" many deaths on the highways, the speed limit is reduced—for the sake of the mortality tables. Medical science strives to prolong life and probably ends by increasing the maximal speed allowed on the highways. These are, however, only the lesser determinants of variations on the surface. Underlying them are the basic laws of population, economic and biological, which control the size of a population under certain conditions. Conditions can change, it is true, but so can the mortality tables. There are many equilibrating forces that tend to stabilize death rates and they must be interdependent. The superstition that the mortality tables validate some law of chance is hardly more than the superstition that my death has nothing to do with yours, an absurd idea.

Sex. The approximate constancy of the sex ratio is so far from having its determinants known that the Principle of Indifference is easily accepted in respect of it. Boy babies and girl babies are supposed to come equally often simply because we do not know why they should not come equally often!

Much more likely is it that girls are born because boys have been born, and conversely. Is there any sense to an approximately equal ratio unless there are equilibrating forces?

Recently Coe (1940, 177 f.) has published an illuminating discussion of sexual development. His thesis is that the organism makes a choice of its sex early in its life, and may occasionally change its mind later, either successfully or with resultant hermaphroditism. Obviously the secret of the sex ratio must lie in the conditions that determine this "choice." For human beings we do not know why the birth of many girls should favor the birth of more boys, yet that must be a fact if it is also a fact that the sex ratio tends toward constancy.[8] Coe cites examples of how the ratio may be maintained in some invertebrates. The snail Crepidula passes through a male stage to become finally a female. If no females are present, the process is rapid, so that there are soon some females with the males. With females present the process is slower. There is equilibration. The determinants which slow the feminizing process of maturation are "the stimuli which the male receives through his sense organs and the associated internal changes occurring at the time of mating," not presumably any transfer of hormonal masculinizing substance. A similar determination of the sex ratio happens with the worm Bonellia. The annelid Ophrytrocha, which also develops through a male stage to the female, may, under unfavorable conditions like starvation, revert from the female stage to the male. It has been noted that when two females are in isolation, the more dominant female may devour the food, thus forcing her companion back into a male stage in which he is able to fertilize her eggs. Would anyone want in these cases to say that the sex ratio is determined by chance, that we must learn to think in terms of indeterminacy, and that it is only the inertia of thought that makes us think that a knowledge of causal determinants is better than a statement of statistical frequencies?

Conclusions

This article is a demand for more energetic discontent when the determinants of the limiting frequencies of convergent statistical series remain unknown. The Principle of Indifference, when it is used to predict frequencies in the absence of observation, is only ignorance masquerading as knowledge. It is, moreover, insidious because it falsely satisfies the discontent that ought to go with ignorance, so that it stops the search for the determinants. Even when the frequency theory of probability has been accepted, the Principle of Indifference may slip in, so habituated to it is thought. The Principle of Independence, appearing perhaps as the Law of Large Numbers or in some other form that works for indeterminacy, is just as great an enemy of research into the causal ground of frequencies as is the Principle of Indifference, but it is a mischief that is not at all generally recognized. With the Heisenberg principle itself one cannot quarrel: When we must be ignorant, we must be ignorant. Let us not encourage ourselves, however, into any patient acceptance of any ignorance that can be dispelled. The use of statistical indeterminacy in most macroscopic science is an unnecessary and premature denial of the effectiveness of determinism.

NOTES

1. Thus Boole (1854, 368–375, esp. 370) called the principle "the equal distribution of ignorance," and von Kries (1886) called it "the principle of insufficient reason."

2. Bertrand's paradox is this. If the ratio of water to wine lies between 1 and 2, then there must be equal likelihoods of its lying between 1 and 3/2 and between 3/2 and 2. But, if the ratio of water to wine lies between 1 and 2, the ratio of wine to water must lie between 1 and 1/2, and according to the Principle of Indifference there would be equal likelihoods of the ratio lying between 1 and 3/4 and between 3/4 and 1/2. Yet these two results are contradictory, since $3/4 \neq 2/3$ (the reciprocal of 3/2). *Cf.* von Mises (1939, 114–117) and the similar example in Keynes (1921, 45).

3. Von Mises (1939). In supporting the frequency theory von Mises rightly ignores the Principle of Indifference, yet the Principle is insidious and I cannot feel that von Mises has got completely free of it. He is too pleased when he finds a model, based upon it, fitting an empirical case, as in his verdict on Marbe's problem, 198–201. *Cf.* also 237–240, 248–250, 280, 283. I am not, however, writing this paper to quarrel with von Mises who is, at this point in the argument, on my side. *Cf.* Reichenbach (1938, 297–357).

4. The theme that no one sequence of events is any more improbable than any other, even though it happens to make some special sense, like a chimpanzee's typing out *Oliver Twist* by accident, has been put forth properly, if humorously, by Maloney (1940).

5. An example of an uncritical and, I think, undefinable use of the terms *random* and *homogeneous* occurs recently in McNemar (1940, 331–365, esp. 335–339, 342) in spite of the fact that he is writing didactically in an effort to increase the sophistication of the users of statistical methods. See also note 7, below.

6. The rule is this. The deck is evenly divided and the cards are alternated, with the card previously on the bottom put down first. Let $n =$ number of shuffles to bring the deck back into the original order; $d =$ number of cards in the deck and an odd integer; $c =$ another odd integer, a constant for a given d. Then $cd = 2^n - 1$. Packs with an even number of cards are taken care of by the fact that n is the same for $d + 1$ (even) as for d (odd). I am indebted to my colleague, S. S. Stevens, for this general formula.

7. See J. G. Pratt, J. B. Rhine, B. M. Smith, C. E. Stuart, and J. A. Greenwood (1940). The distinction between the use of the Principle of Indifference in the mathematics of a model whose fit is subject to test and its aprioristic application to frequencies is subtle, but it is my conviction that an improper use of the Principle occurs repeatedly throughout the book. *Cf.* esp. Ch. 2 on mathematical methods and Appendix 1. For instance: "The method commonly used in evaluating a particular set of data is to calculate the probability that a score as high or higher than that obtained would occur in that number of calls. This probability is based on the number of times such a score would occur, if chance were the only factor operating, in a large number of experiments, each consisting of the same number of calls as the series to be evaluated"

(p. 29); or "The composition of the deck is the same for all calls, therefore the probability of success is constantly 1/5" (p. 363), a sentence which occurs in a context that equates probability to frequency.

8. Von Mises (1939, 198–202) discusses Karl Marbe's problem: Does a man, about to become a father and wishing for a son, have more chance of getting his desire if he finds that the 17 immediately preceding births, registered in his town, were girls, in view of the fact that in 49,152 registrations there has been no instance of 18 or more iterations of registration of the same sex? Von Mises concludes that the chances of a son are still only 50–50 for the expectant father. My question is somewhat different. What are the father's chances of a son (*a*) *if* the sex ratio tends to be equal but (*b*) *if* at the time of the birth it is very unequal? Not 50–50.

The Validation of
Scientific Belief

𝕣𝕣𝕣𝕣𝕣𝕣𝕣𝕣𝕣𝕣𝕣𝕣𝕣𝕣𝕣𝕣𝕣𝕣𝕣𝕣𝕣𝕣𝕣𝕣𝕣𝕣𝕣 1952

I F we are to get clear about these unorthodoxies in science, we must realize that there are different kinds of truth. *Absolute truth* itself is not available to science. There is no one to tell science when it is right and when wrong. Posterity speaks pretty positively about the science of any earlier date, yet even it remains subject to later correction by posterity's posterity. Scientific truth is thus usually *truth by agreement*, a social kind of truth. This sort of truth is simply belief or acceptance. When everyone agrees, then there is no dissent and orthodoxy is for the time being universal. Dr. Cohen (1952) has shown how heterodoxy can change to orthodoxy and back again to heterodoxy, as did astrology through the ages of science, and how a waning orthodoxy, like the belief in the indivisible atom, becomes heterodoxy when it reaches minority status. Our interest, of course, lies in those conflicts where a small heterodoxy challenges a big orthodoxy, and two incompatible truths find themselves in competition. Besides truth by agreement there is also *practical truth*, the truth that works. If Henry Gross can actually find you water, if ESP does actually help you with the stock market, if the next collision of two worlds turns out to have been correctly predicted by Velikovsky, then you have got to take serious account of these new possibilities. Success of this sort promotes agreement, but mostly the limited agreements which constitute the unorthodoxies with which we are concerned are nourished by other food than practical success.

Let me begin, however, by inviting your attention to the question of scientific bias, to the way in which opinion and prejudice and egoism intrude upon and influence scientific belief. They do intrude, as all the contributors to this symposium have made so clear, and it is for this reason, say I that to

Read April 24, 1952, in the Symposium on Some Unorthodoxies of Modern Science. Reprinted with permission from *Proceedings of the American Philosophical Society*, 1952, **96**, No. 5, 535–539 understand the history of scientific thought you need a psychologist at your elbow.

Unconscious Bias

What you face in the disagreements that grow up about the unorthodoxies is a conflict between sincerities. These conflicts between incompatible, staunchly held, sincere beliefs make up what we may call the little wars of science, little wars which, except for size and consequences, differ in pattern no whit from the big wars between nations or, for that matter, from the persecution of a religious minority by a majority.

Herbert Butterfield (1952), the historian, has just given us a vivid picture of the way in which bias and sincerity and intractability and emotion are integrated to form the representative pattern of political and religious conflict. Always you find, he says, "both sides anxious to avoid a war, but each desperately unsure about the intentions of the other party; each beset by the devils of fear and suspicion, therefore; and each side locked in its own system of self-righteousness." Each side is convinced that the other is evil and has habitually been the author of recurrent aggression. So there you have, says Butterfield, "a grand dialectical jam of a kind that exasperates men—a terrible deadlock that makes ordinary human beings even a little more wilful than they ordinarily are." This is "the absolute predicament and the irreducible dilemma," which could "produce the greatest war in history without the intervention of any great criminals who might be out to do deliberate harm in the world" (1952, 19).

Butterfield uses the Royalists and the Roundheads and other great conflicts of the past to illustrate his point that sincere, intelligent, well-intentioned men in conflict hold incompatible views firmly and resolutely and do not surrender them even around a conference table. Yet how, we may ask, is that possible? Do not sincerity and intelligence and good intentions guarantee agreement? No, they do not. The human ego is too much in need of protection. Self-righteousness is its first line of defense, and he who is to assess bias truly must have no stake in the verdict beyond the preservation of his own objectivity.

It is now almost twenty-five years since I undertook to discuss the psychology of psychologists' controversies (Boring, 1929b). I had asked myself: Is egoistic bias so great that the truth must necessarily transcend the thinking of its own individual discoverer, being revealed only to the mature objectivity of posterity? Butterfield might have asked that question, since the historian *is* posterity. At any rate we all know how thoroughly the investigator gets identified with his achievement and how hard it then becomes for him to criticize his own work or to accept criticism from others.

One dramatic instance from the history of experimental psychology—dramatic because it was reinforced by Teutonic acrimony—was the antiphonal polemic in 1890–1892 between Wundt at Leipzig, often called the founder of experimental psychology, and Stumpf, then about to be called to Germany's most important post at Berlin (Boring 1929*b*, 107–111). They disagreed as to whether the psychological bisection of a tonal interval lies at the arithmetic mean of the limiting stimuli or at the geometric mean. The controversy raged through 141 pages, six articles altogether, three apiece. It soon became personal, and each contender was to be found instructing the other as to how he could make of himself a better scientist. Was there any likelihood that the truth would emerge through the smoke of that battle? Fifty years later, however, posterity—mature, wise, judicious posterity—settled the issue. Both men were right—Stumpf for the high tones above 1500 cps, Wundt for the low tones (Stevens & Volkmann, 1940, 343 ff.). Might Wundt have said in 1890: "But Stumpf is surely as intelligent and experienced as I. Both of us cannot be right. Should I not now examine my own position before I reaffirm it?" Hardly. Again and again the simple resolve to be objective yields to the unconscious need for defense of the ego. Wundt and Stumpf had got themselves into a little "absolute predicament," a little "irreducible dilemma," a small one of those "jams" where self-respect forbids compromise. We think at once of Dr. Cohen's (1952) and Mr. Riddick's (1952) citation of Max Planck: "New scientific truth does not triumph by convincing its opponents and making them see the light but rather because its opponents eventually die"—as indeed did both Wundt and Stumpf before posterity's research settled their feud. We, yesterday's posterity, tend to deplore that feud, yet we must remember that it was this same intractable enthusiasm that made Wundt and Stumpf leaders of the new psychology in Germany for three decades.

These little wars can occur in any conceivable pattern of antagonistic relationships—between scientific schools, between groups with leaders, between individuals. When the antagonists are closely matched, the controversy represents nothing more than part of the intellectual turbulence out of which truth is manufactured. For the unorthodoxies and the cranks the battle is, however, unequal. A crank, by definition, is always in the minority. His views may presently be advanced to become an unorthodoxy when they are accepted by a large body of the laity, or by a notable number of scientists, or by a few scholars of distinction, or when the crank himself turns out to possess enough erudition or intellectual energy to continue an enthusiastic promotion of his views.

ESP is no simple crankiness. Dr. Rhine is sincere. There is a Laboratory of Parapsychology at Duke University. Since 1937 the *Journal of Parapsychology* has continued, filled with a variety of researches by a variety of investigators. At least one past-president of the American Psychological Association regards this research seriously and participates in it to some degree. There is great interest among the public. Among both scientists and the public there is also a large group who want mainly to see an underdog have fair play. Altogether ESP provides a perfect picture of an unorthodoxy. Orthodoxy, of course, raises various doubts and objections about ESP, too many for us to consider here. Dr. Kennedy (1952) points to one of them: experimental control needs to be more insulated from the enthusiasm of the investigators than it usually is in ESP. Yet Dr. Kennedy warns without annihilating. An enthusiast could be right for all his enthusiasm.

Then there is Velikovsky. He is nearer crankiness than unorthodoxy; yet his book created a great stir. He had the support of one distinguished philosopher and of many competent newspaper editors—competent as editors but not as scientists. His erudition is quite sufficient to confuse and impress the public, although not Dr. Payne-Gaposchkin (1952) nor the orthodox astronomers. The vehemence of some of these latter may have even won Velikovsky converts, if it is indeed true that there is no such thing as bad publicity. Velikovsky also gains strength with a certain public because he supports a literal interpretation of the Bible in respect of those unusual natural events which he accepts at the expense of orthodox physics, as Dr. Payne-Gaposchkin has made so clear. He has, however, no university laboratory, no special scientific journal running through the years, no great following. He is probably a nova and will soon fade to the dim status of an historical instance of the instability of an intense implausible conviction.

Mr. Riddick did well to confine his discussion of dowsing to Henry Gross' skills, for divining rods go back to classical times and the forked stick to the sixteenth century. This sort of power has been connected with animal magnetism, which in turn has been related to the influence of the planets upon the life of man. *Britannica*, in its article on the Divining Rod, has this to say, and it might indeed have been of Henry Gross: "The best dowsers have generally been more or less illiterate men, engaged in some humble occupation." Certainly Henry does not know how he exercises his powers. Neither did Mesmer in his use of animal magnetism, which served an uncomfortable scientific apprenticeship a full century long before it was admitted to orthodoxy under the nom de guerre *hypnosis* (Boring, 1950a, 116–133). Henry's following was notable but not large. At first it was simply Kenneth Roberts. Later it included Kenneth Roberts' following. Mr. Riddick makes it quite clear how Mr. Roberts stimulated Henry into greater and greater feats, and I can only note that the greater the feat the less indication is there of the use of scientific method to validate the evidence. Dr. Kennedy's advice to the parapsychologists could appropriately be passed on to Mr. Roberts, who needs to know when the seeker after truth must mistrust the effects of his own enthusiasm and when it is in science that humility pays off.

There is, of course, no mystery about Henry Gross' powers. The forked stick snaps down with little muscular pressure, and muscular automatisms are well understood. Henry, as Mr. Riddick makes clear, has good judgment about where to find water, and his muscles and the stick are his means of unconscious automatic communication, though he simply does not know what makes the stick move. That is quite correct, for it is one thing to think and another to know what it is that you think. Only a sophisticated man— and that is not all men—can make his own thinking the object of his further thinking. The best dowsers, as *Britannica* seems to suggest, are those who can perceive water under the ground without the distraction of perceiving how it is that they perceive it.

There are many other unorthodoxies past and present. Some of them Mr. Martin Gardner (1950) has advertised in his paper called "The Hermit Scientist," a title which means that an enthusiasm for an unpopular belief can flourish best when its promoter has become partly inaccessible to the thinking of his colleagues. Best known among these other current unorthodoxies is L. Ron Hubbard's therapy called *dyanetics*, which derives much of its appeal from the desire of men to reduce their own sufferings and worries (Hayakawa, 1951). Not quite out of vogue yet is Dr. Bates, who claims that glasses injure eyesight and that perfect vision is to be gained by throwing your glasses away and allowing your eye-muscles to effect a correction in nature's manner (Huxley, 1942). We cannot, however, undertake here to inventory the better known examples which show that self-assurance is not self-validating.

The Social Nature of Truth

It has become quite clear by now, I hope, that functional, practical truth is social, the truth of agreement, and that absolute truth is actually not available in science. If everyone believes that the sun rises in the east and sets in the west, regularly, every day, why then that is simply the way it is—until some effective skeptical Velikovsky arises to challenge orthodoxy and gets a respectable following.

Now who, it may be asked, does the agreeing? Obviously some in-group. An *in-group* is any group seen sympathetically from inside with regard to its attitudes and beliefs and their causes. An *out-group* is any other group which differs importantly from the in-group in a manner recognized by the in-group. The out-group is always seen critically as from within the in-group. The unbiased eye of history, extolled by Butterfield, keeps shifting its focus, making out-group into in-group, and conversely.

If out-group opposition to the in-group is strong, then the in-group sets up barriers of prejudice against the out-group and unconscious bias reinforces these barriers. The out-group then responds with counterdefensive prejudice. Sometimes enthusiastic innovators, finding no stiff opposition, create a fictitious out-group, straw men against which they can fight, for a movement in science does not move without something to push against. By such positive feed-back are the little absolute predicaments of science's little wars built up.

It is not hard to find good instances of the firm loyalties which hold an in-group together and keep the out-groups at a distance, but I doubt whether there is in science any better example than the in-group that centered upon the ideas and person of Sigmund Freud. It is from Hans Sachs' (1946) charming little life of Freud that you learn how tightly the constraints of loyalty were fixed within that group. Carl Jung never passed the loyalty test and so was never fully admitted. Adler, the crown prince (and that is Sachs' term), had to be banished for his treason about the Ego. Rank succeeded Adler, only to be banished in turn for his belief in the birth trauma. After World War I there were seven of them, six others to whom Freud gave rings resembling his own, so that they might not forget to stand together for the truth of psychoanalysis. Alas, Rank was one of those with the rings! But you see what an in-group is like, a staunch group of believers, passionately sure they have the truth, in this case an unorthodoxy which, after the death of its intransigent leader and only then, is being assimilated into orthodoxy.

In-groups often develop special languages, new systematic terms which begin as shop-talk or laboratory slang, and then, after etymological treatment, emerge as neologisms. The special jargon of psychoanalysis, that runs from the *endopsychic censor* of the early days to the *Super-ego* of the present, is a good example. And a special language promotes in-group solidarity and out-group ostracism. The priests can talk of special things because they know the words. These languages may truly help communication, even when they are promoted by the need for the feeling of solidarity within the group. The best test of their value is their survival. Some neologisms enter the language of science, whereas others are forgotten entirely.

The Scientific Criteria of Belief

To say that agreement is the sanction for truth is really doing little more than to beg the question by saying that people believe what they accept. There is, however, an element of responsibility that enters in here, for agreement is not easy to get, and the agreement of wise men is harder to get, and the agreement of nearly all wise men even more difficult. Some truths are better than others, and we are asking about the criteria for scientific truth, the conditions for agreement in science.

On this matter there are three things to be said.

(1) Scientific agreement means agreement by scientists, by the men best trained to interpret empirical evidence and to see the implications of a new theory for the invalidation or alteration of old theories. The approval of a new

scientific theory by eminent philosophers, novelists, and newspaper editors is approval by inexpert wise men and does not count. Wisdom in one field does not always transfer to another.

In this matter the public is at a disadvantage because its attitude toward scientists is ambivalent. The public tends to respect science but to mistrust the scientist as an impractical academic. The very word *academic* has acquired an opprobrious meaning with the sense of "seemingly true but not really." I have no remedy for this state of affairs which puts the public at a disadvantage in the acceptance of scientific truth. Both Dr. Cohen (1952) and Dr. Payne-Gaposchkin (1952) have already made it amply clear that the traditionalism of the orthodox scientists, egoists though they be, justifies no such unfair verdict as the public often renders of them.

The most important reason for rejecting the authority of the public and of untrained wise men is that they do not know how to evaluate empirical evidence. Not only are they likely to accept the report of a single instance without taking account of negative cases, but they also put too much reliance on the printed word. Take the case of "The Astounding Jimmy Walker," an instance to which Mr. Martin Gardner has called my attention.

In 1950 Jim Walker (1950) was demonstrating telepathy on a radio program. To support his claim for genuineness he reproduced in a magazine two letters from a Dr. George McClenahan, Director of the Board of Research of the Department of Psychology of the University of Texas, letters written on a printed letterhead for this university department. Dr. McClenahan's first letter was incredulous and skeptical and in it he challenged Jim Walker to a test, but in his second letter he ate crow, coming out in full support of Jim Walker's powers. Jim Walker, he wrote, had passed a crucial test, for he had called up Dr. McClenahan and named the five words which Dr. McClenahan had in his mind, all names of bones in the ankle. Could you ask for more convincing evidence? Disbelief, conversion, recantation, conviction. That is indeed one way to convince the public. In this case there was, however, a third letter which another magazine presently reproduced. It was from Karl M. Dallenbach, the chairman of the Department of Psychology at the University of Texas. It had to say that Dr. McClenahan does not exist, that his alleged position does not exist, and that the letterhead had been especially printed for the purpose of deception (1951). So there you are. If the second letter persuaded you to believe, then this third letter probably snapped you over into disbelief. What happens if I now produce a fourth letter which asserts that Dallenbach is a hoax? In short, the printed word is not self-validating, but the public does not fully realize that.

(2) The basic feature that distinguishes scientific observation from other empirical forms of assessing nature is *control*. The scientist mistrusts his own capacity for forming unbiased inferences and he insists on control as a way of protecting his conclusions from his predilections. Control may mean keeping conditions as constant as you can. In its technical sense, it means substituting

the more accurate relative judgments for the inaccurate absolute ones. You observe best a difference between events, not simply an event. You see, for instance, how the experimental group differs from the control group, or the experimental series from the control series. Dr. Kennedy has described the need for control in research on ESP. In general he warns all scientists to mistrust the effects of their own biases and so to design their experiments that personal predilection, if it enters into significant differences, can at least have its effects measured.

Not all wise human action can be scientific. Control may be impracticable. The institutions of government, medicine, and education all have frequently to act in the absence of evidence obtained under controlled conditions. Society is not yet ready to use scientific method on all possible occasions, and in many situations controlled experiment is actually impossible.

(3) The third thing to say about the validation of scientific belief is that you must not fail to consider the weight of the total evidence. This is Dr. Payne-Gaposchkin's point about Velikovsky, a principle that has also been stressed recently by Laurence Lafleur who, like Dr. Payne-Gaposchkin, has a special interest in Velikovsky. All of Lafleur's seven criteria boil down to the necessity for suspending judgment about a small consistency which contradicts a great mass of interrelated other consistencies (1951). Velikovsky, we have seen, throws away Newtonian mechanics in order to support the Biblical narrative. What substitute, ask both Payne-Gaposchkin and Lafleur, has he got for Newtonian mechanics? Are we to abandon the more fully confirmed larger system in order to believe in a smaller and imperfectly plausible contradiction?

That is all I have to say. The thing to do with the little wars in science is, in my opinion, not to try to eliminate them but to understand them and their participants. Scientists are human beings. Enthusiasm, and insecurity, and egoism, and the desire for adventure and change as well as the desire for security and no change, and the need for companionship in intellectual endeavor, and sympathy for the underdog, and the intolerance of intolerance— all these and many other human attributes and needs contribute to that form of turbulence which posterity ultimately sees as scientific progress. The unorthodoxies come, and many of them go, and a few are absorbed into an orthodoxy which keeps changing under progress. It would not do for us to attempt to police enthusiasm, but it is important to understand it and its effects, to criticize it and to point out its dangers. Velikovsky may yet do us a service by becoming a paradigm for how a scientific belief is not to be induced, and Rhine, if I may here introduce my own opinion on ESP, may become the paradigm for the waste of energy when boundless enthusiasm is directed upon a poorly formulated problem. As to Henry Gross, he has already become a specimen of the way in which unconscious motivation can influence action and leave but little trace of its own course.

The Mind-Body Problem

᠁᠁᠁᠁᠁᠁᠁᠁᠁᠁᠁᠁᠁᠁᠁᠁᠁᠁᠁᠁᠁᠁᠁᠁᠁᠁᠁᠁

*I*F others than philosophers should work on the mind-body problem, who should they be? To represent the mind, a person thoroughly schooled and experienced in introspective psychology—a representative of the great effort to make a science of conscious experience. To represent the body, one erudite in physiological psychology. To represent the times, one who understood the grounds of behaviorism's revolt against introspectionism. Boring is all of these, and in these papers he uses these skills to present a coherent resolution of the mind-body problem.*

To be fair to the philosophers, we should also acknowledge that E.G.B. brings more to the task than scientific skills. His solution is colored by philosophical commitments. He is a vigorous positivist, operationist, and physicalist. He is a vigorous opponent of dualism, particularly in ontology, but also in epistemology, and his physicalism tells the monism he chooses.

If this description makes him sound like a behaviorist rejecting conscious experience, then the picture is incomplete. For with his positivism, physicalism, monism, he continues to work on the problems of the introspectionist— on perception, memory, sensation, imagery. In behaviorism, the positivistic reform was achieved by avoiding such problems; in Boring, by applying to them improved criteria of meaningfulness.

E.G.B.'s position of 1922–1937 ends up in general agreement with Feigl's position of 1958 (Feigl, 1958), except that Boring is even less dualistic. Feigl's "dual aspect" or "synthetic identity" principle, while ontologically monistic, partakes of what has been called an epistemological dualism. Even this de-

253

gree of dualism E.G.B. rejects and avoids, most explicity in the final paper of this section.

We have placed the four papers of this section in chronological order, since they are spread out enough in time to constitute a developmental sequence. In "The Stimulus-Errror," originally published in 1921, E.G.B. deals exhaustively with a major methodological problem bequeathed by the dying introspective psychology in which he had been trained. The clarification of this problem provides the earliest use of his approach to the mind-body problem and his positivistic methodological orientation. This is also his first influential paper. Eleven years later, he attempts to shock dualists by his title "The Physiology of Consciousness." This paper provides the most convenient introduction to the common theme of this section, and represents briefly his views as they appear in his 1933 book, The Physical Dimensions of Consciousness. The two final papers "Psychophysical Systems and Isomorphic Relations" and "A Psychological Function is the Relation of Successive Differentiations of Events in the Organism," represent definite developments beyond the 1933 book. They provide the final statement of his monistic resolution of the mind-body problem.

The Stimulus-Error

🝆🝆🝆🝆🝆🝆🝆🝆🝆🝆🝆🝆🝆 1921

THE purpose of this paper is to discuss the "stimulus-error," to indicate something of its history (though limits of space will preclude
more than a bare outline), to add something by way of definition (since
definition has remained implicit and there are some who do not understand
this term), to inquire, at the level of the scientific experiment, into the significance of the attitude which is thus styled an "error" (relying as much
upon experimental observation and as little upon epistemological conviction
as is possible), and to arrive, it may be, at an evaluation of the stimulus-
error or stimulus-attitude in its relation to the psychology of the present day.[1]
This is not so large an order that it does not need filling. Some psychologists
put out of court experiments that involve the stimulus-error; others refuse to
see any "error" at all and discount the works that stress this "merely epistemological" distinction. And when we seek a sanction for the one view or
the other, we are at a loss whither to turn, for the "stimulus-error," although
it has a long history, has been left to make its way without any very formal
introduction.

Undoubtedly much of the confusion and disagreement has been brought
about by the term itself: "stimulus-error." It implies something that is right
and something that is wrong, defending one position and impugning another.
It serves, and was intended, to throw two positions into contrast, to insist
upon an important distinction that is often overlooked; yet does not stop
with definition, but goes on to pass a judgment. In this dual function of the
phrase there has been both an advantage and a disadvantage. To those who
accept both the implied distinction and the explicit evaluation the notion
has been exceedingly useful, for it has enabled them, not only to separate the
methodological sheep from the goats, but also to dispense with the goats—
a telescoping of procedure that is convenient and economical. On the other

Reprinted with permission from *The American Journal of Psychology*, 1921, **32**, 449–471.

hand, those psychologists who have staked their fortunes on the goats of stimulus are not to be reformed by being found in the way of the "stimulus-error." They simply deny the "error" and in so doing miss the more fundamental distinction between opposing positions that must be made out before judgment can be passed upon either. We ourselves must not be thus misled, whatever our ultimate judgment may be.

This implied opposition, which we must now bear clearly in mind, is the fundamental opposition in psychology—or between psychologies—of mental process and meaning, of content and object, of *Beschreibung* and *Kundgabe*. Titchener, who is responsible for the term "stimulus-error," puts the case thus:

> We are constantly confusing sensations with their stimuli, with their objects, with their meanings. Or rather—since the sensation of psychology has no object or meaning—we are constantly confusing logical abstraction with psychological analysis; we abstract a certain aspect of an object or meaning, and then treat this aspect as if it were a simple mental process, an element in the mental representation of the object or meaning. . . . We do not say, in ordinary conversation, that this visual sensation is lighter than that, but that this pair of gloves or this kind of grey paper is lighter than this other. We do not say that this complex of cutaneous or organic sensations is more intensive than that, but that this box or package is heavier than this other. We do not even say, as a rule, that this tonal quality is lower than that, but rather that this instrument is flat and must be tuned up to this other. Always in what we say there is a reference to the objects, to the meaning of the conscious complex. It is not the grey, pressure, tone, that we are thinking of; but the grey of leather or paper, the pressure of the box, the pitch of the violin. . . . What is more natural than to read the character of the stimuli, of the objects, into the "sensations" with which certain aspects of the stimulus or object are correlated? . . . This is what Fechner did. . . . [He] transferred to sensation a point of view that is right for stimulus, but that introspection refuses to recognize in psychology (Titchener, 1905, II, i, xxvi ff.).[2]

We commit the stimulus-error if we base our psychological reports upon objects rather than upon the mental material itself, or if, in the psychophysical experiment, we make judgments of the stimulus and not judgments of sensation. At the more complex levels we may make a similar error, a "meaning-error," which consists of describing objects, reporting meanings, stating *Kundgabe*, instead of describing mental process or giving *Beschreibung*. We cannot, however, in this paper, extend the discussion to include this complex level, but must content ourselves with the conviction that whatever applies in the controversy between judgment of stimulus and judgment of sensation, applies also to introspection and its rival, the statement of meaning. We may concede that the psychophysical experiment in its simplicity represents the ideal ultimate in the psychological experiment, where control of conditions and adequacy of observation are maximal; and that we should be glad to reduce all psychological observation to this degree of rigor at least.

At any rate any extension of this discussion to the "higher" processes must wait, for the history and application of the stimulus-error are at the level of psychophysics, and the interpretation of the "stimulus-error," up to which we are leading, shows most clearly here.

The Quantity Objection and the Stimulus-Error

It is not surprising that a psychophysics, which seeks to establish the relation between the mental and the physical, should emphasize the distinction between sensation and stimulus. What is surprising is that the opponents of psychophysics should have raised this very distinction for the confounding of psychophysics and should have claimed that the psychophysical relationship (the logarithmic relation of the Weber-Fechner law) was an artifact created, not by the attempt of the psychophysicist to distinguish between sensation and stimulus, but by his confusion of the two. Yet such is the substance of the "quantity objection" to psychophysics, which had later to be met with the psychological sense-distance by Müller, Titchener, and others, who thus turned the tables and brought the argument for the distinction between mental and physical materal to the support of a Fechnerian psychophysics. This was a long and tedious battle, and one might have expected that the resultant emphasis upon the two-fold nature of psychophysics would have determined the psychophysical universe for a time. On the contrary, however, the confusion between sensation and stimulus persisted. Cattell was fathering a psychology of the stimulus, and it was in the tradition of the work of Fullerton and Cattell that Urban did his experiments. Now that behaviorism has come into vogue, it is not apparent that we do not have two kinds of psychophysics—a psychophysics of process that gives, as Fechner wanted, the correlation between mental and physical data, and a psychophysics of behavior that seeks to identify response with its stimulus. That this psychophysics of stimulus-and-response needs also, if it is to be scientific, to take account of the error that has been called the "stimulus-error" is the thesis of the present paper; but the thesis must wait upon the perspective of the preface.

A clear recognition of the distinction between mind and body, between consciousness and objects, was the key-note of Fechner's position. There was for him at least this dualism in the universe, which may be regarded from one standpoint or the other. The case is not unlike, Fechner argued, the Ptolemaic and Copernican worlds. The geocentric and heliocentric solar systems are different systems, and we may at pleasure take either point of view that we choose. The worlds remain distinct. Or the matter is like a circle, which may be viewed from the inside or the outside. In the one case we see only concavity, in the other only convexity. Such a dualism can be resolved only by the law of relationship that holds between its two aspects, and, just as the relationship between concavity and convexity can be stated geometrically for the circle, so the logarithmic law resolves the dualism of mind and body. There is no doubt, therefore, that Fechnerian psychophysics stands or falls according to its success in distinguishing between measurements of mind and measurements of body, or between sensation and the object of sensation, the stimulus (Fechner, 1889, I, 1–12).

The vigorous opposition that developed to Fechner's psychophysics took its stand firmly upon the distinction between mind and body, but denied the possibility of a quantitative correlation between the two on the ground that mind was not possessed of magnitude and that mental measurement was an impossibility. This argument came to be known as the "quantity objection" and was the main source of opposition to quantitative psychology in the eighties and nineties of last century. Introspection, the objection runs, does not show that a sensation of great magnitude ever contains other sensations of lesser magnitude in the way that a heavy weight may [supposedly] be made up of a number of smaller weights. "Our feeling of pink," said James (1890a, I, 546), "is surely not a portion of our feeling of scarlet; nor does the light of an electric arc seem to contain that of a tallow-candle in itself." "This sensation of 'gray,'" remarked Külpe (1895, 45), "is not two or three of that other sensation of 'gray.'" "A blue surface," Ebbinghaus commented, "is something other than a green, but the latter has in itself, apart from memory of the colors, nothing of the doubleness or threefoldness of the green. . . . A low tone sounds different from a high tone, and in like manner a loud tone different from a soft" (Ebbinghaus, 1890, 323). In other words increase of magnitude in no sense means increase of complexity. A sensation is just itself no matter what its degree. The tone produced by many instruments in unison is not of itself composed of more units than is the tone from a single string, nor is the tone of many vibrations per second more complex than the tone of few vibrations. In this form the objection seems obvious enough. Sensational magnitude is certainly not multitude, and intense sensations are not integrated of more sensory stuff than are weak.[3] How then was psychophysics to defend itself?

Its immediate defense was a display of the factual material. Here were the experimental measurements. If they were not observations of the magnitudes of sensation, what were they?

To this question the raisers of the "quantity objection" replied that psychophysicists had created an artificial mental magnitude by a confusion of the sensation with the stimulus, that is to say, they had committed in their experimental work the "stimulus-error." This was a serious charge against a discipline that depended for its existence upon a sharp distinction between the mental and the physical. Let us see how the accusers dared to raise it.

Von Kries put the matter clearly:

An illusion is thus very easily brought about by the fact that one tends in general to estimate objective values (measurable in objective terms) according to the sensation. If one, however, excludes this source of error, and in so far as possible things not at all of the objective process serving as a stimulus, then one must necessarily admit that a quantitative relation does not exist between the different parts of an intensive series. This fact is most obvious to us when we do not attempt objectification as, e.g., in pain. Whatever it is called, a pain exactly ten times as strong as another does not admit of such absolute statement (von Kries, 1882).

Ebbinghaus, somewhat later, was even more explicit:

In general one designates the brightness of a flame or a surface as 10 or 12 times another brightness, and could just as easily, it appears, designate a loud tone as the double or treble of a soft tone. But what occurs here is no longer an immediate sensation or an immediate judgment of sensations, but depends upon the introduction of experiences. We can readily experience, and we do every day experience, the fact that the arousal of a brightness or a loudness depends upon a diversity of just those physical things or processes that in limited number call forth the impression of darker or softer. In order to have an impression of greater brightness for a surface, one can increase the number of gas-flames illuminating it; in order to strengthen a tone; one multiplies the instruments carrying it. Such experiences with respect to the causes of sensations we have always in immediate view, and we believe that we have the numerical characteristics that always attach to the one occurring without anything further in the other. It is psychologically difficult to get rid of them, just as it is difficult not immediately to see in a grass-green apple its sourness. But if one succeeds in the perfectly possible separation of the thought context, then it is clear that, as the bare visual impression of an apple has no sourness in it, similarly the bare impression of brightness does not consist of the multiplicity of candles upon which, of course, it frequently depends (Ebbinghaus, 1890, 323 f.; 1905, 71–79).

We have already seen what, fifteen years later, Titchener had to say in the same vein and how, although defending mental measurement, he makes the charge of the stimulus-error against Fechner. And there were many others.

Exner put forward the general argument (1879, 242) followed by Boas (1882, 568 f.). Tannery (1883, 138) said: "It is the objective study of the excitation and its variations that leads to this definition of number that measures the sensation. At bottom it is by excitation that sensation is defined." On epistemological grounds both F. A. Müller (1882, 46–56) and Meinong (1896, 96 f.) concluded that mental magnitudes, unlike physical, were indivisible. And long before any of these, Brentano, the father of modern intentional psychology, had said: "If one measures, as Fechner did, the intensities of colors, tones, etc., then one is measuring the intensities of physical phenomena. The color is not the seeing, the tone is not the hearing, the warmth is not the sensing of warmth" (Brentano, 1874, 91).

Nevertheless this still seems a surprising charge to bring against Fechnerian psychophysics. If the fundamental task of psychophysics is the discovery of the relationship between the hitherto unrelated body and mind, is it not astonishing that psychophysics should have confused the two, the two whose very separateness was the *raison d'être* of psychophysics? Yet the critics stuck to the point and were at pains to show the readiness with which these incommensurables did duty, the one for the other. Ward, pointing out that the psychophysical limen expressed in terms of stimulus was physical quantity, concluded: "There is no trespass harder to avoid than that across the lines dividing the subjective and objective aspects, and none more disastrous to the offender" (Ward, 1876, esp. 460). Other writers urged the same point, and Külpe even brought the prevalence of objectification into an experimental study (Külpe, 1902). It is no wonder then that objectification was thought of as a source of error and that Titchener coined for it the term "stimulus-error."

The Answer to the Quantity Objection

The fundamental and final answer to the quantity objection was Weber's law: $S = k \log R$. In so far as the relationship had been observed, no amount of explaining could explain it entirely away. It might be that the function was not exactly logarithmic or that it held only within certain limits; it might not be certain just what was the nature of S, or of R; but the unescapable fact was that there were an S and an R, which were covariant and which were not identical since the mode of variation of the one was not the mode of variation of the other. To charge the stimulus-error and say that S was contaminated by R was not enough, since the confusion of S with R was not enough to explain the discovery of this difference in variation. The psychophysicists, therefore, had the stronger position, and had only to show where the difference actually lay. There seem to be five ways of accounting for the difference and thus of establishing psychophysics.

1. Systematically one may argue for a physiological interpretation of Weber's law, as Müller did (1878, 224–403). Excitation varies somewhat as does the logarithm of the stimulus. No one doubts that excitation may have magnitude, and thus the quantity objection is met. Moreover the logarithmic relation between physical dependents is not unknown.[4] Excitation, however, does not happen to be open to immediate observation, so we must observe its correlate sensation. We deal therefore with stimulus and sensation, which we must keep apart, avoiding the stimulus-error; and we escape from the formal objection that sensation does not have magnitude by making it a mere qualitative indicator of excitation which must have magnitude.

2. Wundt's psychological interpretation of Weber's law meets the quantity objection by the introduction of *Merklichkeitsgrade*. Sensations do not have magnitude, but if they did the matter would be irrelevant to psychophysics. It is apperception that gives a quantitative aspect to mind; there

are degrees of noticeableness to sensations or to the differences between them.[5] The sensation scarlet is not more than the sensation pink, but is more noticeable than the pink; and the difference between the scarlet and a pale pink is more noticeable than the difference between the scarlet and a rose. To introspection it is just as obvious that apperception has degree as it is obvious that sensation has not, and it is between these *Merklichkeitsgrade* and the physical values of the stimulus that the logarithmic law holds.

3. What was Fechner's answer to the quantity objection? To deny the stimulus-error, which the quantity objection implies. In the *Revision* he wrote:

> One must take care not to try to count relations that exist in the physical realm between physical units as existing within the mental province because they can be grasped only by the mind; for in so doing one loses the ground for distinction between the two provinces. Even the physical, within which the relations exist, must be grasped by our minds in order to exist for us and to be spoken about. Yet we discriminate on the basis of this community between outer and inner phenomena as between two provinces, and have to distinguish properties as belonging in the one or the other, not merged with each other or interchangeable, as might sometimes seem to be the case under a philosophical point of view. At any rate psychophysics takes this point of view and thus avoids confusion. Whenever something like a relation, a change, a difference, a unity, or a fusion, etc., appears as characterizing the physical or psychical world, it is abstracted from the province of the one or the other, or it is counted into the one or the other province; it may occur just as readily in psychology as in natural science. Hence it is perfectly possible that the pitches should be represented in one province by something in the other province without our identifying the two. The relations of periodicity between vibrations, which occur as the psychophysical representatives of melodic and harmonic sensations, are the most obvious; the one is something very different from the other (Fechner, 1882, 5 f.).

In other words it is all in our point of view. We can judge the stimuli or we can judge the sensations; and, according as we do the one or the other, we constitute for ourselves the physical or the mental world. It is nonsense to assume that, because we make judgments of physical phenomena in building up natural science, this natural science is a science of judgments and therefore mental. The two are distinct, and the discovery of the difference that is summarized by Weber's law attests the distinction.

To the writer of this paper it seems that Fechner's argument, turned a different way, becomes at least as invincible as any of the other ways out of the difficulty. The trick for escaping the force of the quantity objection, when directed against mental phenomena, is to turn it upon the stimuli themselves. Suppose sensations of weight do not under observation exhibit magnitude; what of the physical weights themselves? To physical observation ten grams is *a* weight and one gram is *a* weight; it is only in common sense, which is assuredly not physics, that ten grams is ten one-gram weights. Because physical phenomena, like mental, are referable to objects, is no excuse for reading the objects into them. Physical weight is as little the number of objects in the scale-pan as mental weight is the number of weights in the hand. The physical quantity is just as simple and unitary as the mental, and if sensation lacks magnitude so must stimulus. We can hardly, however, deny measurement to physics, and it thus appears that the quantity objection is not valid either against the measurement of sensation.[6]

4. Undoubtedly the most general way of meeting the quantity objection while saving mental measurement is by the substitution of the sense-distance for the sensation magnitude. Historically this conception dates from Delboeuf's *contraste sensible*. It is not necessarily incompatible with any of the foregoing accounts of mental measurement and is endorsed essentially by Wundt, Boas, Stumpf, Ebbinghaus, James, Meinong, Höfler, Stout, and G. E. Müller (Titchener, 1905, II, ii, cxxxii). It is the basis of Titchener's quantitative psychology where it finds its clearest exposition (Titchener, 1905, II, i, xxi–xxvii; ii, cxvi–cxliv).

This position holds that sensations, although they do not possess magnitude, may lie within a continuum, and that, although we can form no quantitative estimate of any sensation, we can nevertheless estimate the relative degree of separateness of two sensations within the continuum. Sensations are simply themselves and are not summed of various numbers of increments; the distances between these sensations, however, do vary and can be estimated in amount. The simplest case of mental measurement occurs when, for a series of three sensations, A, B, and C, occurring in a continuum, we estimate the sense-distance AB as equal to the sense-distance BC. Here we have measurement, for we have laid off the unit AB = BC twice in the distance AC, and it is the correlation of such estimated sense-distances with the corresponding values of stimulus that gives Weber's Law.

5. All the foregoing modes of meeting the quantity objection are successful without sacrificing the possibility of mental measurement; the fifth mode of defense consists in joining the enemy. We can give up the measurement of mind, substituting the measurement of sensitivity or of capacity-for-discrimination. Fullerton and Cattell give us our orientation here.

They declare, in the first place, that both sensation magnitudes and sense-distances are undiscoverable:

> If an observer can, in fact, estimate quantitative amounts of difference in sensation, apart from association with known quantitative differences in the stimuli, a relation between mental and physical intensity can be determined. The writers, however, agree in finding that they cannot estimate such quantitative differences in sensation in a satisfactory manner. We can indeed say when one weight seems approximately double another, but this is doubtless because we have often lifted first one volume, and then two, and the like. But we cannot say when one sound seems twice as loud, or one day twice as hot as another. We have made experiments to see how nearly different observers

would agree in adjusting one shade of light midway between two others, and have found hesitation in coming to a decision and great divergence of opinion. Most men will think that a just king is happier than a tyrant, but few will agree with Plato in considering him 729 times as happy (Fullerton & Cattell, 1892, 20).

What is left? The observed *stimuli* (Fullerton & Cattell, 1892, 9 ff., 20, 153) and errors of observation incurred in observing the stimuli (Fullerton & Cattell, 1892, 14 ff.; Cattell, 1893, 287 ff.). There is no constant just noticeable difference or threshold. We have only errors of observation as we fail to observe an actual difference in the stimuli or, less often, observe a difference that is not there. These errors can be treated under the ordinary calculus of probabilities and follow the normal law of error. The amount of the average error is always determinable and it increases with the magnitude of the stimulus. It is the law of the dependence of the average error of observation upon the magnitude of the stimulus that Weber's law seeks to state, although the mathematical form of Weber's law is actually incorrect (Fullerton & Cattell, 1892, 11, 12 ff., 150, 152, 153 ff.; Cattell, 1893, 285, 290).

Such a quantitative psychology of error is of necessity a psychology of capacity (Titchener, 1905, II, ii, cxxxiv note)—of the capacity of the organism to respond correctly to stimuli. This point of view has since developed into the statistics of mental tests and of behaviorism, which is a psychology of stimulus and response. It is a point of view for which there is no stimulus-error since quantitative judgments can be made only of the stimulus, and it is one that touches other sciences very closely since it concerns itself with observation, the method of every science (Fullerton & Cattell, 1892, 9; Cattell, 1893, 285).

The Two Psychologies

Thus it becomes evident that the answers to the quantity objection have divided along the traditional cleft in psychology. We have not only a psychology of datum and a psychology of capacity, but we have quantitative psychologies of datum and of capacity (Külpe, 1920, 5; Titchener, 1921, 108–120).

The quantitative psychology of datum ["the given"] insists upon a truly mental measurement. When further it correlates these mental measurements it is the true psychophysics. It may answer the quantity objection in any of the first four of the five foregoing ways, because any one of those four insists upon or explains the existence of mental quanta. It is a part of the larger psychology that is variously called structural or introspective, the psychology of process or of *Beschreibung*.

The quantitative psychology of capacity admits the quantity objection and denies—or at least ignores—mental quanta. This psychology sees no distinctively mental measurement, but undertakes the physical measurement of bodily response as a function of the physical quantities of the stimulus. There is no sharp epistemological line discernible between this sort of measurement and other physical measurement, and it thus meets the requirement of modern behaviorism that psychology interpenetrate physical science without sensible demarcation (Watson, 1913*b*, 177; 1913*a*, 427; 1919). The psychology of capacity is also the psychology of mental tests (Titchener, 1905) and of Urban's psychophysical experiments.[7] These latter seem strange mates, but the influence of Cattell is apparent in both. If the germ of the tests was in Galton, nevertheless it was Cattell, in the interests of the psychology of individual differences, who planted it in American soil where it has brought forth fruit abundantly. Urban's origin is less apparent. It is trivial to remark that he began his psychophysics in the laboratory that Cattell had founded years before. The evidence is internal and not explicit, but the seeker after information can find it.[8] In the broad, we may add, the psychology of capacity may become a functional psychology and deal, when it is experimental, with *meanings* and *Kundgaben* instead of mental processes and *Beschreibung*.

As a term the "stimulus-error" is the property of the psychology of datum. It characterizes the attitude of the psychology of capacity as being concerned observationally with the stimulus and admonishes against it. Of course the psychology of capacity ignores this admonition, for in making observations of the physical stimulus it is simply fulfilling its self-appointed task. The "stimulus-error" is no valid charge against this psychology, nor does it raise within it a question of right and wrong. No more can be expected of either psychology than that it hold to its premises.

In practice there is a difficulty, however. No matter how distinct the two psychologies may be, psychologists can scarcely hold strictly to the one or to the other. The psychologist of the datum can not be expected to attack a new perception without recourse to judgments of stimulus or of meaning (Hoisington, 1920), and statements of meanings moreover may themselves become the object of psychological investigation (Weld, 1917). As to whether the psychology of capacity might remain wholly faithful to the stimulus, it is not so easy to say. This attitude is more natural and it is possible to complete entire experiments without once trespassing upon the realm of mental process. On the other hand, the functional psychologies for all they have to say of the inadequacies of structural psychology, seem usually unable to complete the systematic mental picture alone, and a recent system of behaviorism has drawn unhesitatingly upon the psychology that it seeks to supplant (Watson, 1919). In general, what is fundamental to the one can not be ignored by the other, and on this account the writer of this paper would urge the attention of the psychologist of capacity to the "stimulus-error."

The Effect of the Stimulus-Error

If we are now to urge upon the psychology of capacity the avoidance of the stimulus-error, it is a fair demand that we state first the probable penalty that is incurred by a failure to accept our advice. Here we can not stand upon the epistemological ground that psychology observes mental processes and not stimuli, and that judgments of stimulus are therefore *a priori* inadmissible. This historical warning against the stimulus-error does not apply to the psychology of capacity which protests against a scientific dualism and deals by preference with stimulus and response. What we have to show is rather that the stimulus-error works against the establishment of the univocal correlations between stimulus and response that a psychology of capacity demands, that it interferes with the prediction of the response for a given stimulus. Here the ground is broadly scientific: we are dealing with the constancy of experimental conditions and the reproducibility of results.

When we go frankly to the literature, however, asking just what in numerical terms may be the effect in mental measurement of allowing judgments of the stimulus or of instituting them, we meet at first disappointment.

The psychology of datum is set to avoid, rather than to measure, the stimulus-error. It tells us where the stimulus-error is most insidious, *viz.*, in judgments of supraliminal sense distances (Titchener, 1910, 218). We may have trouble with the limens; we are almost sure to have it in comparing large sense-distances. Sometimes a special technique is necessary to avoid the error. In Martius' experiment on the apparent size of objects at different distances from the eye, all the stimulus habits for the estimation of the size of objects in everyday life are appealed to, and a special method is required "in removing the initial tendency of the observers to reflect on the actual size of the comparison rod in relation to the standard rod" (Martius, 1889; Titchener, 1905, ii, 262 f.). In Angell's (1891, 438) experiment on intensive distances between sounds one would expect concrete reference to the stimulus to enter much less readily; on the contrary, however, the observers tend to judge the height of fall or the angle of fall of the stimulus, and to neglect the mental datum. For this error special remedies are presented. Müller urges that the amount of intensive difference be taken as the *Kohärenzgrad*, the *Leichtigkeit des Kollectivaufgefasstwerdens* of the two sounds (1903). Titchener (1905, II, ii, 198, 203 f., 230) suggests letting the observer blunder into the stimulus-error and then rescuing him by individualized treatment, his protocols in hand. These experiments are striking cases, but even the psychologists who have no special measures of reform to offer cry out against the evils of judgments based upon secondary criteria, upon associates of the processes judged, or upon surrogate processes (Fechner, 1889, II, 318 ff.; Angell, 1891, 438; Ament, 1900, 173; Müller, 1903; Fröbes, 1904, 259). A surrogate, they complain, can even render incommensurables artificially commensurate, as seems to be the case when the intensities of weights and noises are compared in terms of *Spannungsempfindungen* (Münsterberg, 1900, 56–122).

Now it is not likely that there could be so much smoke without some fire; yet we are still at a loss to estimate the amount of danger. It would be reasonable for these psychologists of datum to seek to avoid stimulus for no other reason than that they are interested solely in "mind," but it is not to be supposed that the matter would have been taken so seriously had the quantitative results, and Weber's law which is dependent upon them, been unaffected by the kind of judgment given. Indeed this belief came to the surface when Grotenfelt, in defense of Weber's law, accused Merkel of the stimulus-error and inclined to the belief that results that followed Merkel's law might possibly indicate that they were based upon judgments of stimulus (Grotenfelt, 1888, 111 f.; Titchener, 1905, II, ii, lxxviii f., 219). The data that we wish, however—the comparison in quantitative terms of results of judgments of process—are, in the earlier history of psychophysics, lacking.

(The psychologists of capacity, we may note in passing, are not to be asked for this comparison. Cattell and Fullerton denied the possibility of mental measurement. They can not therefore be asked for its comparison with any form of physical measurement.)

On the basis of recent literature, however, there is something to be said, in answering this question, for the case of lifted weights, and very much to be said for the case of the limen of dual cutaneous impression. We may mention the lifted weights at once and reserve the two-point limen for the next section.

Friedländer (1920) undertook a comparative study of lifting weights under different *Einstellungen*. He employed a *"G-Einstellung"* in which the attention was directed upon the lifted object (*Gegenstand*, hence G), and an *"A-Einstellung"* in which the object was abstracted from (hence A) and the attention directed upon the sensory aspect of the experience (*Druck-, Spannungs-, Kraftempfindungen*). Here we should expect to find the results we are seeking, for the *G-Einstellung* is the stimulus-attitude, the attitude demanded by a psychology of capacity and called the "stimulus-error" by the psychology of datum; and the *A-Einstellung* in its various forms is the process-attitude which avoids the "stimulus-error." There is not the least doubt that the two attitudes give different results. "Differential sensitivity on the whole is somewhat finer for the G-series" for a standard weight of 500 g., Friedländer tells us, but a standard of 1200 g. may give a finer discrimination under the *A-Einstellung*. The data unfortunately are for one observer only. They are based on too few cases—41 series after the practice-effect was presumably constant. The observer did not always succeed in maintaining the required attitude, for the stimulus-attitude was difficult for him (!) and he sought to make his finer discriminations under the A-*Einstellung*. The resultant psycho-metric functions are not smooth ogives; one just barely misses inversion in its central portion.[9] We are not yet ready, then, to generalize as to the exact effect of attending to the stimulus in making psychophysical judgments. All we can say is that there is an effect, that a shift in the observational attitude alters the numerical results significantly. We shall not dare, therefore, if we wish to predict response from stimulus, to leave attitude out of account.

My colleague, Professor Fernberger, has recently completed similar experiments in the Clark Laboratory. He had three observers, and extended his series through many fractions to take account of progressive practice and to give an adequate number of cases. His resultant ogives are smooth and regular, and his procedure seemed calculated to yield all that could be desired methodically. He gets differences for the different attitudes—more striking differences in some cases than Friedländer's. More than this I cannot say in advance of the publication of his results. Perhaps in his final analysis he will discover a generalization, which is not apparent to casual inspection of the functions and constants. The results indicate unquestionably that an alteration of attitude by instruction may result in an alteration of the psychometric functions, which is significant in the mathematical sense of being many times its probable error, but which for a given observer is unfortunately quite unpredictable. Attitude may be very important even when we cannot say just why.

Fortunately the case of the two-point limen is less mysterious.

The Stimulus-Error as Equivocal Correlation

The limen of dual impression upon the skin furnishes the case for which we are looking. We know not only that judgments of stimulus may here make a difference in the quantitative results, but we know further how great this difference may be and something of its conditions. We are in a position, moreover, to generalize from these facts with some assurance and to assert that the effect of the "stimulus-error," from the point of view of a psychology of capacity, is—under similar conditions, at least—to render the correlations between stimulus and response equivocal and thus to jeopardize the rigor of conclusion that science demands.

We may proceed to the point by reference to the visual schema of the figure reproduced herewith. The diagram is intended merely to assist in the analysis of the factors involved and not as an actual picture of neural or psycho-physical fact.

One deals in determining the two-point limen with a series of stimuli, A, B, C, D, E, pairs of stimulus-points at different separations, with perhaps a single point, A, at the extreme of the series. From the work of numerous investigators (Tawney, 1895; Henri, 1898*b*, 6; Foucault, 1910, 122–145; Gates,

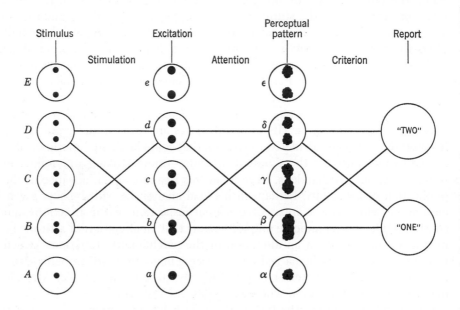

1915) we know that there is a similar series of perceptual patterns, α, β, γ, δ, ε, which passes, with approximate regularity, from a sharp point to a blunt point, to an oval, to an elongated oval, to a double-paddle, to a dumb-bell, to two separated points. We may best think of these perceptual patterns as the process material of the psychology of datum, but they exist also for the psychology of capacity as inscrutable "middle terms." Intermediate between stimulus and process we are accustomed to assume some sort of excitatory process, a, b, c, d, e. Of these there must also be a series, and knowing little about them, we may picture them as somewhat like the perceptual processes. Finally there is the verbal report which is generally limited experimentally to the words *One* and *Two*. It seems, moreover, that we keep within the limits of scientific good sense if we say that stimulus, excitation, mental process, and report form a dependent series, and that each is the resultant of the preceding.

If now we choose for special consideration the stimuli B and D, we may note that they most frequently, perhaps, give rise to the dependent series "B-b-β-One" and "D-d-δ-Two," but we must note further that cross-connections are possible.

Stimulus gives rise to excitation by way of stimulation. Here variation may tend either in the direction of fusion or of separation. On the forearm, for example, the angular shifting of stimulus toward the longitudinal axis may result in fusion and D may give rise to b; if the rotation is toward the transverse axis, d may follow upon B (Tawney, 1897; Boring, 1916). Location as well as angular orientation also yields these differences. Near the elbow D gives b, say; a little further down B may give d (Henri, 1898*b*, 26 f.; Boring, 1916). It is also possible that the chance impingement of the stimulus-points upon multiple innervated spots in the skin gives rise to multiple excitation (B to d) and that the stimulation of less complexly innervated spots may lead to a simpler excitation (D to b) (Henri, 1898*b*, 64 ff.; Boring, 1916).

At the next phase of our series excitation culminates in perceptual pattern under the selective action of attention. These terms sound strange of course to the psychologist of capacity, but we may ask him to accept them or to find substitutes for them. They stand for factors that affect the correlations with which he is working, and he must take scientific account of them, whatever he calls them.

It is experimentally demonstrable that under inattention potential *Twos* become *Ones*; one stimulating point or the other catches the attention and thus withdraws it, as it were, from the other (Brückner, 1901, 54 f., 60; Boring, 1916, 88 f.). The converse occurs in the well-known *Vexirfehler*, the paradoxical judgment, where two points close together or even a single point gives a perception of duality. Henri and Tawney referred this phenomenon in part to attention, and its dependence upon certain suggestive factors seems to indicate that it is of this order (Henri & Tawney, 1895; Tawney, 1897; Henri, 1898*b*, 61–66). Griesbach (1895) and others supposed that fatigue reduced the limen (1918), but Friedline has shown that the effect of fatigue is operative only among the perceptual forms at the lower end of the series, say a and β. Here fatigue acts in the direction of fusion and may perhaps be another factor that operates within the attentive phase (Friedline, 1918). Thus the perceptual pattern is not wholly dependent upon conditions at the periphery, the mode and place and nature of the stimulation. Certain more central factors also come into play and justify us in adding to the cross-connections B-d and D-b the connections b-δ and d-β.

Finally, now the perceptual pattern issues in a judgment in accordance with criteria of judgment that have been established. The available factor here lies in the setting up and the preservation of these criteria. Left to himself there is no guarantee of what the subject will do, as the studies of Titchener (1916), deLaski (1916), and Friedline (1918) all show. Perhaps the most normal criteria for sophisticated adult subjects would be such that the perceptual δ of our chart would lead to the judgment *Two* and the perceptual β to the judgment *One*. It is a reasonable inference that McDougall's savages in Torres Straits, under the competitive incentive to do well, assumed such criteria that even our β would have led to the judgment *Two*, for plainly β is larger than the pattern which a single point most often gives (McDougall, 1903*a*, II, 189–193; Titchener, 1916). An overzealous subject can interpret perceptual patterns lying very low in the series as meaning the presence of two points upon the skin; in fact, as Friedline has shown, he can do amazingly well under the influence of both practice and incentive, provided he is not fatigued (Friedline, 1918, 408 ff., 414 ff.). On the other hand the sophisticated subjects of the laboratory, and, it may be, therefore the Englishmen, whom McDougall compared with the savages, tend to define *Two* by reference to a perceptual pattern higher in the scale (McDougall, 1903, 192 and note; Titchener, 1916, 211). We should hardly have been bold enough to have predicted this result; to the writer, however, it seems reasonable enough now that it has been pointed out. Is it not to be expected that the savage would try to "do well" by discriminating as finely as possible and that the sophisticated person would try to "do well" by discriminating as accurately and consistently as possible, though less finely? In any case the point is that the acceptance of a criterion is an unavoidable experimental condition in determinations of cutaneous spatial sensitivity, and that the criterion must therefore be controlled, since when uncontrolled it gives uncertain significance to the verbal responses *Two* and *One*. In fact it appears that the apparent limen for cutaneous duality may be very much more than quartered by a variation of criterion, and it seems further that the conflicting results in the literature with respect to the effect of fatigue and the effect of practice upon the limen are to be explained in this way.

This leads to a conclusion. If only the end-terms of stimulus and response are controlled, a univocal one-to-one correlation between stimulus and response is not possible. In the terms of the diagram, both the stimuli *D* and *B* may condition the response *Two*. There are eight paths leading to *Two*, four from *D* and four from *B*. If we consider the other factors of the schema, the situation is enormously complicated. There are over a hundred modes of connection from *A*, *B*, *C*, *D*, and *E* to *Two*. Certainly the actual possibilities must be legion. At this level of work the best we can do is to remain in the dark and to deal with relative frequencies, yet relative frequencies do not yield the predictive correlation that science demands. The only way to get out of the dark would be to study the effect of stimulation, of attention, and of criterion by taking hold of these dependent series at their intermediate points, thus providing ourselves with a more complete knowledge and control of the entire psychophysical situation. Now the psychologist of capacity habitually controls stimulation, the various adjustments of the stimulus to the sense-organ, but the psychologist of datum also controls by instruction both attention and criterion. He does not, to be sure, reach the ideal of 100 per cent certainty in the prediction of the response to a given stimulus, but he is able greatly to increase the precision of these stimulus-and-response correlations. On the other hand, the failure to control the attitudinal factor implied in the acceptance of a criterion and the attentional factor again and again results perforce in an equivocal determination of these responses, which is nothing more nor less than a "stimulus-error."

In the psychology of capacity, then, the danger of the "stimulus-error" reduces to the danger that judgments of stimulus will prove scientifically equivocal. Experimentation will show when they are and when they are not. When they are equivocal, the problem is soluble by refinement in the control of conditions. The modern technique for the control of attention and attitude is a method that satisfies scientific standards of accuracy of prediction better than any available substitute. To shut our eyes to this technique in the absence of a substitute would be to refuse to accept scientific methods that have already yielded practical results. Certainly if the psychologist of capacity is to be a successful experimenter, joining hands with the biologist and physicist, he must in some way take account of all the means of experimental control that have been demonstrated as essential to the securing of accuracy.

Summary

Scientific psychology in its inception assumed a distinction between mind and matter and the separate existence of observable mental data and observable physical data. Fechner's psychophysics sought to measure the mental data and to establish their correlation with related physical data. The opponents of this point of view raised the *quantity objection*, arguing that mind is not possessed of magnitude and is therefore not measurable. Most of these objectors were attacking only the quantitative status of psychology and seeking to establish it as an essentially qualitative, but mental, science. Other objectors preferred, however, to keep psychology quantitative by conceiving of it as physical, as the psychology of the *capacity* of the organism for response to stimulus. The older psychology met the quantity objection by showing that the nonexistence of mental magnitude does not preclude mental measurement, and then sought to protect itself against incursions of the physical observational attitude of the psychology of capacity by styling that attitude the *stimulus-error*. The implication would be that a psychology of capacity does not need to avoid the stimulus-error, but rather should cultivate it. The thesis of this paper is, however, that recent researches have shown that the observational attitude which is directed upon the stimulus—the attitude of the stimulus-error—may sometimes lead to equivocal correlations of stimulus and response which, because equivocal, are unscientific. In the case of the limen of dual impression upon the skin, for example, a psychology of capacity must make use of introspective data if it is to attain its own ideals.

NOTES

1. The present paper is the outcome of a promise to deal specifically with the nature of the stimulus-error, especially with its relation to psychological measurement and psychophysics (Boring, 1920a, 27 ff.; 1920b, 447–449).
2. *Cf.* Titchener (1910, 202f.). Titchener first uses the term stimulus-error = "R-error" (1905, II, ii, lxiii, 198 f., 203 ff., 207, 219, 223, 230 f., 262, 450). For Titchener's further use of the term (1910, 218, 350, 398 note, 522). J. v. Kries characterized the objectifying attitude as a "source of error:" "Wenn man aber diese Quelle des Irrthums ausschliesst und möglichst an den objectiven, als Reiz dienenden. Vorgang gar nicht denkt . . . ;" (1882, 275), and Titchener seems to refer to this discussion as a sanction for the term "stimulus-error."
3. Titchener (1905, II, ii, x, lviii–lxiii) mentions as raising the quantity objection: G. E. Müller in 1878, Exner in 1879, Stadler in 1880, Zeller in 1881, Boas and F. A. Müller in 1882, Stumpf in 1883, Tannery in 1884, Elsas in 1886, Grotenfelt in 1888, James, Münsterberg, and Ebbinghaus in 1890, Sully in 1892, Külpe in 1893, Wahle in 1894, Meinong in 1896, Höfler in 1897, and Lehman in 1902.
4. Müller (1878); Ward (1876, 452–466); Titchener (1905, 66 f.). The autocatalytic theory is more recent. Robertson (1909, 372 ff., 384 f.).
5. Wundt's theory passed through successive stages and no brief statement does it justice. For summary and discussion, see Titchener (1905, II, ii, lvi ff., lxxiv f., lxxx ff., 69 f.; for summary and genesis, lxxxii, note).
6. The more thorough exposition would show that magnitude and measurement are systematic matters and are not found immediately at the observational level of science. The confusion is not unlike that of the systematic "sensation" with the observational "attribute:" Titchener (1915). On the other hand, it is hardly fair to physics to say: "No sensation is a sum of sensation-parts or of sense-increments; no sensation is a measurable magnitude. Fechner has transferred to sensation a point of view that is right for stimulus, but that introspection refuses to recognize in psychology:" Titchener (1905, II, i, xxvii).
7. The present writer has already had occasion to refer to F. M. Urban's position (Boring, 1920b, 27 f., esp. note 77; 1920a, 446 f.). It is well to repeat that no reference is intended here to Urban's later position, which involves an acceptance of the epistemology of Mach and Avenarius (Urban, 1913a; 1913b).
8. On psychophysical judgments and random events, compare Fullerton & Cattell (1892, 12 ff., 23 ff.) with Urban (1908, 17 f.). On the meaning of the just perceptible difference, compare Fullerton & Cattell (1892, 11) and Cattell (1893, 288 f.) with Urban (1908, 70). On mental measurement compare Fullerton & Cattell (1892, 20, 152 f.) and Cattell (1893, 293) with Urban's ignoring of the issue. [Or could he have thought that Titchener (1912) had settled it for the sense-distance?] On judgment as directed upon stimulus, compare Fullerton & Cattell (1892, 20) and Cattell (1893, 293) with Urban (1908, 5, 17; 1910, 27 ff.). On recording degrees of assurance, compare Fullerton & Cattell (1892, 11, 151) with Urban (1908, 5 ff.). On the relation of psychophysics to physics, compare Fullerton & Cattell (1892, 151), Cattell (1893, 285) with Urban (1910, 243 f.).
9. In fact it is not even clear that Friedländer's cautious generalization is not in part

an artifact. If we compute the data of Table 10 by Urban's procedure for the *Konstanzmethode*, we get:

	A-Einstellung	G-Einstellung
Av. measure of precision (h)	0.0138	0.0147
Interval of uncertainty (grams)	35.39	37.13
Point of subjective equality (grams)	500.8	509.9

There is not much difference in precision or discrimination by this method. The striking difference is in the effect of attitude on the point of subjective equality.

The Physiology of

Consciousness

𒑰𒑰𒑰𒑰𒑰𒑰𒑰𒑰𒑰𒑰𒑰 1932

M Y thesis this evening is that scientific psychology needs more than to become the physiological psychology that Wundt originally called it, and that we are not entirely without the means of proceeding in this direction. Psychology, it seems to me, needs to save for its own uses both consciousness and the nervous system, and it must have both if it is to survive.

Once upon a time psychology had some hope of getting along without a nervous system. There was a time when introspectionists like Külpe and Titchener would have hailed with avidity any step that brought psychology nearer to being a descriptive science of the facts of experience, a science that could get along with introspection as its only method and could leave the nervous system and the stimulus ruthlessly in the outer darkness of physiology. There is no need to explain to this audience that the introspective method unsupported failed to yield a psychology, or perhaps even a single factual generalization.[1] The most satisfactory introspective experiments were those that resulted in the correlation of sensory or perceptual data with stimulus. The best theories were formulated in terms of the nervous system or the sense-organs. Unaided introspection proved inadequate in crucial cases, as in the problem of thought where we were left with only a "physiological" determining tendency as a principle of explanation.

The reaction of behaviorism against this state of affairs by the complete rejection of the introspective method was very natural, even though it represented a throwing out of the baby with the bath. Theoretically you can answer for animals, by tests of discrimination or by observation of conditioned reflexes, any of the questions about sensory or perceptual capacities that have been answered for human beings by the use of the introspective method.

Reprinted with permission from Science, 1932, **75**, 32–39. Address of the retiring vice-president and chairman of Section I—Psychology, American Association for the Advancement of Science, New Orleans, December 29, 1931.

And what can be done with animals in general can be done with human animals. Nevertheless, the behavioristic method is not always advantageous. Sometimes it yields results that are less univocal than those gotten by an introspective method.[2] Sometimes it is terribly laborious and no added precision is gained for the added pains. If you will imagine a behavioristic method which determines, without the use of words, the occurrence of difference tones, or the wave-length of one of the three pure spectral colors, you will see what I mean when I say that these objective methods can be clumsy.[3]

It is worth noting that behaviorism owes its *ism* to consciousness. And what would it be without its *ism*? Well, it would be physiology. Behaviorism has preserved itself as psychology and as something that is not physiology— I speak of the historical fact, whatever may have been the wishes of the behaviorists—by persistently attempting to solve the problems that originated as introspective problems of the psychology of consciousness. The attitude of the behaviorist for introspection has always been ambivalent. He has hated introspection for the love he bore it.

On the other hand, if we bring consciousness back into "physiological psychology," without ridding ourselves of the old-fashioned Cartesian dualism, we get no farther along than we have always been. Now there is nothing new in my objecting to dualism. Perhaps the majority of you had thought of dualism as already rooted out of psychology. Nevertheless, you see that the behaviorist, who would have us ignore consciousness in psychology, is thereby a dualist because he has to believe in consciousness as something different from the "objective" world in order to dismiss it as irrelevant. In this way behaviorism has often emphasized the fundamental dichotomy of mind and body by its insistence that the mind is not the body, and that you may take the one and leave the other. *Gestalt* psychology certainly has no use for dualism, and yet it is impossible to read Köhler (1929) or Koffka (1930, 161–187) on the correspondence of "direct experience" to "underlying physiological processes" without feeling that the old dichotomy is still fundamental to their thought. The step I am asking you to take, in the interests of getting to a physiology of consciousness, is ever so much more radical than these imperfect attempts to avoid the Cartesian curse: I am asking you utterly to abandon dualism, sincerely, so that if there be a consciousness that could be ignored you will let it into the total system that is your scientific monism.

It is the introspectionists who have been primarily at fault in this matter. Wundt talked about "immediate experience," and Köhler talks about "direct experience." In such phases there is an implication that there is some way of taking hold of experience, immediately, just as it is per se, and of keeping it for scientific purposes, and that in doing so one has introspection. Physical science is supposed to deal with entities that are mediate to experience, to be indirect in the sense that its subject matter consists of inferential "constructs." The formula that Külpe and Titchener took from Avenarius, that psychology deals with all experience regarded as dependent upon the experiencing individual, is really not so much different, because experience really is dependent upon an experiencing individual for its existence, and when so regarded is thus being taken more immediately, more in its own right rather than as a ground for inference. I am quite serious when I say that this view of introspection seems to me to be nonsensical. The view implies that there is nothing important to introspection, that to have an experience is the same as to be aware of having it, that observation of conscious processes is nothing other than being conscious.[4]

However, the difficulty of regarding "direct experience" as the subject-matter of any science becomes more apparent when we note that we are landed by it in a circle of dependencies. At one time those who hold to this view will tell you that there is experience from which all science is derived, that psychology deals immediately with experience, and that the materials of physical science are mediately derived from experience. The view seems to make psychology prior to all the other sciences. Thus Köhler (1929, 3–69) tries to prove that behaviorism is really introspectional because its data were originally experiential. Nevertheless, these introspectionists may at another time hold to the opposite point of view that experience is dependent upon the activity of a brain or a nervous system. "No psychosis without neurosis" used to be the phrase. What then have we?

We have first the assertion that the brain, a physical entity, is a "construct," like an atom or an electron, which is not as such given in experience but which may be regarded as real and as generated from experience in the way that all scientific realities issue out of experience. In this sense the brain is dependent upon experience. However, in another sense, experience must be considered as dependent upon the brain. To have each dependent upon the other is not a relationship that is going to help us much. Either dependency alone is valuable, but the two negate each other (Boring, 1931).

On the other hand, we avoid this circle at once if we admit that psychology is not peculiar among the sciences, that introspection is as much a method as any of the other methods of observation, that it is a method whereby on the basis of experience we establish the existence or occurrence of mental "realities," like sensations or seen movements or any of the other phenomenal objects which introspection yields. The old-fashioned introspectionist will not like my calling a sensation a "mental object," but I mean that it is as much an object as ever a molecule is a physical "object." Certainly the sensation as such is not given in experience itself.

If any of you doubt this statement, you have only to think how science is always proceeding by indirection. It uses experience, yes; but always as symbolic of something else. The behaviorist misses this point when he tries to make behavioral observation more immediate than introspective. Watson said that introspection is verbal behavior, as if there were some virtue in preferring the immediate datum that the experimenter observes, the spoken words, to the conscious processes signified. The behaviorist who uses "objective" methods of recording is just as indirect as the introspectionist: the immediate datum may be a kymograph record, yet it is for him merely a symbol of behavior.

Now, at last, I come to the main issue of this paper, my thesis that *introspection is a method for the observation of certain events in the brain*. Traditional introspectionism would protest such a statement. If I see a red circle, it would say that I am not seeing the brain; no part of the brain is red, presumably no event in it is circular. Nevertheless, I may be observing the brain, just as I can observe animal behavior by looking at records from a kymograph, or as I can observe an electric current by looking at the black and white pattern which is a pointer on the scale of a galvanometer. In scientific observation we always come face-to-face with symbols, and usually we ignore the symbols and talk about the realities that they signify.

Such a symbolic function of introspection may, of course, be sound epistemologically and yet utterly wrong. A relationship of this kind either does, or does not, grow in the structure of a science. We can not force its acceptance by argument. All we can do is to find it implicit in thought and to bring it out into the open. Even when it is exhibited and accepted by every one, it remains as tentative and temporary as does all scientific truth. It is our task, therefore, to consider the extent to which this view has already found its way into psychological research and whether it has seemed to be thus far successful.

We can best understand what has been going on within psychology if we return to the dualistic tradition, and see that in it there were, roughly speaking, three principal loci for psychological events: (1) the sense-organs, (2) the central nervous system, and (3) consciousness. The three are causally related: stimulation of the sense-organ gives rise to a central neural process, which in turn may be said to "cause" a conscious process. In the less exact parlance of the laboratory, we are always thinking about stimulus, brain and consciousness.

The events in the brain, the middle term of this dependent series, have been largely inaccessible to observation. There has been of course some extremely important "direct" experimentation, from Fritsch and Hitzig to Lashley. There has been clinical observation. The rest of what we "know" about the brain is at a higher inferential level. The physiologist holds to the faith that the brain, being made up of neurons, is capable only of that excitation which is the sum of the excitations of many neurons, and that these central neurons obey the same laws and are excited under the same limitations as apply to the peripheral neurons which have been experimentally studied. To this article of faith the psychologist sometimes opposes another belief, that the organization of cerebral excitation corresponds to the organization of phenomenal experience. These two hypotheses are not neces-sarily consistent, and often we have to choose between them.

The two end-terms of the dependent series, the stimulus and conscious-ness, have been much more accessible to observation. The result is that the largest body of precise information within experimental psychology consists of correlations between these two terms. These correlations are the facts which make up the chapters on sensation and perception in any psycho-logical handbook.

If the scientific mind could be satisfied with correlations, physiological psy-chology might have ignored the brain as inaccessible to its methods, and have remained content with correlations between stimulus and sensory process in the old days and between stimulus and response later on. The experimental method itself yields, in the first instance, mere correlations; nevertheless, the scientist demands something more. He wants insight into the relationships, a complete and immediate understanding which seems to leave no further ques-tions to be asked. Many persons, in learning to extract square roots by the use of a calculating machine, discover for the first time the rule that the sum of a given number of consecutive odd numbers equals the square of the number of numbers summed; the sum of the first *three* odd numbers, 1, 3, 5, is 9, the square of 3. Such a relation is a mere correlation and it seems, when first dis-covered, a great mystery. Even the proving of the general rule by algebra may seem to leave the mystery intact. If, however, one draws big geometrical squares made up of unit squares, one sees at once why to any square one must add a "next odd number" of squares in order to get the next larger square. The mystery has gone and we have what I am calling insight.

It is this need for insight that has forced the brain upon psychologists. The gross psychophysical correlation must be made more intimate. We want, in Fechner's phrase, an "inner psychophysics." Nevertheless, even if we had this knowledge of the brain and the resultant correlations, we should still be wanting insight in both parts of the picture. We should, on the one hand, want more intimate knowledge of the relation of stimulus to brain, and this sort of knowledge we are now actually beginning to get in the all-or-none law of neural excitation, in the frequency theory of intensity that Adrian has so ably promoted, and in the experiment of Wever and Bray on the nature of the impulses in the auditory nerve. Very slowly this physiological continuity is getting worked out. On the other hand, the correlation between consciousness and the events in the brain shows no signs of yielding to insight because there is no conceivable way in which insight can transcend the dualistic gap be-tween mind and body. If there were any ground for dualism, if immediate ex-perience as such seemed capable of scientific study, we might shrug our shoulders and decide to make the best of an unsatisfactory situation. Since, however, dualism seems both to fail to give us a satisfactory scientific dichotomy and also to exclude insight from psychophysiology, we ought, it seems to me, to make all haste to abandon it.

Let us now get down to business and see what there is to be said, for the purposes of psychology, about events in the brain. We had best accept, I think, four of Titchener's dimensions of consciousness [5] as setting the main topics for investigation. Consciousness is organized in respect of four dimensions: quality, intensity, extensity, and the temporal dimension which Titchener called "protensity." We may begin with intensity.

Twenty years ago the physiology of intensity offered little difficulty. A strong stimulus gives rise to an intense sensation; presumably the middle of this causal sequence must consist of strong excitation. However, this simple view became untenable with the acceptance of the all-or-none theory of excitation of the neuron. It seemed at first as if a multiple-fiber theory of intensity were the only remaining possibility, that degrees of sensory intensity must depend upon the number of fibers stimulated. Then came the frequency theory, the generalization, now well established, that a stronger stimulus may excite a greater frequency of impulses in a single fiber (Adrian, 1928). It is not necessarily true that the frequency theory of intensity must displace the multiple-fiber theory. Some of Hecht's conclusions (Hoagland, 1930, 354–359) point to the possibility that the stronger stimulus gives rise both to the excitation of a greater number of fibers and to a greater frequency of excitation in the fibers stimulated. The volley theory of Wever and Bray (1930*a*) is also such a view.

When such theories are being discussed, it is natural to ask whether there must not be a summation of separate impulses in the brain. I believe that such a question generally indicates the existence of an implicit belief that introspection gives direct information about the brain, that, since sensory intensity is not anything like a frequency or a spatial dispersion, the brain ought somehow or other to collect the separate impulses in order to get some single unitary state that corresponds to what phenomenal intensity itself seems to be. The multiple fiber theory calls for the summation of the impulses in separate fibers; the frequency theory calls for the summation of successive impulses in the same fiber; and any combination of the two theories calls even more for summation, since, when different causes give the same effect, we want some insight into how the different causes are effectively the same.

Now I think we can indicate positively the sense in which summation must occur on any theory of intensity, but before I go into that matter I wish to point out how already prevalent is this view of the direct correspondence between consciousness and the brain.

Most psychologists have accepted this conception as a matter of course. It is the common assumption in different physiological theories of Weber's law, the theories of Wundt and G. E. Müller. Köhler is the most courageous modern to state the general view. He thinks of intensity as the electrical charge of a concentration of ions in the nervous tissues. He dislikes a constancy hypothesis between stimulation and central excitation, and so he suggests how the logarithmic relation of Weber's law might occur on the purely physiological level. However, Köhler (1920) likes a "constancy hypothesis" of the relation of consciousness to the brain (of course, he does not call his hypothesis by that term), so that there he supposes a simple relation between gradients of intensity and of electrical potential. This notion of Köhler's, that there is a direct and simple correspondence between consciousness and events in the brain, only just misses what I take to be the necessary denial of dualism.

The physiologists are apt to avoid the problems of consciousness, but when they consider them they tend to make the same assumptions as the psychologists. Let me illustrate by reference to a recent article of Hoagland's on the Weber-Fechner law. This law requires that the plot of the measure of sensation against the logarithm of the stimulus should be linear. Hoagland (1930), citing Hecht, points out that the Weber-Fechner law is known not to hold at the extremes, and that this semi-log plot may be not linear but sigmoid in shape, thus corresponding to other functions familiar to physiologists. He cites certain cases where what we may call "excitation" does show this kind of dependence upon the logarithm of the stimulus. He cites Hecht's analysis of König's data for the visual discrimination of brightnesses as proving the same point. What can one conclude? That Hecht and Hoagland, at least, have rejected dualism and are ready to accept introspection as a measure of physiological excitation, for König's data were introspective, and they are ready to bring them under a physiological generalization.

Certainly then it is good form to assume that sensory intensity is a symbol of neural excitatory intensity. Can we justify the view further?

Here it is, I think, that we need to appeal to the physiology of introspection. Let us suppose that the occurrence of a given sensory intensity leads to a judgment of its degree. It does not matter whether that judgment is a word spoken aloud or written on paper, in English or German, or whether it is the pressing of a key connected with an apparatus, or whether it is some imaginal form of note-taking which only later leads to expression. The judgment differentiates *the* intensity from other intensities, and as such it is a response to *the* intensity. In the absence of such response there can be no knowledge that the intensity occurred and hence no introspection.

However, the discriminative response is a response *to* the intensity, which one must now think of in physiological terms. Do the excitations of many fibers have to be summated in order that a response may occur to them? Do the successive excitations of a single fiber have to be summated to lead to a response that depends upon the frequency? Not necessarily in any objective sense, if summation implies that all the impulses are collected together into one place at one instant. On the other hand, there is summation in the sense that the response is to the totality of the impulses, that all the impulses are collectively effective in producing a single response which is characteristic of them all as a totality. For instance, if the neural impulse is electrical in nature, there need never be a summation of ion charges, but there must be a functional summation into a single physiological effect.

The experiment of Wever and Bray illustrates this point beautifully (1930*b*). They hooked an electrode on the central end of the cat's auditory nerve where it enters the medulla; they talked to the cat and greatly amplified the currents of action in the nerve, leading the amplified currents to a loud speaker. Human speech was heard over the cat's nerve with little distortion and tonal frequencies up to 4000 cycles were accurately transmitted. It is still extremely doubtful whether a single auditory fiber can transmit a frequency greater than 1000 cycles. However, Wever and Bray transcend this difficulty in their "volley theory" which combines the multiple-fiber and the frequency theories of intensity. I can not expound this theory here, but the point of it is that, if a tonal frequency and amplitude, corresponding respectively to a given pitch and intensity, are put into the ear, the resultant excitation in the auditory nerve is utterly different, consisting of a number of frequencies in a number of fibers, and yet a simple electrode is able, out of the total effect of the excitations within the nerve, to pick up the original frequency and amplitude. The electrical circuit "responds" to the totality of events in the nerve, without the original frequency and amplitude ever being reinstated in the nervous tissues. In the same way the physiology of sensory intensity must be at least a simple totality of degree of excitation, even though it may not be summated at any point at any one instant of time.

If we turn from the problem of intensity to the problem of extensity we find that ever so much more has been written about this problem and that the solution is less certain.

The oldest theory of extensity is the projection theory. It is a theory that was helped a hundred years ago by the theory of the specific energy of nerves, for, if the mind perceives, not objects, but "the states of the nerves" (as Johannes Müller said), it can "perceive" spatial pattern only if it be projected upon the brain. Nowadays, Köhler (1929, 64), while denying projection, nevertheless keeps our thought in the same channels by his principle of correspondence between the spatial order of phenomenal experience and the underlying physiological processes. It is certainly good form to suppose that the perception of shape and size is dependent upon spatial differentiation in the fields of central excitation.

There is not the same amount of supporting evidence for this view as there was in the parallel case of intensity. Nevertheless, I think that the conclusion for intensity helps us to a belief in a broad conception of correspondence for all the dimensions of consciousness. It looks as if some sort of physical intensity (like electrical potential) were the physiological fact of sensory intensity. It looks as if spatial differences of stimulation were the occasion of spatial differences of central excitation, and temporal differences of stimulation, of temporal differences in central excitation. We are not in such a statement making an appeal to analogy; we are saying that the physical dimensions of peripheral stimulation are likely to be the dimensions of the organization of central events, that there are not enough possible dimensions for us to expect a change of kind, and that the adequacy of perception to certain dimensions of the external world is thus readily explained.

The projection theory of extensity would thus be a very acceptable theory were it not inadequate to the facts. Since we can not undertake to review the entire field of space perception, let us select for consideration two special problems: the problem of the third dimension in vision and the problem of visual size.

Koffka (1930) has recently suggested that the existence of the third dimension in visual perception implies a tridimensional neural pattern in the brain. Such a view is consistent with Köhler's theory of correspondence, but I think that a stronger case can be made out for it than a mere appeal to an uncertain generalization. So much has been said about the dependence of the perception of depth and distance on convergence, accommodation, and retinal disparity, that Koffka is at pains to take the cases of depth that occur in simple drawings, where neither accommodation nor any binocular *differentia* is possible. He shows that you may see the Necker cube in either perspective, but that you practically can not see it as a flat geometrical design in the plane of the paper. What is the difference then between the plane design and the two perspectives? As projections they would be identical. If the two-dimensional pattern means a two-dimensional field of excitation, it is almost inevitable to look for a tridimensional field when the third dimension comes in immediately to the perception.

The case becomes stronger when we consider how retinal disparity works in stereoscopic vision. Let us think of the case of the truncated cone, which stretches out convexly toward the observer in stereoscopic vision. Each eye sees only a small circle within a large circle, but the relation of the small circle to the large circle is disparate for the two eyes. When the eyes first view the two drawings, there may appear two completely separate images in perception. Then the eyes move in respect of each other until there is seen, let us say, but a single large circle. At this stage the small circles may remain double within the single large circle. Thus far the experience fits the projection theory. The two large circles appear as two circles until the eyes move so that they lie upon corresponding points; then there is but one circle, because the two circles are projected upon the same locus in the brain. Moreover, we see that the eyes tend to move so as to bring similar images upon corresponding points. It is as if the mechanism of vision operated in the interests of simplification.

However, the eyes can never move so as to make both the large and the small circles coincide at the same time. If the small circles coincide, the large circles must be double, and vice versa, if we keep to projective geometry. However, projective geometry is just what perception does not preserve. Presently both small and large circles coincide and we see the truncated cone as a solid. Is not the conclusion almost inescapable that the tendencies for the large circles to combine and the small circles to combine are realized by the establishment of the circles in different fields, which for bidimensional figures would have to be separated in a third dimension? [6]

Now let us turn to the problem of visual size. It seems probable that the perceived size of stimuli at the same distance from the observer is proportional to the size of the corresponding retinal images. As usual we can begin with a projection theory.

However, a projection theory breaks down when we consider size in relation to distance. As a stimulus-object is moved away from the observer its perceptual size decreases, but it decreases not nearly so fast as does the size of the retinal image. The alley experiments have worked out the law of the dependence of phenomenal size upon distance. The facts are as if perception compromised between the projection theory and some other theory, under which a given object would maintain its size, irrespective of distance.

There is another way in which size varies. The moon in the zenith is perceptually smaller than the moon on the horizon. For all the controversy that has gone on about this illusion, it seems fairly accurate to say that the size of the moon or of any other stimulus-object is diminished when the head and the eyes assume the strained position required for looking at the zenith and *when distance is indeterminate.* It is this second condition that has fooled the experimenters. The illusion fails, or is reduced to a few per cent, for an artificial moon a few feet from the observer. Schur showed that the illusion may be as much as 50 per cent for cardboard moons 33 meters from the observer. Beyond 33 meters in the vertical it is not possible to carry most experiments, but the implication of Schur's results is that position of the head and eyes makes a difference to size when distance is indeterminate, as it becomes when it is great. With shorter and determinate distances, the laws of the alley experiments hold. With the moon, distance is completely indeterminate and the illusion is maximal.

It thus appears that perceptual size is a complex function of retinal size, of distance, and at times even of the position of the head and eyes. Moreover, there is some ground for belief that this variation in size applies to three-dimensional fields. It is very hard to adjust this sort of physiology to the conventional notions of neuron reflex arcs. These phenomena accord much better with Lashley's (1929; 1931) principles of equipotentiality and mass action in the cerebral cortex. Hunter (1930) has criticized Lashley's views on the ground that it is possible to explain the animal behavior in question in terms of a more conventional physiology. The difficulty with Hunter's position, so it seems to me, is that conventional physiology, even if it can explain Lashley's data, can do very little else for the theory of perception. What, for instance, can it do for these problems of the visual perception of solidity and of size?

I am not proposing that we disregard facts in favor of theories. I am proposing merely that we accept, tentatively, the most productive hypotheses, those with the greatest resolving power. We may need some day to abandon the hypothesis that consciousness always involves some kind of brain action. However, I think that this view should be kept just now, and with it the more explicit view that spatial and intensive phenomena, given in introspection and representing respectively spatial and intensive aspects of the stimulation, are symbols of spatially and intensively differentiated events within the brain. The evidence for such an hypothesis is scanty enough, goodness knows, but I think it is greater than the grounds for faith in the simple reflex-arc theory of the brain. If we must choose an hypothesis, let us choose one that gives us some insight into the extensive knowledge of perception which experimental psychology includes today.

There is no time for me to discuss the other two dimensions of consciousness. Of protensity, the temporal dimension, we know but little. We should be looking, with Köhler, for durations in the brain when introspection shows duration to be a characteristic of the perception.

Quality has had no acceptable physiological hypothesis for itself since the theory of the specific energy of nerves and the related theory of sensory centers broke down. All we can be sure of is this: whatever quality is within the brain, it must be differentially dependent upon whatever quality is within the stimulus. In tonal hearing this view means a frequency theory of quality, and Wever and Bray have shown how such a view is not necessarily incompatible with the theory of peripheral frequency for intensity. In the other senses we are dependent upon more knowledge of the receptor processes.[7]

Let me see if I can now, in closing, repeat all that I have said in the compass of a few words.

Dualism is dead. It ought to be buried. It can not work for us any more and we do not need it.

The great delusion of psychology has been the belief that we can have a science of direct experience. Scientific facts come out of experience, but they are then no longer in it. Science does not attempt to reconstitute experience; it builds up inferentially a world of constructs which are its realities.

A careful examination of the introspective process shows that introspection, like any other observation, is the taking note of symbols that mean occurrences in this constructural or real world.

We are, therefore, free to examine these symbols, the phenomenal data of introspection, to see what they can symbolize with the greatest profit for scientific psychology; and we conclude that neural events are the sort of mental constructs that introspective data most effectively "intend."

We can then set out to test this view, to see what it will yield us in the way of a physiological psychology. Such a view is necessarily subject to test and to correction, in the same way that a galvanometer is subject to test and correction as to how it means or "intends" the strength of an electric current.

When we go to the physiological theories of psychologists (and of some physiologists, too) we find many views consonant with the thought of the present paper, as indeed we could have known from the start, since the paper has been written to explicate and evaluate these views.

In general, the most plausible theory of the brain seems to be that the four conscious dimensions find reality there in four physical dimensions of intensity, extensity, duration, and an uncertain fourth which must have an immediate dependence upon the physical variable for quality in the stimulus.

Such a general view is most definitely explicable for intensity. Sensed intensity must represent degree of excitation in the brain. Such excitation does not, however, have to be localized at a single place at a single time, except that it must all be effective in producing a simple subsequent neural event, which is the first physiological term of the introspective process.

In respect of extensity, the notion that introspection tends approximately to mirror the brain is, at the present day, a plausible view and a useful one. A more conservative physiology not only leaves one without an hypothesis for most of the facts of space perception, but implies certain limitations which are contradicted by the facts.

Finally, in urging this view upon you for serious consideration, I would make bold to remind you that scientific hypotheses and scientific truth are temporary and provisional, and that hypotheses that are false today have been largely instrumental in leading us to what is true today. However, I doubt if a false hypothesis ever led far toward the truth unless it was at the time believed to be true. You have in that statement both my admonition and my apology.

NOTES

1. There never were any laws of introspective psychology other than those that state the correlation of conscious processes with the stimulus or with events in the nervous system, with the possible exception only of the law of association. Nowadays it is superfluous to claim that association is solely a law of conscious events, when we are

so constantly being reminded of its physiological counterpart, the conditioned reflex.

2. On the behavioristic method as more equivocal than the introspective method in the determination of the two-point limen, see Boring (1921).

3. *Cf.* the awkward (imaginary) experiment that J. B. Watson describes for the determination of difference tones (Watson, 1919, 78). I have forgotten who it was in the Harvard Psychological Colloquium who suggested that an animal could be tested for *Hauptfarben* in the following manner. If one is after the wave-length for pure yellow, one would train the animal to respond positively to the yellower of two oranges, and would see how far along the spectrum this relational response would be given. Obviously, it should break down at the pure yellow, since a yellow-green is not yellower than a yellow.

4. Philosophers have made this same objection, but introspectionists have found little force in it ever since the argument for immediacy was put so trenchantly by Mach (1886).

5. E. B. Titchener never explicated his doctrine of conscious dimensions beyond his twelve-line note (Titchener, 1924).

6. There is a very simple system of geometrical projection in which a disparity, which is like retinal disparity, actually gives the projection in the third dimension, but I forego its discussion since I cannot make it seem like acceptable physiology.

7. Perhaps this view accords with Nafe's objections to the theory of the specific energy of nerves and thus with his quantity theory of feeling; *cf.* his discussion in "The Foundations of Experimental Psychology" (1929, 395–399). I have never understood Nafe's theory; but if he means that quality must ultimately be understood as a function of the quantifiable aspects of nerve-conduction and the relationships that are quantitatively statable between excitations, then I suppose that all scientifically minded psychologists would immediately agree with him.

Psychophysiological Systems and Isomorphic Relations

▨▨▨▨▨▨▨▨▨▨▨▨▨▨▨▨▨▨▨▨▨▨▨▨▨ 1936

THIS comment on the nature of psychophysiological hypotheses grows out of an interest in the concept of isomorphism, the tenet of Gestalt psychology that the pattern of experienced perception corresponds in some of its formal relations to the pattern of the neural excitation that gives rise to it (Köhler, 1929, 60–67; Koffka, 1935, 61–67). This hypothesis had seemed to me insufficiently validated for the seriousness of the consideration that is given it. I suspected in it the existence of some unrecognized premise, some habit of thought so familiar that it escapes detection in common sense, and I set out to look for it. I found myself studying isomorphic physiological relations at the periphery, or, more often anisomorphic relations that had earlier been regarded as isomorphic when speculation had had very little fact of which it could take account. Thus I was brought to a consideration of psychophysiological hypotheses in general, regarding isomorphism as nothing more than a very special case. However, I found that I wanted to see how hypotheses of this sort are formed, what kind of validation can exist for them in advance of the discovery of direct empirical proof, and what happens historically to them as knowledge increases. Such is the origin of this paper. The outcome is an attempt to restate the problem of psychoneural isomorphism in physiological monistic terms, showing that the operational substitute for dualistic isomorphism (although no longer an isomorphism) is of such a nature as to explain the ready plausibility with which the original concept has been accepted.

First, however, we must sketch a picture of psychophysiology, one that will show the nature of its central problem and the general form of the solution. We must begin with a comment on the sort of systems that appear in the scientific description of psychophysiological events.

Reprinted with permission from *Psychological Review*, 1936, 43, 565–587.

Cause-and-Effect vs. Systems

It is the conventional view that psychophysiology seeks the description of
causal chains of events that occur in connection with the action of the
nervous system between an antecedent stimulus and a consequent response.
While this conception often serves its purpose satisfactorily as an approximation, it involves a great many difficulties that prevent its employment for
rigorous description. Let us see what some of the difficulties are.

(*a*) The initial limit, the *stimulus*, cannot be fixed definitely, but must
be chosen in accordance with the convenience of the problem. For instance,
in vision the stimulus may be the proximal stimulus (Koffka, 1935, 79 f.) of
the excitatory pattern at the retina, or the light as it enters the eye, or the
object that reflects the light to the eye.

(*b*) The terminal limit, the *response*, is also not fixed. It may be the
movement of a muscle, or the consequent movement of a bodily member,
or a subsequent mark on a kymograph, or a spoken word. If *E* writes down
the word that *S* speaks, perhaps *E*'s movement is the "response," which thus
depends upon the nervous systems of both *S* and *E*.

(*c*) Even when the initial and terminal limits have been fixed in a given
case, the series, as we know it, is never actually continuous. There are all
sorts of gaps likely to occur between stimulus and response, and our ignorance of the intermediate neural terms is so great that Skinner (1931) has suggested that psychologists had better give up the nervous system and confine
their attention to the end-terms of such series, where observation is more
immediate and the temptation for insecure speculation is less.

(*d*) When consciousness is introduced into this series—and surely *psychophysiology* ought to have something to do with consciousness—it is separated
from the rest by gaps, and unprofitable speculation arises as to whether consciousness parallels some part of the causal chain (parallelism) or is a link
in the chain (interactionism).

(*e*) The lateral limits of the causal chain are also indeterminate. Hardly
ever can a receptor cell and an afferent nerve fiber be supposed to act alone.
The retina acts as a whole, or at least in Hecht's "unit areas." A pure tone
spreads its effect in the organ of Corti. It is doubtful if a cutaneous receptor
can ever be separately stimulated. Nor can a sensory effect always be limited
to a single sense. The analysis of an orchestral harmony is much easier when
sight of the instruments supplements the sound.

All these difficulties arise because we are actually dealing with a *system*
whose interrelationships resist description as a simple series of causes and their

effects. Most events are systemic. Even so simple a relationship as that expressed by Newton's "third law," that action and reaction are equal and opposite, does not show clearly a distinction between cause and effect. However, the nature of a system is best seen in those complexes where interrelated variables can be understood without the possibility of analyzing them into dependent and independent variables associated in pairs. Figure 1 shows an example of an electrical system. The resistances, R, are constant, and we can imagine that a fixed input voltage, E_1, is maintained across the terminals A and B. The current through each of the seven branches can be calculated, but only by considering all the currents simultaneously. A change in the resistance of any one branch affects the current through every branch. No one of the branches is independent of the others, so that it can be considered first, with the others regarded as successive dependences. We have to set up seven equations expressing the interrelationships between the currents and their dependence upon the seven Rs, and solve them simultaneously. This notion of a system as superseding the conception of cause-and-effect is quite fully established in modern science. It has been introduced into psychology as Gestalt. Excellent discussions of the nature of a physical system have recently been given by Humphrey (1933, 7–39) and by L. J. Henderson (1935).

Ideally there is only one system, the universe, including all time and all

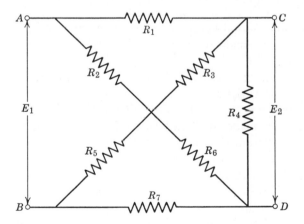

Fig. 1. *An electrical system. The seven resistances, R_1, R_2, R_3, . . . ; and the input voltage, E_1, are known. When E_1 is kept constant across the network, the problem is to determine the currents through each of the seven branches, and how they change when any one R is altered. The output voltage, E_2, is any other potential difference in the network across which another system can be coupled. See text for conditions under which this network is (1) a closed system (2) an open system, and (3) an incomplete system.*

space (Humphrey, 1933, 20 f.). Everything is related to everything else. Practically, however, it is necessary, for the solution of particular problems, to distinguish small finite systems. There are two ways in which this limitation can be effected. First, we may omit the consideration of "lateral" terms whose effect within the principal system is negligible because it is small with respect to the probable error with which the other terms are established. It is possible for such a system to be *closed*, containing within itself all the forces, as well as all the properties, that come into consideration. In such a case the system is an equilibrium. However, psychology is concerned for the most part with the disequilibria of action. Such systems have forces entering them at some point or points and leaving them at some other point or points. Otherwise they too would be in equilibrium. The forces that are derived from a prior system must have negligible effects on the prior system; otherwise they would react upon the prior system, alter it and change its effect upon the principal system—which is to say that the two systems would be so related by interaction that they would have to be treated as a single system. The same point applies where the principal system affects a posterior system. There must not be more than a negligible reaction of the posterior system upon the principal system if the two are to maintain their integrities as separate systems. In this manner we come upon a practical rule for the establishment of systemic boundaries: a disequilibrium must be an open system, accessible to influence by some external system and able to affect another external system, but these external relations must be asymmetrical if the system is to retain its isolation. Action between systems must be one-way; if it is mutual, the systems do not remain discrete. Let that statement stand for the definition of a system.

These distinctions can be made clearer by a further consideration of Fig. 1. E_1 is the input potential across the terminals A and B. We can regard E_2 as an output voltage across the terminals C and D. If E_1 is kept constant and no connections are made to C and D, we have a system, but an *open* one accessible to the system that supplies the voltage E_1. Then, if the potential across A and B is furnished by a battery, E_1 will vary when some R is changed, because E_1 will depend upon the internal resistance of the battery. In this case the net-work does not represent an isolated system; the battery must be included with the other seven resistances in the system. The relationship is similar with regard to the output. If a voltmeter is connected across C and D, it draws a negligible current and alters E_2 a negligible amount: it does not violate the integrity of the system. But, if some other apparatus of low resistance is put across C and D so that an appreciable current is drawn, then the new apparatus reacts upon the system and must therefore be included within it.

It now becomes apparent that in psychophysiology we have after all to do with causal chains, chains in which the links are such systems as we have described in the preceding paragraph. These systems are open disequilibria which transmit action in the general direction of "stimulus" to "response." The complete action is a progression from system to system, with the reaction of any system upon its preceding system regarded as negligible. "Lateral" systems beside the principal train must be related to the train only in negligible ways. Negligibility is relative; what is negligible for one problem may not be for another. Thus at a sufficiently high molar level we find that we have after all the essentials of the cause-and-effect relation holding between open systems. This general pattern applies in the present instance because the nervous system is insulated laterally into pathways, and synapses or changes of media in receptors or effectors provide boundaries across these pathways where action is forward and reaction is negligible. In other words, the successive systems approximate each the network of Fig. 1, where E_1 is maintained by a preceding system and is independent of the value of any R in the network, and where E_2 is unaffected by any of the properties of a subsequent system. If these conditions in respect of E_1 and E_2 are not met, then the system must be enlarged until they are.

Correlation and Sufficient Reason

This conception of causal systemic series puts us in a position to understand why some effects seem to be founded upon sufficient reason and why an observed correlation seems in itself an insufficient reason for an effect.

Observed correlation is the basis of all scientific fact. The simplest law of the functional dependence of one variable upon another is nothing more than the observation of the concomitant variation of the two, usually by an experimental method where the independent variables (cause) and the dependent variables (effect) are distinguished. The notion of cause-and-effect in science is based upon the pairing of a dependent variable with an independent variable in experimental observation, which always requires the isolation of the variables from the continuity of nature. However, the method of correlation also extends to the establishment of systems. We have said of Fig. 1 that, if the input voltage and the resistances and the connections of the network are known, the seven simultaneous currents can be computed. The input and the seven resistances are eight simultaneous conditions of the seven simultaneous currents: change any condition and you change all currents. However, the system involves no appeal to the notion of a serial cause-and-effect, for the currents are concomitant functions of all the properties of the system.

The objection to correlation is sometimes urged that it is discontinuous, that it represents action-at-a-distance. However, this supposed "defect" is inherent in the nature of correlation, which obtains always between isolated variables. Nevertheless, these discretely correlated terms may be used to infer continuity, just as the plotted points of some functional relation come to be regarded as implying a smooth curve. In the same way a molar system is considered to be continuous spatially, temporally, and in respect of every other dimension of variation. (The discontinuities of electrons and quanta need not concern us here.) Thus one has, by an inference of continuity, very much more in a system than has ever been actually observed. In a statement of the properties of a system, one establishes, from a finite number of observations, dicta about an infinitude of cases. And these generalities remain established so long as new instances continue to satisfy them. It is this reification of discrete observations into systemic continuities which seems to provide a sufficient reason for the new facts which are subsumed under the properties of the system. Let us have an illustration.

The sun rises in the east. That is merely an observed correlation except as its two terms are intended to be generic. *That flaming orb always rises over that hill* is a correlation and thus a fact, but it seems senseless. There is no sufficient reason for it. But to say *The earth rotates toward the east in respect of the sun* is to describe a system and thus to provide a sufficient reason for the flaming orb's always rising over the eastern hill. In other words, a reason is sufficient if there is enough of it! A system is so much larger than a correlation that it will bring any observed relation, which can be subsumed under it, well above the threshold of credibility.

Psychophysiological Progression

We have said that psychophysiological events tend to progress through the organism in the afferent-efferent direction. This progression is represented by the successive excitation of a series of systems. The action gets from one system to a next because there is some term common to the two successive systems. If Fig. 1 represents an electrical system, then its input, E_1, must be the output of some preceding system; and its output, E_2, may, if the progression continues, be the input of a succeeding system.

Let us consider as an example present-day knowledge of the systems participating in auditory perception (Davis, 1934).

We may take as a first system the air. It is displaced initially by some vibrating body, perhaps a loud-speaker, which involves various mechanical systems that in turn depend upon electrical systems. It is because we must start somewhere that we begin arbitrarily with the air. If the sound is a continuous tone, produced in the presence of reflecting surfaces, standing waves are set up. The stimulus available at the drum-skin is therefore a function of the whole aerial system. It is not wise for us to try to divide this system into smaller ones.

The middle ear may be taken as a second system. The displacement of the drum-skin is a common term for the two successive systems. The action is essentially one-way, for the nature of the aerial vibrations is not altered more than a negligible amount by the properties of the middle ear. Thus we can put a boundary between the two systems. However, the middle ear has such properties that the wave-form at the drum-skin is distorted by the time it reaches the oval window.

The cochlea is the third system. Its mechanical action has to be regarded as a whole. Its presence does not radically affect the action of the middle ear (anterior system), and the presence of the receptor cells (posterior system), does not radically affect its action. It can therefore be distinguished as a separate open system between the oval window and the receptors.

The "cochlear response" is the name given to the electrical phenomena found at the round window and other parts of the cochlea, a response observed by amplification of the resultant potentials (Davis, 1934, 970–976). It is supposed to represent events in the receptors cells, since it is known not to correspond with events in the nerve. It would seem, therefore, to be a fourth system.

Then comes the action of the VIIIth nerve, as it is now understood by the amplification of its action potentials. It is quite clear that it is a fifth system, separate from that of the "cochlear response," and that the one-way criterion is satisfied at the joint boundary.

There is some indication that the auditory tract at levels above the VIIIth nerve is divided into several subcortical systems (Davis, 1934, 980), but the data are meager.

The question arises as to what we are to do with *consciousness* in such a progression. In any monistic view, consciousness, if the term is used at all, becomes a word for some neural system or relationship between neural systems. However, the word generally connotes a dualism, and thus a difficulty arises. Enough has been said about the laws of consciousness, from the Associationists to Wundt and from Wundt to the Gestalt psychologists, for us to realize that consciousness is a system. Moreover, it is not a closed system. According to parallelism, its input is open. According to interactionism, both its input and output are open. Nevertheless, a dualism forbids a common term which joins the psychical system to the physiological, and consciousness is thus placed in a unique systemic position. There is nothing novel in the discovery of a uniqueness of consciousness under a dualism, but it is plain that this relationship forbids the possibility of there being a "sufficient reason" for consciousness being as it is. Consciousness can be correlated with a neural system, but its action can not issue from the action of a neural system in the way that the action of one neural system issues from the action of another.

We must return to this problem of consciousness later when we discuss psychoneural isomorphism and the possibility of a sufficient reason for consciousness. Let us pass now to the meaning of isomorphism in general.

Isomorphic Relations

Isomorphism is a term invented by Köhler (1929, 60–67) to stand for the theoretical notion that the spatial order of perceptual experience corresponds to the spatial order of the underlying neural processes. It signifies a particular hypothetical form of the unique psychoneural correlation. We shall examine this hypothesis later on, but at present we may stop to consider the nature of the conditions under which we should find the isomorphic relation between events in different systems.

The fundamental rule is very simple. In the case of the sort of open systems in series that we are discussing, *any event in one system is a joint function of the properties of that system and of the input which the system has from the preceding system.* Events between two successive systems can not very well be isomorphic in respect of any attribute unless the systems have similar properties. This rule would seem to make the isomorphic relation rare, and so special a case as not to be interesting as a topic of general discussion. However, there are three reasons why the principle can not be ignored.

(1) Isomorphism is the rule and not rare in the *propagation of an irreversible change through a constant medium.* The transmission of light in vacuo or the transmission of the nerve impulse along a single fiber are instances. In the latter case one is free to take any segment of the fiber as a single system, since it satisfies all the criteria of a separate system. Assuming that the membrane hypothesis of conduction holds, we find that the impulse in any segment of nerve fiber is isomorphic with the impulse in preceding segments and succeeding segments. In other words, the isomorphic transmission of an event is possible, and consists in the maintenance of the form of the event during its propagation. This special case fits the popular notion of causal chains which we have had, in general, to abandon in favor of systemic serial action.

(2) Because this simple kind of transmission is an hypothesis easy to imagine in the *psychophysiology of perception*, it has often been employed in the history of speculation about perception. The next section of this paper takes up this topic. In it we must remember that the presumption always lies against isomorphic correspondence between serial events in successive systems. The burden of proof to show adequate reason for isomorphic relationship rests upon those who would apply this hypothesis to a given case,

and the general rule is that events are not likely to be isomorphic between systems unless the properties of the systems are known to be similar.

(3) Finally there is the specific question of *psychoneural isomorphism*, which assumes importance because it has historical prestige and distinguished advocates. We shall consider this conception presently.

Isomorphism and Parsimony

The outstanding characteristic of perception is its correctness. Its chief function is to provide a correct picture of the external world. Illusion is the exception, for ordinarily the mind is adequate to reality. This fundamental truth invites the introduction of isomorphic relationships into perceptual theory. In what simpler way, the theorist asks, could perception be correct than by mirroring the external object? If his conception of mind is predominantly empiristic, then it is quite natural for him to think of perception as an isomorphic transmission of the properties of the perceived object.

Such indeed was the *image theory of perception* held by Epicurus and later by some of the scholastics. Epicurus' view was that fine images, exact replicas of the perceived bodies, are discharged from the surfaces of the bodies and reach the soul by way of the organs of sense. The isomorphic principle here involved is so natural that it has persisted in some form or other until the present, and most progress in the theory of perception has consisted in the overthrow of this principle in some special context. Locke's doctrine of primary qualities involved the principle, but his doctrine of secondary qualities gave notice that isomorphism between the object and perception cannot be regarded as universal. It must have been Epicurus' view, embodied in common sense, that Johannes Müller was combating in his theory of the specific energy of nerves. Müller's theory was not new: Thomas Young and Charles Bell had held it as a matter of course before him, and yet Müller had to polemize in favor of the theory and Helmholtz had later to proclaim its fundamental importance, all because the Epicurean view was so strongly established in common sense. What was it that Müller said? That we are directly aware, not of the objects of sense themselves, but of the states of the nerves that these objects affect. That does not seem a very difficult doctrine to get accepted; but it was difficult for Müller because he had to prove that the states of the nerves and the properties of their stimulating objects are anisomorphic, as he did by marshalling the evidence for "inadequate" stimulation (*cf.* Boring, 1929, 76–94).

Recently Köhler (1913) has criticised what we have come to call the "constancy hypothesis," the assumption that perception and its stimulus have a constant relation, and that the form of the perception depends only upon the properties of the stimulus. This objection is the proper objection of Gestalt psychologists to isomorphism: the perception depends in part upon the laws of the system to which it immediately pertains and only in part upon the properties of the stimulus.

A special constancy hypothesis that has long dominated psychology is the view that the attributes of sensation—quality, intensity, extent and duration —are correlated one-to-one with dimensions of variation in the stimulus. For example, the pitch of a tone was supposed to be a function of stimulus frequency only; loudness was supposed to vary only with stimulus energy. Now we know that pitch and loudness are each joint functions of frequency and energy, and that other tonal attributes like volume and density are also joint functions of the same two stimulus variables (Stevens, 1934). I have shown elsewhere—partly in penance for my own too ready acceptance of attributive constancy in the past—that theoretically the number of attributes of a sensation is entirely independent of the number of effective dimensions of variation in the stimulus, and that, as long as the attributes have different laws of functional dependence upon the stimulus, they will remain distinct (Boring, 1935). This relationship holds because the attribute may be a function, not only indirectly of the properties of the stimulus system, but also of the properties of all those other systems in the progression that are antecedent to the establishment of the attribute.

Isomorphism is a parsimonious concept; it is a simple relation that economizes thought. When no contradicting facts are known, it is the natural assumption to make. "Entia non sunt multiplicanda praeter necessitatem." That is William of Occam's "razor" and Sir William Hamilton's *law of parsimony*. However, there are in this case so many contradicting facts. The total system that includes the event called a perception involves many smaller, different, successively excited systems, and these systems impose their nature on the event. "Entia sunt multiplicanda propter necessitatem," we had better say. In view of the complexity of the media, simplicity of transmission is suspect (*cf.* Boring, 1929, 487).

My point is that these isomorphic relationships are natural and easy to assume in the face of ignorance, but that they generally prove false when detailed knowledge of the systems involved begins to be available. To make this point quite clear, I beg the reader's patience while I give an historical illustration.

Isaac Newton (1677) proposed what we should call now a theory of color vision. At that time Newton knew about the periodic nature of light and believed light to be vibratory, for he had not yet espoused the corpuscular theory. He suggested that the various rays of light would excite vibrations in the retinal terminations of the optic nerve, "the biggest, strongest, or most potent rays, the largest vibrations; and others shorter, according to their bigness, strength, or power"; and he concluded: "these vibrations will run

. . . through the optic nerves, into the sensorium; and there, I suppose, affect the sense with various colours, according to their bigness and mixture; and the biggest with the strongest colours, reds and yellows; the least with the weakest, blues and violets; the middle with green, and a confusion of all with white—much after the manner that, in the sense of hearing, nature makes use of aerial vibrations of several bignesses to generate sounds of divers tones, for the analogy of nature is to be observed." Newton supposed that there were seven colors, analogous with the seven musical notes of the octave. He had discovered the now classical laws of color mixture, including the then astonishing one that white may be a mixture of all the colors—presumably of all seven colors. What could have been more natural in the face of the ignorance of that day than to suppose that these frequencies are conducted by the optic nerve to the "sensorium?" So Newton assumed isomorphic transmission and put forward a theory that had at this point some resemblance to Epicurus' image theory of perception.

A century and a quarter later Thomas Young faced the same problem. There had not been much increase in relevant knowledge, but the many black absorption lines in the spectrum (later measured by and named for Fraunhofer) had been discovered, and it was known that there is an "infinitude" of kinds of light, not merely seven colors. Newton could suppose after the analogy of tones ("and the analogy of nature is to be observed") that seven colors could fall upon a single spot in the retina and their individual frequencies be maintained, so that the sensorium could perceive the specific "confusion" that is white. Young could make no such simple assumption for the infinitude of colors that compose white light, and he was thus obliged for a retinal theory of color to appeal to the properties of the retinal system.

Young wrote (1802): "As it is almost impossible to conceive of each sensitive point in the retina to contain an infinite number of particles, each capable of vibrating in perfect unison with every possible undulation, it becomes necessary to suppose the number limited, for instance to the three principal colours, red, yellow, and blue, of which the undulations are related in magnitude nearly as the numbers 8, 7, and 6; and that each of these particles is capable of being put in motion less or more forcibly by undulations differing less or more from a perfect unison; for instance, the undulations of green light, being nearly in the ratio $6\frac{1}{2}$, will affect equally the particles in unison with yellow and blue, and produce the same effect as light composed of those two species; and each sensitive filament of the nerve may consist of three portions, one for each principal colour."

Thus was born in its essentials the theory that is now called the Young-Helmholtz theory and which is the accepted principle today for hypotheses concerning color vision. Newton, believing in the existence of only a few colors, could suppose their isomorphic transmission at the retina. Young, knowing that there are very many colors, could make no such assumption. He had to look to the retinal system for properties that would so change the form of the event as to provide a "sufficient reason" for the laws of color mixture.

Psychoneural Isomorphism

The notion that there is a similarity between perceptual relations and the underlying relations in the brain is so nearly implicit in the doctrine of psychophysical parallelism that it would seem that this hypothesis must be quite old. At any rate, G. E. Müller (1896, 1–4) formulated five axioms concerning it. However, the principle has recently been given great importance by the Gestalt psychologists. Köhler (1920, 173–195) laid down the rule and coined the word isomorphism for the psychoneural correspondence of spatial orders (1929, 60–67). Koffka (1935, 61–67) espouses the principle in general. Wertheimer (1912, 246–252) made use of it in discussing a physiological hypothesis for the phi-phenomenon.

It should be plain from what has been said that the presumption lies against an isomorphism that represents a correlation between the two terms of a dualism. If consciousness and the brain are the terms of a metaphysical dualism, then we have two incomparable systems that would not be likely to have the identical properties that are implied by the isomorphic relation. If consciousness and the brain differ merely as the terms of an epistemological dualism, still one should not expect such different operations of knowing to imply identical properties. The presumption is strongly against isomorphism in a dualism, and, since *psychoneural isomorphism* describes a dualistic relation, the presumption must lie against it.

However, a fact can easily annihilate a presumption. Let us therefore examine the factual situation in respect of psychoneural isomorphism. There are three cases to consider.

(1) There are the cases where the terms of both the phenomenal and the neural systems are alleged to have been observed and correlated. This is the sort of observation that would immediately rout a presumption to the contrary. The difficulty is that there are almost no such cases that are univocal. As far as I know there are none at all for intensity, duration, or quality (what would quality be neurally?). There may be some for space, but they are very general, approximate, and inferential. Koffka (1935, 61) cites experiments that show that some principles of spatial organization in the brain resemble principles of spatial organization in perception. Much of Lashley's work can be given similar implications (*cf.* Boring, 1933, 94–107). Perhaps it may be said that recent research tends more toward the support of the theory of the projection of the periphery upon the center, and thus perhaps, in view of the adequacy of perception, to imply an isomorphic relation between the projec-

tion field and the perception. On the other hand, temporal, qualitative, and to some extent intensitive differences are also supposed to have spatial representation in the brain, so that it appears that this evidence cannot be directed toward any simple isomorphism. This paper is not the place to review a large literature that is equivocal as to the point in question. Perhaps it is enough to say that the hypothesis of isomorphism hardly needs to be considered in this case. It is certainly not yet proved. Much more exact neurological knowledge is needed. If it could be proved, the isomorphism would probably be forgotten in the presence of the observed correlations. The present stress on the hypothesis shows that it is still speculative.

(2) On the other hand, there are cases where no claim is made for a directly or indirectly observed neural term. In them, I think, the presumption against the isomorphistic hypothesis applies in all its force. Perhaps one such case is the correlation of "experienced order in time" with corresponding temporal relations in the underlying physiological context. I think that this is the relation that Köhler (1929, 65) has posited, although he is so guarded in his sentences that I am not sure. In any case it is a common parallelistic view, and there is no observational evidence for the neural term. Such inference as is available makes it appear that the temporal factors ought to become spatialized in the brain before they are discriminated, as even Koffka indicates (1935, 452). Operationism has a way of avoiding this difficulty of the neural spatialization of time, but the principle is not an isomorphism (or isochronism) and so does not form a proper digression here.

(3) A special class of cases is where the observed terms are all phenomenal but appear to be connected by physical laws. Wertheimer's assumption (1912, 246–252) of a cortical short-circuit as underlying the phi-phenomena is a case in point. Here it appears as if a final perception drains an initial one when the time between the two is not too short nor too long. (This argument is strengthened when Korte's laws are also known, but we shall not complicate it here.) However, the notion of drainage or short-circuiting is physical, and it may have appeared more plausible to Wertheimer to suppose that a relationship of a physical order within phenomenal experience must, since it is physical, imply an isomorphic basis in the brain.

It seems to me that Köhler's discussion (1920, 211–227) of the physiology of the Weber function is a similar instance of this sort. The phenomena are such relationships as they would be if certain physical principles applied to them, and these principles, being physical, can be localized in the brain. Similar comment can be made on the mnemonic trace which Köhler (1923, 137–148; 165–174), Koffka (1935, 423–464), and others have considered as a neural entity, following physical laws of growth, decay, and assimilation. Both these views imply an intensitive isomorphism that is founded, not on the observation of neural states (e.g., summed cortical action potentials), but on purely phenomenal data.

In these cases, I think, it is fair to argue that the presumption against isomorphism should be respected. If the data are phenomenal, let the explanatory concepts also be localized in the phenomenal world without the use of insecure isomorphic bridges across the dualistic gulf to the brain. A trace is a reasonable hypothesis. It is the residue of a no-longer-conscious sensation. It exists because it continues to have determinable functional capacities. Why force it into the brain when we have no physiological evidence for it, if we *as dualists* do not localize phenomena in the brain?

My general conclusion is that psychoneural isomorphism has not in general been validated, that as an a priori hypothesis it is too improbable to be safe, and that dualists should be warned against it. (Monists will not need it.)

A Restatement of Psychoneural Isomorphism in Physiological Terms

It is obvious that the difficulty which lies beneath the general assumption of psychoneural isomorphism is the impossibility of finding in physiology any sufficient reason for phenomenal consciousness. If consciousness is a system that is not identical with the underlying neural system, then there is no reason to suppose that events in the one system will mirror events in the other unless the two systems can be shown to have similar properties. But how can the two horns of a dualism be supposed to have similar properties, except as similar properties are separately and empirically established for each? What we need, if we are to assume psychoneural isomorphism, is (*a*) some knowledge of the properties of phenomenal experience, a knowledge which we are only beginning to have; (*b*) some knowledge of the properties of the underlying neural system, a knowledge which is also just beginning; (*c*) evidence that the properties of the two systems are similar, evidence which we have not got; and (*d*) at least a plausible theory as to how the two systems intercommunicate, whether by common terms or otherwise. If we could put all these neural and phenomenal events into two communicating systems, then we should have the "sufficient reason" for consciousness. However, I do not see how dualistic modes of thought can ever provide a plausible conception of psychoneural communication.

Nevertheless, I think we can have a sufficient reason for consciousness if we want it. In order to get it, we must first inquire concerning the nature of the "immediate experience" that lies apart from the rest of scientific reality, that can be correlated (it is said) with physical reality, but not systemically integrated with it. That inquiry is answered—and I do not see how else it can be answered—by the defining of *immediate experience* in terms of the operations by which it is known (Stevens, 1935, 520–523). Since introspection is neural and behavioral, consciousness must be too. Consciousness is the capacity of the organism for specific differentiated response (discrimination), for an organism knows what, as an organism, it distinguishes, and what it cannot distinguish does not exist psychically for it (*cf.* Boring, 1933, 221–236). Thus the problem of psychophysiology becomes the problem of discovering what differentiation in one system implies a specific differentiation in some antecedent system. With such conceptualization consciousness becomes, like every other event, a matter of systemic relationships. It is not so much that consciousness is integrated with neural systems as that it *is* certain integrations of neural systems (*cf.* Lashley, 1923, 330–343).

On this view the problem of isomorphism dissolves in a knowledge of the functional relationships which obtain between variables of neural systems, and I urge that it requires some such view to strip isomorphism of the mystery of magic that has always clung to any bridge between the body and the soul (think of Descartes! think of Fechner!). Psychology will certainly face reality more securely if it can achieve this release from domination by the magic isolation of an insubstantial soul.

On the other hand, there is a monistic and systemic conception of the relation of introspection to the brain which is a physiological account of "psychoneural" isomorphism. I offer it as the proper substitute for a concept that seems to me to become less and less plausible and useful the more its meaning is examined.

Consciousness—immediate experience—introspection—they arc all, I have argued, matters of discrimination. Discrimination can always be reduced to choices between A and *not*-A. In fact, in science discrimination usually is dichotomously limited. All readings of scales are choices between coincidence and not-coincidence, and other observations are most reliable if reduced to the discrimination between identity and difference. Though we may have more convenient gross descriptive methods, at least we can say that all science could be realized if the observer's discrimination were always directed upon the dilemma between *same* and *different*.

Thus introspection can be envisaged as action of the kind A-or-*not*-A in a terminal system. The determinant of A-or-*not*-A lies not in the properties of the terminal system that is directly observed but in an antecedent system. We know that specificity of reactions of this sort is not determined in peripheral efferent channels. The efferent neural paths may be quite different: A may be the movement of the right hand, and *not*-A the movement of the left hand. It is also possible by instruction to shift the differential response from the hands elsewhere, perhaps to the feet or to the vocimotor apparatus. Still the same discriminations remain. It thus appears that the crucial determiner of the specific response must lie in a system anterior to the peripheral efferent systems. The determination of the dichotomous discriminatory choice must be pre-efferent, because the alternative efferent paths are isolated from each other, and because the particular pathways used are irrelevant since a given discrimination can be switched onto various pairs of paths. It is plain that behavior at the periphery *qua* movement is not significant. It is significant only in respect of what it implies in the system whose differentiation determines the discriminatory behavior.

It is important to note at this point that, in a series of communicating open systems, the differentiation of some particular system, Q, may be determined by the differentiation of some other system, K, antecedent to Q. For instance, the event k_1 in K may determine the event q_1 in Q, and k_2 may determine a q_2. There need be no similarity between K and Q, nor between the ks and the qs. There is merely a one-to-one correlation of a casual order between each k and its q. In such a relation the events in the system K *imply* the events in the system Q; or, we may say, the events in K mean the events in Q; or, in still other words, K describes Q.

In this sense it is true that *introspection implies, or means, or describes, the differentiation of some pre-efferent neural system*. The relation is not isomorphic because the events in the terminal system (introspection) are not like the events in the crucial antecedent (central neural) system. However, it is true that the meaning of the introspection—its meaning, not its content as motor events—does resemble the "brain" pattern in the sense that it refers to it.

There are two ways of regarding this situation, and one seems to be isomorphic and the other not; yet there is really no essential difference between them. (1) We can say that, on the basis of introspective data, a set of psychic reals is set up. Such a real might be a sensory trace, which diminishes in degree with time. The trace is described by those dichotomous discriminations which are the immediate motor content of introspection. However, these discriminations are determined by and therefore imply (mean, describe) the crucial central determining system. Hence the neural system and the psychic reals are isomorphic. (2) On the other hand, it is apparent that we gain this psychoneural isomorphism by means of an unnecessary step. We do not have to posit the independent existence of the psychic reals at all. The argument that shows that the psychic reals are isomorphic with the determining neural system is an argument that makes introspection directly descriptive (implicative) of the neural system itself. Thus there seems to be nothing more to isomorphism than the tautology that, since introspection means (is determined by) an antecedent neural system, the meaning of introspection is that neural system.

Here, in the logic of this last paragraph, lies I think the explanation of why the hypothesis of psychoneural isomorphism retains importance in spite of insufficient evidence. There is no ground for it in the known systemic relations of two dualistic systems. However, the Gestalt psychologists, though speaking dualistically of phenomena and physiological processes, doubtless intuit the fact that introspection itself is a physiological event which reflects the differentiation of central processes, so that it becomes a description of the neural processes themselves (*cf.* Köhler, 1929, 67). The paradox of this kind of isomorphism is that you can establish it only by annihilating it. To establish it you have to let dualism go and consider intercommunicating neural systems; and then you find that the isomorphism which you have is the implication by a terminal system (introspection) of the state of an antecedent system (brain). Psychoneural isomorphism reduces to nothing more than this: *description implies its object!*

A Psychological Function Is the Relation of Successive Differentiations of Events in the Organism

1937

THE trouble with the concept of cause-and-effect is Newton's third law. The reaction of the effect upon the cause matches the action of the cause upon the effect, so that we have, not a serial progressive action, but that mutual interdependence of two events which makes them into a system. Everything is interrelated in this way. The universe is a system, and to partition it into part-systems is a falsification. If a man is ever to utter the whole truth about a natural event, he must not shut his mouth until he has expressed all nature.

Nevertheless man has perforce to be content with much less than that mouthful. He describes events within limits, and he succeeds again and again in distorting them only by an amount that is negligible. There are practical lateral and terminal limits that can be set to events. One can think of a neuron as a system and not commit any great error. Of course, the neuron is not insulated laterally, for its recovery after excitation is dependent upon the circulation, and the restorative power of the blood depends upon nutrition, and nutrition upon food, and food upon food supply, and food supply upon economic legislation, and the legislation upon world politics, and so on. This extension of the neuron-system is not imaginary: the nerves of the man who is dead from economic want do not react as they did in prosperity. Similarly we fix the terminal limits of a neuron-system at the synapses, although it is probable that even there some reaction occurs to alter the action. Even though systemic limitation may be arbitrary and only approximate, no one will deny its practical necessity nor the fact that we may sometimes make accurate scientific progress by accepting the fiction that a system can be isolated from the rest of the world.

It would seem that these fictitious systemic boundaries can be interpolated successfully when there is great disparity between the events in adjacent sys-

Reprinted with permission from *Psychological Review*, 1937, 44, 445–461.

tems, and in some such cases we can actually recover for practical use the convenient relation of cause-and-effect which the universality of systemic relations had caused us to abandon.

Sometimes this disparity is temporally from the great to the small. The big event has a small effect. The effect then reacts upon the event, but its reaction is negligible to the event. Thus approximately we have one-way action. Take the series of miniature systems affected when a sound from a loudspeaker excites the organ of Corti. The diaphragm (1) of the speaker sets up a vibratory pattern in the air (2), which by way of the tympanic membrane moves the ossicles (3), which through the oval window set up a resonating pattern in the cochlea (4), which, moving the hairs of the hair cells, arouses the electro-chemical disturbance known as the cochlear response (5), which excites the VIIIth nerve (6), which excites the lateral lemniscus (7), and so on. We do not know much about reaction at a synapse, but it is plain that there must be some reaction back from the cochlear response to the speaker diaphragm. The electrical energy dissipated in the cochlear response must increase the resistance to movement of the organ of Corti (just as it is harder to turn a generator when the switch in its output circuit is closed and current can flow); and the increased resistance of the organ of Corti must diminish the movement at the oval window, at the tympanic membrane, in the air, and at the speaker diaphragm. It is conceivable that the vibration of a loud-speaker might be diminished because a man fifty feet away turned his attention to the sound! The point is that in the first five of these systems there is a disparity between the events: reaction affects the antecedent system only a little because the antecedent system is relatively large. Destroying the apical tip of the cochlea does not greatly alter the action of the tympanic membrane for low tones.

On the other hand, the disparity is sometimes from the small to the great. This is the case of the release mechanism, the case that is typical for the nervous system. Now the antecedent system simply pulls the trigger or throws the switch, as it were, and there results an effect that is huge with respect to the energy derived from the preceding system. The magnitude of the effect depends, of course, upon energy resident in the consequent system. There must be reaction here too, but it is only of the order of magnitude of the energy required to trip the switch and is therefore negligible.

For these reasons it becomes possible to understand many psychological events as if they were cause-and-effect relations between serial systems in the living organism. Even though theoretically there is only one system, the universe, we can make progress by means of the fiction that the organism is a system separated from the rest of the universe, that the nervous system can sometimes be regarded apart from the total organism, and that portions of the nervous system can also be separated from each other for the purpose of studying their correlative relations.

The Organism as a Systemic Series

It is the purpose of this paper to depict the organism as a series of open communicating systems, transmitting action in the direction of stimulus to response. Figure 1 is the paradigm. Partial systems of the kind that can be separated practically from the rest of the universe can appear in any one of three ways. Such a system may be *closed*, that is to say, it may represent an equilibrium that is maintained essentially independently of events outside the system. The system may be *incomplete* in the sense that it cannot be inde-

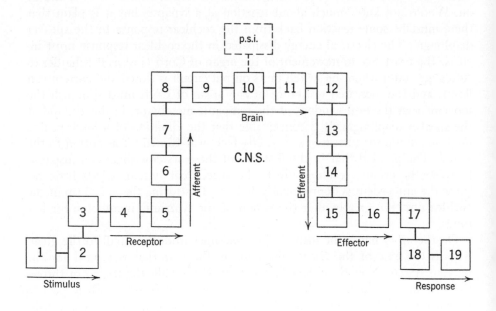

Fig. 1. *Schematic diagram of the organism as a series of communicating systems.*

pendently described, and so must be enlarged. Or a system may be *open* in that it communicates with antecedent or consequent systems in such ways that reaction is negligible in comparison with action. Successive neurones with synaptic communication are in this sense open systems. An electrical network may form an open system. It is a system because the relation of the current in the various parts cannot be determined by any simple logic of cause-and-effect but only by the solution of a set of simultaneous equations. On the other hand, such a system *B* can communicate with an antecedent system *A* in the sense that *B* derives its initial input voltage as the output of *A*; or *B* can communicate with a consequent system *C* in the sense that some difference of potential within *B* may become the input of *C*. Ordinarily such electrical systems would be incomplete and would have to be combined, but their separation might properly be made if, for example, the antecedent system were a compound-wound generator which approximately maintains its voltage whatever current is drawn from it, and the subsequent system were a vacuum-tube voltmeter which does not appreciably reduce a voltage in measuring it. The open systems of the nervous system tend to show relationships of this sort (Boring, 1936, 566–570).

The meaning of Fig. 1 will become clear if we apply to it the auditory illustration of the preceding section. Suppose that an organism presses a key which mechanically moves a signal when the organism hears a change in the pitch of a tone given by a loud-speaker. In the list below we can place tentatively successive systems with numbers corresponding to the numbers of Fig. 1.

1. Loud-speaker	8. Aud. radiations	15. End-plates
2. Air in room	9. Cortical system	16. Muscle
3. Ossicles	10. Another system?	17. Finger
4. Cochlea	11. Another system?	18. Key
5. Cochlear response	12. Motor area	19. Signal
6. VIIIth nerve	13. Pyramidal tract	
7. Lateral lemniscus	14. Efferent nerve	

The list is schematic and suggestive only. There must be other systems that should be introduced. Some of these systems, like the cochlea and the ossicles, are perhaps so incomplete that they need to be combined.

Of course the great omission from the table is the *Aufgabe*, the "switcher." An organism making such a specific response is following an instruction or acting in accordance with an attitude. An instruction, given as the meaning of words, is an afferent series that may come along various routes (visual, auditory; English, German) but ends up in the same excitation, since the meaning is the same. Somewhere in the region 8–12 this excitation determines what set of efferent patterns will be discharged (13–19) as the response to the stimulus (1–7). An attitude persists in the region 8–12 as a trace of the organism's past. So does every other available trace of memory. The tremendous complication of the fact is well known. Nevertheless the simple scheme of Fig. 1 serves as the paradigm to show how the organism can be regarded for the purposes of psychology.

Isomorphic Relations

When an event is transmitted through a systemic series like Fig. 1, it some-times remains with its essential form unchanged in successive systems. It is then possible to say that the successive phases of the event are isomorphic with each other. Transmission across a synapse may be isomorphic since, under the all-or-none law, neural excitations are pretty much alike. The general rule is that, if two successive systems have the same properties and the output of each is like the input, then transmitted events should be isomorphic. Thus the mechanical events of the first four systems listed for hearing are anisomorphic, for the properties of the systems change and output is not like input (Boring, 1936, 572–579).

In general when isomorphic relations between systems are known to exist, there is no need for the word. The term is more often applied as a hopeful hypothesis in the face of insufficient knowledge of the properties of the systems involved.

Discrimination

Discrimination is the psychical function of the organism. It is the criterion of mind, of consciousness, of knowing. Animals, children and irresponsible adults are recognized as conscious only as and in as far as they discriminate, that is to say, as they react differentially (discriminatorily) to a differentiated situa-tion. The contents of the unconscious mind can be asserted to exist only in as far as they appear in differential response. Even the "immediate, private experience" of introspection can be defined only operationally, and the opera-tion which indicates its existence is differential reaction. The mere fact of psychical relativity shows that the contents of mind have no meaning apart from differentiation. If color were constant, there could be no awareness of color. It is only as color is differentiated that it provides a possibility of dif-ferential reaction. If color and size always varied together, they would never be recognized as different. Differentiation among the attributes is got by their independent variability. The psychophysical judgment is always relative. Either a standard is given as a frame of reference, or else—as in the so-called "absolute" judgments—the frame of reference is constituted by the traces of immediately past judgments. This point has been argued elsewhere (Stevens, 1935; 1936, 94–98; Boring, 1935, 240–244; Boring, 1933, 229–233) and does not need extended consideration here. The fact is that all the soluble problems of psychology can be reduced to problems of differentiated reaction if one wants so to reduce them.[1]

The only persistent opposition to the view that the subject-matter of psychology is the discriminations that organisms make comes from those persons who wish to maintain that there is scientific significance to the concept of immediate (direct phenomenal) experience. These persons are answered by the fact that even private experience is not immediate. There is not even a private meaning to a sense-datum, except as it is given in relation to some extrinsic frame of reference.

Successive Differentiation in the Nervous System

The term *discrimination* is, however, not the most fortunate. It is a functional term representing the dependence of a consequent differentiation upon antecedent differentiation, a relation such that the later differentiation indicates the existence of the earlier. Only in this descriptive sense is the word useful. Unfortunately it tends to pick up a "subjective" or "dynamic" context, partly because *discrimination* has long meant a capacity which belongs to a world of private or sensory experience, and partly because dynamic or functional concepts are intuited as "energetic," whereas in scientific description they are nothing more than relationships. We get rigorous description only by avoiding the "anthropomorphism" of "dynamic" psychology, and the word *discrimination*, as it enters into this discussion, does not mean that the organism as a whole is doing the discriminating. The cochlea "discriminates" among events in the middle ear when it responds differentially to the action of the ossicles. The VIIIth nerve "discriminates" as to what goes on in the organ of Corti, and efferent events may be "discriminations" of afferent events. It is therefore probably best to abandon the word *discrimination*, which implies a freely acting, conscious observer, and to limit ourselves to the descriptive terms of successive differentiation and the relations between them. It is these relations between differentiations that are the subject matter of psychology.

It is obvious that the differentiation of events within any one of these seriated systems of Fig. 1 is a joint function of (*a*) the properties of the system and (*b*) the differentiation of the antecedent communicating system. Three things can happen as an event is transmitted through the series.

(1) Additional differentiation may be *gained* as a result of the properties of the system in which it first appears. For instance, the mechanism of the middle ear may "add" a difference tone to a complex of two tones; that is to say, the system of the ossicles distorts the transmitted wave-form, so that resonance to it will now yield three tones instead of two. In the same way,

when the two dimensions of the tonal stimulus (frequency and intensity) yield a four-fold differentiation in the organism (pitch, loudness, volume and density), it is plain that the final differentiation reflects some properties of the transmitting chain as well as properties of the stimulus. If the four attributes are initially dependent, as Stevens has suggested, upon the differentiation of the pattern of excitation in the cochlea, then the differential observation of these attributes can be regarded as an observation of the properties of the cochlear mechanism.[2] So much has been said about the stimulus-response relation being the organism's discrimination of its environment, that it is high time to remember that a great deal of what counts for error on the part of the organism in discriminating its environment is really its correct perception of properties of its own self.

(2) On the other hand, differentiation may be transmitted part of the way and then *lost*. There is a great deal of differentiation in the stimulus which has negligible effect upon the organism, like the polarization of light and the phase relations of tones heard monaurally. There must also be many incidental properties of the parts of the nervous system that do not get passed on. It seems probable that the frequency of a tonal stimulus below 1000 c.p.s., although recoverable from the VIIIth nerve, is lost at higher levels of the auditory tracts. In such a case the frequency would be incidental to the physics of transmission but would have no further significance in the psychic life of the organism.

(3) There remains the case in which differentiation is *maintained* and thus transmitted. Although some psychologists are interested in such relations as the adequate response of the cochlea to the auditory stimulus, psychological problems for the most part are based upon overt differentiation that appears in effector mechanisms—behavior, both concrete and verbal. Any discriminatory behavior that reflects adequately the properties of the stimulus means that differentiation in the stimulus has been carried all the way through the stimulus-response series. Sometimes differentiation in the response reflects a property of a phase of the train subsequent to the stimulus, as would be the case if a judgment of tonal volume is dependent upon the spread of excitation in the organ of Corti. In other words, there is always a problem as to where the final differentiation originates within the organism or before the organism. Any judgment that depends upon learning is a differentiation in response that has originated at some post-afferent point, for to learn something is to change the properties of the brain.

These three cases represent three fundamental psychological problems. Is one "conscious" of the stimulus, or of the processes in the sense-organ, or of the engrams in the brain? The *Aufgabe* and attitudes introduce still other problems, of course, but it is already clear that it is important to know where differentiation originates in the organism, when it is known to appear in response. The place of origin of the differentiation determines, at least in the common-sense meaning of terms, *what* it is that is being discriminated.

There is no possibility that, by observing stimulus and overt response at the organism's periphery, we should ever be able to localize properties within the organism. If something comes out that did not go in, who shall say where it entered the series? We can find out only by tapping into the series at some point. The discovery of the method of amplification of action potentials has taught us a great deal about auditory stimulation. We can tap the series by observation at the hair cells, at the VIIIth nerve, at various higher levels in the auditory tract. Mechanical interference with the cochlea gives us more information, and physical methods enable us to know much that goes on outside of the tympanic membrane. Observation of peripheral nerves shows us that the differentiation in the response must be fixed at some pre-efferent level. The *Aufgabe* as a switching mechanism must act in the brain, and what the *Aufgabe* affects in the response could not be added in the efferent tracts. There is then considerable advance in the localization of these special properties in the nervous system, but this knowledge could never have been gained except by breaking into the stimulus-response series with a new method of control (e.g., *Aufgabe*) or of observation (e.g., action potential).

Psychoneural Isomorphism

The foregoing argument contains the lethal objection to the theory of psychoneural isomorphism, and indeed to any parallelistic dualism of consciousness and brain. Figure 1 represents consciousness (phenomenal experience) as *Psi*, paralleling the brain system, no. 10. Such is the usual assumption of parallelism. Psychoneural isomorphism assumes that certain essential differentiation in *Psi* corresponds to similar differentiation in 10. There are various ways in which we can learn about the neural system 10, but there is no way of learning about *Psi* except by introspection, and introspection is differentiated response in the 15–17 region (Fig. 1), and can reflect differentiation in *Psi* only as it is transmitted through 10. Hence only those events in *Psi* which are represented by events in 10 could ever be known. We must conclude that, if there were a *Psi* paralleling 10, then the only events in *Psi* that could ever be known would be those that are isomorphic with events in 10. We see here why psychoneural isomorphism is plausible. However, the theory is not only plausible; it is also untenable, for there is no possible way in which *Psi* can be given a separate existence from 10, since all information about *Psi* must pass through 10. If we could put an electrode on the "psychoneural joint" between *Psi* and 10, in order to find out what originates in *Psi* and what in 10, then—and then only—should we have the opportunity of proving or disproving psychoneural isomorphism.[3]

Consciousness

An objective theory of the mind, such as this paper presents, does not reject consciousness! Let us get that matter straight. Instead it ingests consciousness. Its chief value is that it provides so good a definition of consciousness that the rigor of the definition turns out to be preferable to the uncertainty of the term. Thus we have the paradox that a system invented to account for consciousness seems to get along without consciousness. There is, however, another reason for abandoning this precious word.

Consciousness as traditionally used is an ambiguous term, as is also every other term applied to "immediate," "direct," or "phenomenal" experience. The two definitions of consciousness are

(A) *Consciousness = awareness of an object.*
(B) *Consciousness = awareness of the awareness of an object.*

Let us see to what sort of psychological events or relations these two different concepts apply.

Consciousness as Awareness of an Object

To define consciousness as awareness of an object is to equate consciousness to discrimination, and thus—in the terms that this paper sets down—to the relation of differentiation in response to differentiation in stimulus. The man who says "I see green," and who in such a saying consistently reflects a variable property of the stimulus, is conscious of the green in the stimulus, because he is responding adequately to it. This is what most laboratory introspection is, and it would seem therefore to be a useful definition of consciousness. The difficulty is that the definition includes so many other cases that are not ordinarily regarded as examples of consciousness.

Under this definition A the following events would all be conscious. (1) The recognition of a familiar face among strange faces, an instance which would be disputed by none. (2) Looking toward the door when there is a knock at it. (3) Eating raisins while absorbed in conversation after dinner. (4) Pronouncing the word *the* as it occurs casually in the middle of a glib *ex tempore* speech. (5) Winking when the eye-ball is dry. (6) Continuing to swallow when food is half-way down the œsophagus. (7) The phototropic turning of the protozoan toward the light. (8) The movement of the iron filings toward the magnet. We can paraphrase these situations. For instance, we can say: "he knows that the raisins are there though he is too absorbed to notice them"; "he has not time to choose his words, but his voice chooses for him"; "the eyelid knows that the eye is dry"; "the iron filings know where the magnet is." The list runs from the discriminatory relations that are ordinarily called conscious, down through the habituations and automatic actions which are supposed to be less conscious, on through the tropisms which have for forty years been only hesitantly classified as conscious, to the inorganic relations which differ in no whit from the conscious ones but which are never called conscious.

Here then lies the first difficulty with this concept of consciousness. Persons who accept the definition for the top of the hierarchy are unwilling to go through with it to the bottom. Yet the series is continuous and there is no essential difference between the human and the inorganic pattern. We are meeting here with the conventions of usage and not with logic. It is obviously best to abandon the word *consciousness* in the sense of awareness of an object and to deal instead with relations between systemic differentiations where there can be no dispute about terms.[4]

Consciousness as Awareness of Awareness of an Object

The reason why people will accept definition A as meaning consciousness in man and reject it as meaning consciousness in iron filings is that they have been trained from an early age to think of consciousness as an essential attribute of man, a probable attribute of animals (especially vertebrates), an improbable attribute of plants, and an impossible attribute of inorganic things. Definition B, however, practically limits consciousness to man and is therefore likely to be more acceptable. Certainly there are many cases in which consciousness is attributed to a response solely because the organism is conscious of being conscious of an object.[5]

The crucial instances here lie in automatic behavior. Take the case where the eye runs down columns of proper names in order to note all the *Smiths*. The names, we shall suppose, are arranged in random order. The inspection can be rapid and yet no errors be made. Not a single *Smith* is missed. Is every other name, therefore, perceived as *not-Smith*? Yes, in the sense of definition A. To be correct in not stopping at a name that is not *Smith* is to react adequately and differentially to that name, to perceive the name, to be conscious of it in the sense of A. Yet most persons would prefer not to attribute consciousness to these responses where there can be no recall or recognition of the noncrucial names. What is the difference between the *Peterson* that goes unnoticed and the *Smith* that is noticed? It is possible for the organism to react correctly to his reaction to *Smith*; he knows that he reacted; he is aware of having been aware. No such statements can be made about *Peterson*. The best that the organism can do about *Peterson* is to read the list slowly again, single out the name, and infer that he must have reacted to the word because he was correct in not noting it.

It would be possible to develop this conception through a great many intricacies that would not be worth our exploration. The self-conscious introspector is aware that he is aware that he is aware of the object. By empathy one organism is aware at once that another organism is aware of an object. An animal reacting to his reaction would come under this definition. Yet altogether the definition marks off a class of mental events that are normally human, and it serves for the human being to differentiate the conscious from the unconscious.

Of course the unconscious, in so far as it can be known, is dependent upon differential response for its revelation. Definition A would make the unconscious conscious; but definition B preserves the distinction between the conscious and the unconscious. When a person acts in accordance with a repressed idea without knowing the reason for his action, he is said to be motivated by the unconscious: he is aware of something (definition A: adequate response), but he is not aware that he is aware (definition B). But, when the motivating idea is fully conscious, then he is aware of the something, and aware that he is aware of the something. On this second definition of consciousness depends the important distinction between the conscious and the unconscious.

We have to understand this second definition of consciousness in order to realize what has become of consciousness in the objective system that this paper sets forth. Having understood, tough-minded rigorous thinkers will, I think, want to drop the term *consciousness* altogether. A scientific psychology is scarcely yet ready to give importance to so ill-defined a physiological event as an awareness of an awareness. This concept might never have come to the fore had not people tried to interpret others in terms of their own "private" minds—that egocentric Copernican distortion which properly leads to desolate solipsism.

Private Experience

Let us now ask ourselves the direct question: Have we, by explaining consciousness out of existence, by transforming it into a physical relation as we do when we give it its rigorous operational definition, have we by such an amœboid ingestion of consciousness proved that private experience does not exist? I think the answer is clear: Private experience does not exist, in any useful meaning of the term existence (Holt, 1937, 46 f.).

The term is a contradiction. Perhaps, when an atom of oxygen woos two atoms of hydrogen, its need appears in a consciousness that is over and above the fact of the dynamic relation between hydrogen and oxygen; but, if that is so, such consciousness is truly private. It never becomes public, and for all practical purposes of science and philosophy it does not exist. The human consciousness for which common sense asks our belief can have useful meaning for us only in so far as it is *not* private.

Nevertheless common sense still meets us with the assertion that private experience is the obvious ineluctable certainty of every person. "You do not mean to tell me," it says, "that you stand there, talking to me, without being intimately aware of me, without a complement of perceptual experience that is immediately your own before you even begin to think how to impart knowledge of its nature to anyone else? A denial of private experience is a *reductio ad absurdum*." The answer to this demand is more than Yes. It involves the demonstration that the person who is so sure of his immediate awareness or private experience, nevertheless has difficulty in determining just when he has been aware or has had experience. When he rapidly scrutinizes a set of visual objects to pick out a familiar one, and thus successfully ignores all the others, was he aware of every one of the others in order correctly to ignore them? We have noted above that he must be aware of the others, but not aware of his awareness. He himself will be puzzled to say of what he was aware. There is nothing obvious and certain to this "experience" whose owner has to reason out its existence just as the public might do. Awareness is not necessarily immediate or private. A doubt occurs as to where the boundary of privacy is to be drawn, and, if some "private" experience can be attested only by an inference that might as well be public, then the whole concept becomes shaded with doubt.

Still the stubborn man of common sense will say: "But some experience at least is immediately given. To have it is to know that you have it." To this I can only say that I do not find the world thus. My private experience is always an inference as to what is just past—in the last minute or the last half-second. That experience can also be the knowing of it does not make sense. Moreover, with all these contradictions popping up about immediate and private experience, I think the burden of proof lies with the person who insists on the existence of ineffable private experience. I feel sure that an intimate facing of the facts would reduce all personal experience to retrospection and inference of the kind that can be shared publicly.

In any event—and this is my *coup de grâce* to privacy of experience—can there be a useful meaning given to any private experience that does not possess the property of potential publicity? The experience can be, and in science must be, published, and the operation of publication is physiological and therefore physical, so that the means of publication come to provide a physical operational definition of experience. In this way experience inevitably loses its privacy, its immediacy and its nonphysical character. Nor do I find anything in introspection to confound this conclusion.[6]

Summary

For psychological purposes the organism can be regarded as a series of communicating systems in which the action is in the afferent-efferent direction. Causal interpretations can without undue falsification be applied to the relations between these systems, if the systems are properly chosen.

Discrimination, the psychic function of the organism and the criterion of psychological events, can be understood as the differentiation in a consequent system that adequately reflects the differentiation in a prior system. Differentiation can be begun, continued or ended at any point in the nervous system, and one of the primary tasks of psychology is to determine the place of origin of such differentiation as issues in overt response. Only by entering the systemic series by other observational methods can these places of origin be determined. For this reason psychoneural isomorphism turns out to be a meaningless concept, since there is no method by which the psyche can be differentiated from the brain.[7]

Consciousness is an ill-defined, equivocal term. It may mean adequate discrimination, but this definition includes inorganic relations as well as animal and human. It is sometimes used in the sense of awareness of awareness (reaction to a reaction) and the distinction between the conscious and the unconscious is of this kind. On the other hand, both kinds of consciousness are explained and the use of the term *consciousness* is avoided, if we speak more rigorously in terms of the dependence of the differentiation in one neural system upon the differentiation in another. With such a set of simple physical concepts we avoid the danger of founding a scientific account of mind upon these vague intuitions of the nature of private consciousness, which common sense has stamped upon the intellectual predilections of every man.

NOTES

1. E. B. Holt (1937, 42 ff., 47 ff.) holds a similar position, although he singles out verbal-motor processes as characterizing consciousness.
2. See Boring (1935, 240–245). Stevens' suggested correlation of the tonal attributes with the pattern of excitation in the organ of Corti is: pitch—place of maximal excitation along the basilar membrane; loudness—number of nerve fibers excited; volume—spread of excitation along the basilar membrane; density—number of fibers excited per unit of spread.
3. See Boring (1936, 574–586). I wish I could substitute the paragraph above for pp. 582–586 in this article, for I think that I have now got the matter stated more clearly and succinctly.
4. *Cf.* here Holt's (1937, 39–42) citation of Souriau: "Vision is an absolutely uncon-

scious act," and "Sensations are, therefore, by their very nature unconscious." His argument is similar to mine. In general let me say that I have always owed Holt a greater intellectual debt than I have ever been able to acknowledge by citation of article and page in his writings.

5. Again *cf.* Holt (1937, 40) who rejects this regress: "Thinking and knowing are processes in their own right: to think is not to think that I think that I think; and to know is not to know that I know that I know—into all eternity. In short, these considerations convey the gentle hint that philosophers and psychologists might improve themselves by learning not to stammer."

6. Privacy tends to reduce to the alleged self-validation of consciousness, the view that it is "impossible for any one to perceive, without perceiving that he does perceive" (Locke). *Cf.* Holt on the persistence of this dogma (1937, 33–35).

7. This argument is closely related to the contention that the concept of psychophysical parallelism is self-contradictory, because mind and brain cannot be distinguished unless they can be shown to vary independently, whereas psychophysical parallelism asserts that they do not vary independently although they are distinguished.

The Psychology
of Communicating Science

𝄢𝄢𝄢𝄢𝄢𝄢𝄢𝄢𝄢𝄢𝄢𝄢𝄢𝄢𝄢𝄢𝄢𝄢𝄢𝄢𝄢𝄢𝄢𝄢𝄢𝄢𝄢𝄢𝄢𝄢𝄢𝄢𝄢𝄢𝄢𝄢𝄢𝄢

*F*ROM *its inception in January 1956 and for six years thereafter, E.G.B. served as editor of Contemporary Psychology: A Journal of Reviews. Through the medium of a regular, monthly feature, "CP Speaks," he called attention in almost 300 essays to a variety of current issues. Many of them concern problems of the psychology of communicating science. These problems are not peculiar to psychology alone, justifying the broader title for this section of his papers. In this very direct way, E.G.B. found himself involved in an application of the psychology of science.*

The papers that follow were concerned with various facets of this application. The theme of static-free communications with dissent confined to ideas, not men, is expressed with a fugue-like development, appearing here in one guise and there in another. The principles that guided him in his editing of "A Journal of Book Reviews" is a paper which sets the stage for those that follow. A more specific problem is next considered: that of the "Social Predicament" created for the reviewer when he writes an unfavorable review. A counterpoise for the reader of Contemporary Psychology has been provided by another feature of that journal, "On the Other Hand" wherein critical letters and informal, counter-reviews make their appearance. This feedback of counter-criticism to that given in the original review makes possible "Cybernetic Justice" which is discussed in another essay. According to the form of communication, there are to be discerned various levels of "Tolerances for Inaccuracy," which is the concern of the next paper. That the scope of his interests in communication extended beyond the limits of American Psychology is explicit in his application of the concept of "Ortgeister" and national differences and in an appeal not to let ignorance of language make for increased "Isolationism." Two thematically related papers to those in this section which originally appeared in Contemporary Psychology, "Good Writing" and "Humanizing Psychology," are reprinted in Psychologist at Large (Boring, 1961a).

E.G.B.'s excellence as a dramatic, forceful lecturer to undergraduate and graduate students is attested to by generations of Harvard University students. His television series, recorded for Boston's educational TV station, has been shown in various parts of the country. This was but one of his excursions into communicating with the general public. During the Second World War, along with Marjorie Van de Water, E.G.B. wrote Psychology for the Fighting Man (1943), which addressed itself as the title indicates. They used the more technical contributions from a number of psychologists as a base from which to compose the book. In selling 380,000 copies, this book proved the point that the academic psychologist in the person of E.G.B. can communicate clearly and explicitly with the general public.

A Journal of Book Reviews

丱丱丱丱丱丱丱丱丱丱丱丱丱丱丱丱丱丱丱丱丱丱丱丱丱丱丱丱 1961

S IX years ago *CP* began life with an alias, *A Journal of Book Reviews*, a qualifying specification that indicated the medium through which the contemporary scene in psychology would be viewed. Except for an occasional rationalized self-indulgence, *CP* has not ventured beyond this pale. There are many ways in which contemporary psychology can be presented and perceived, but in general *CP* has abided by its instructions: it has reviewed books.

There are, however, a good many different ways of reviewing books, and it seems appropriate, as *CP* now passes from childhood to adolescence, to examine its early years as to what it has been and especially as to what it has not been. Now, if ever, would be the time to begin working on its worse faults. Altogether *CP* has thought of eight ways in which it might have been different, in which a choice was made with consequences, but each of them is connected, at least indirectly, with the major question of *CP*'s primary goal. Is it *CP*'s chief function to purvey information, or does it rather undertake to stimulate thought, trusting that discussion and criticism will carry with them enough information to leave its readers sufficiently informed as well as stimulated? It is this second alternative that *CP* chose in 1955 when policy was being laid down, and now is the time to consider whether the choice was good, whether *CP* cheated by giving its readers too much excitement and too little peaceful fact.

For the most part *CP*'s mail has brought in praise, ever since the first year when readers complained about the pictures, the large-type citations, the review titles, the aphorisms, and all the white space that goes along with this posh style of living, but incidental praise is no poll, for protest usually lingers quietly below the threshold until it builds up enough pressure to explode. Last summer, however, one reader did indeed explode in his own behalf and on be-

Reprinted with permission from *Contemporary Psychology*, 1961, **6**, 428–429.

half of many other "disgruntled readers" (so he said), wishing CP would settle down to facts and stop talking about reviews' being inevitably idiosyncratic (Boring, 1961c). He knew what he wanted, this correspondent did, and, of course, he was already getting quite a lot of it, although not enough— not enough fact and too much opinion.

CP in those days used to say of itself that it was not a "service journal," but in this context *service* was not the right word. Is stimulation no service to a mind that needs excitement so badly that it builds up its own hallucinations under extreme sensory deprivations? It is for this reason that dissent, by stimulating, performs a service, as CP has just remarked (Boring, 1961b). Doubt too is good—Descartes thought it was—for its occurrence is proof that mind is alive. Said Judge Jerome Frank thirty years ago: "The acceptance of everything as transitory, the welcome of new doubts . . . the zest of adventure in investigating the conventional—these are the life-cherishing attitudes . . . the attitudes of the so-called scientific mind . . . the emotionally adult or mature mind" (Boring, 1961d).

Now what are these eight choices that CP says it made and has tried to hold to?

(1) *Criticism.* From the start CP told its reviewers not to abstract the books but to criticize them. A reviewer was to talk about a book and in doing so to indicate the range and nature of its content. He was to note the book's purpose and assess the author's success in achieving it. He was to place the book in perspective, historically and within the contemporary scene. Solid criticism of this sort should carry enough information with it to satisfy the reader's need for description.

(2) *Truth's Servomechanism.* To encourage value-judgments about books is to open the way for idiosyncrasy in assessment. Even when the reviewer tries to found his assessment firmly on fact and inexorable logic, his unconscious biases will slip in and his conclusion will differ from the equally careful judgment of another critic. Plainly this difficulty results from CP's having invited criticism. CP insists that the remedy lies in repeated criticism and counter-criticism, in dissent to dissent to dissent, in the columns of "On the Other Hand." With continuing rejoinder and riposte, the Spielraum within which disagreement can persist gets smaller, and agreement between dissidents, which is all that "truth" is in this context, is approached.

(3) *Stimulation.* It is thus in the clash and interaction of ideas that criticism and dissent produce stimulation. CP said in January 1956 that it aimed to be interesting (Boring, 1956). No small part of the interest that it has aroused in its readers comes from this freedom to criticize and dissent. The letters in 8-point type get read as fully, perhaps even a little more carefully, than the reviews in 9-point. Criticism provides a social stimulus, and there is always interest in a contest.

(4) *Responsibility.* Freedom for idiosyncrasy needs to be coupled with re-

sponsibility. CP has perhaps not always kept every reviewer in line and the most bitter dissents have arisen when the first critic was blind to the book author's values or even to his stated facts. On the other hand, those who find CP's reviewing too uniformly favorable argue—some of them do—that CP's criticism is not objective enough and would be more valid if it were given anonymously. CP has steadily set its face against anonymous reviewing, choosing candid honest onymity as preferable. Anonymity can cloak prejudice and personal hostility fully as easily as onymity yields to generosity or the fear of giving offense.

(5) *Depreciation.* Every now and then a counter-critic remarks that a book, if it is really as poor as its reviewer made out, should not have been reviewed at all. Of course CP has preferred to review the more important and the more psychological books, and the really bad books as a rule have been screened out by a succession of sieves—the author's and his friends' superego, the publisher and his readers, the editor and his reviewers. Nevertheless an important bad book ought to be reviewed and also some others at the lower level in order to keep the perspective of contemporary published psychology clear, and also because the negative judgment about the book in the first place may be idiosyncratic, needing to be corrected presently by the servomechanism of dissent.

(6) *Length.* CP has favored longish reviews—from 500 to 2000 words, sometimes longer for special reasons, almost never shorter except by inadvertence. It is almost impossible to be interesting by furnishing perspective and developing well-founded criticism in less than 500 words. Some length is necessary if these goals are to be gained, and CP thinks that many reviewers enjoy the freedom of being able to say their says without severe constraints. Nevertheless it is still true that the 4000-word man finds a 1500-word ceiling excruciating. There was one reviewer who tried—but in vain—to fill a 1500-word assignment with 10,000 words.

(7) *Idealism.* The reviewers and consultants have all worked for CP without pay—in these days when consultants' fees can be enormous as compared with earlier academic standards. At first CP was frustrated: how could it command talent with so little to give in return? Must psychology's poverty keep CP inferior to the *Saturday Review* and the *New York Times Book Review?* During the last four years this feeling has, however, evaporated. CP believes that it has had the best talent psychology had available, even though some of psychology's most talented wise men steadfastly refuse to undertake reviewing. Psychology's best is, moreover, better and more abundant that CP ever expected it to be. The pay has been found partly in prestige, but also in the fun of being involved cooperatively in a largish common enterprise. Describing the reviewers, because readers of 1956 said they did not know who the reviewers were, turned out unexpectedly to be prestige-pay. Reward has, moreover, been autocatalytic. An important talented reviewer increases CP's prestige, which

helps CP then to secure another important able reviewer. CP has no reason to be despondent over psychology's modern commercialism.

(8) *Training.* When CP was choosing its goals in 1955 it included among them a desire, somewhat diffidently expressed, to contribute to good writing among American psychologists. It asked: "Can not psychologists write well?" and commented further: "The embryo CP wondered, hoped, and was not too sure. CP means to be interesting, and interesting writing is good writing" (Boring, 1956). This bit of CP's mission had an educational slant, and CP thinks its effort has had an effect, that American psychologists are less diffident about trying to write well than they were when C. P. Snow's "two cultures"—science and humanism—were supposed to be incapable of symbiosis. There have been two processes at work. The good writers have been coming out of hiding and asking for space. The poor writers have been trying to write up to the good writers, and CP has been enormously gratified by the tolerance with which so many reviewers have accepted heavy editing, given arbitrarily in accordance with CP's own assured idiosyncrasies as to what would make the review clearer and more interesting. So the good writers have become bolder and the poor writers better, and CP looks upon its sexennium with the conviction that so much progress has now been made that American psychologists might just as well keep on along the same path. How much better is intelligibility than dubiety! And how much lovelier is fun than hard work! If it is the duty of the scientist to communicate his results, why should he not also take on the responsibility for getting his communications read, for being interesting? At any rate CP chose this mission among the others and sees no reason to believe that American psychologists cannot command the English medium—or that those who do not cannot learn.

None of these aspirations of CP's was essential. You could have a journal of short, uncritical, anonymous, dull abstracts, and it would perform an important service function. Not everyone likes CP for what it has been, but CP has had goals, has tried hard to reach to them, has failed on occasion but succeeded on others, and now leaves the old home to live with a new editor where certainly some of the old aspirations will seem obsolete. Let the Zeitgeist control. Trust him. He has Fillmore Sanford [1] to guide him and what more could CP ask?

[1] (*Editor's note*) Fillmore Sanford was to succeed E.G.B. as Editor of *Contemporary Psychology* with the next issue.

The Social Predicament
of Book Reviewing

🝫🝫🝫🝫🝫🝫🝫🝫🝫🝫🝫🝫🝫🝫🝫 1960

THE other day a reviewer, sending in a review that disparaged a book, wrote: "It was hard for me to write such an unfavorable review. I know only one of the two authors, and him only slightly, but I have a feeling that I have lost both of them as possible friends. Since we all have to live together for the rest of our careers in a rather tightly knit professional society, I felt strongly impelled to win friends rather than alienate people. Perhaps some day CP will discuss the social psychology of book reviewing and the emotional factors in it." All right. CP will. This is it.

Recently in its July issue (Boring, 1960) CP raised the question of whether poor books should be reviewed at all, of why and when unfavorable reviews have a use, and it also touched once again on the business of why it is opposed to anonymous reviewing. The question now before us is: How much sacrifice is the onymous reviewer making when he writes an unfavorable review, and is it reasonable to ask him to surrender his peace of mind to objectivity or at least to conscience? Conflict in these cases can be very real indeed. CP knows of two competent reviewers, each of whom, when he discovered what the book to be reviewed was like, found himself quite unable to give the author the offense that intellect demanded. In one case CP lost the review. In the other it was able to find another reviewer for a late review. Such a conflict is no casual indecision; it can be very real abulia.

Of course there are occasions when disparagement is not difficult for the critic. The book may have made him so angry that he needs release. That can be all right. Anger can be a legitimate idiosyncrasy among the values of book reviewing. Sometimes the book is something to release latent aggression. That may not be so good, yet you would not wish entirely to decontaminate reviewers. There still remains, however, this question of whether this process of "honest" negative criticism is to be given full expression or be softened. Need the negative reviewer lose friends and alienate people?

Reprinted with permission from Contemporary Psychology, 1960, 5, 290, 291

The solution of this dilemma lies in the impersonalization of attitudes in reviewing, in the intellectualization of discussion. It is part of the great motivational predicament of scientific activity where the pride of conviction wars with the humility of objectivity. "Enthusiasm is the friend of action and the enemy of wisdom." It takes egoism and a spark to make the scientific machine go, yet too much egoism stalls the motor. The only way around this predicament is to understand it, so as to know when to have plenty of pride and when to throttle it down.

What most observers of the dilemma fail to appreciate is that the critical reviewing of books is unescapably idiosyncratic as far as the value-judgments go. Try as he will to be objective, no reviewer can claim to be delivering "truth." You can get eventually the pragmatic substitute for truth by the process of "cybernetic justice," with the counter-review that sees the book differently, dissent and dissent-to-dissent, gradually narrowing the region of play toward an ultimate "just" value.

Such a process as it goes on is virtually a game, a kind of verbal tennis, or perhaps chess. "Check!" says the reviewer. The author or his champion replies with a letter and moves out of check. If he is mated, inwardly he suffers, but outwardly he smiles and lets the issue go until next time—for he is a good loser.

Americans are apt to think that the British are better at this business of sportsmanship than most others, but CP's British friends do not seem to think that any such national difference exists. In England the disapproved author feels hurt and may sulk, so they say. Perhaps it is harder to be a good sport in print than it is in talk. The ear may hear a jolly good attack that the eye sees in print as malign, and after a debate opponents may leave together in friendly or even amused discourse. Certainly the public lecture in England is more of a sporting event than in America. There the British chairman first anoints the speaker with oil as he introduces him; then after the lecture he offers him a little wine mingled with myrrh, yet never so bitter as to incapacitate him for repartee. Sportsmanship can begin as soon as you have rules for the game.

Meanwhile what has become of our honest reviewer who started all this discussion? Have we rescued him from the life-long disapprobation of the two men he thinks he ought to criticize? No, not yet, but CP has in hand the principles from which he can proceed. He should send in his review and let it be printed. Then he should go to the next annual convention, seek out these two men, and, having practiced for them a special urbanity, meet them in a friendly way that shows that he does not for a moment suppose that his disparagement of a book implies disapproval of its authors. In such a manner he can promote the concept of good sportsmanship in book reviewing and thus do his additional bit for civilization. But he must not in the first instance have criticized the men themselves, just their product. No man has a spare self to substitute when his one-and-only self gets wounded.

Cybernetic Justice

🔲🔲🔲🔲🔲🔲🔲🔲🔲🔲🔲🔲🔲 1958

THE readers of this journal do not see the 1900-word *Comments to Reviewers*, which every reviewer receives, which most reviewers study, and which outlines CP's policies more definitely than this page has ever done. This hortatory essay contains the following admonition:

> Good criticism requires tact, objectivity, and a sense of good taste. Personal aspersions are taboo. Criticize the text, the ideas, the logic, the accuracy, not the author. Always try to see how nearly the author has realized his own aspiration, whether you approve of the aspiration or not.

In short, criticism should be *ad verbum*, not *ad hominem*. It is more important to note whether the author achieved his own goals than to say how much you disapprove of his goals. A letter in this issue of CP makes these same two points as it dissents from two critical reviews that CP published in 1957.

CP is delighted to have this letter for it is an instance of the "hunting" servomechanism of criticism and countercriticism that CP is struggling to promote. The only truth toward which CP can lead its readers is the limit upon which opinion and dissent from opinion and dissent from dissent converge. CP wishes to maintain the free market of opinion, with the victor, if any, him who sells his wares.

CP has space for this counterarguing, but not instantaneous space. The author waits until his review is published to know his fate, unless the reviewer sends him a copy of the review. The reviewer who is to be admonished for error does not know what he is in for until the wagging finger is exposed in a later issue of CP. Then there has to be another lag before the dissent to the dissent can come out, and so on. Is there any better way? If you hold up criticism to get sincere dissent, do you not have to hold up the dissent for the possible counterdissent, and that for the rejoinder, which must then wait for

Reprinted with permission from *Contemporary Psychology*, 1958, 3, 55–56.

the riposte? What is fair? When can you break into this conversational tennis? At present CP keeps mum when it has dissent in hand until publication has occurred. Then it tells the target that he may reply or not as he chooses, depending on his personality and on his judgment as to whether a firm declaration or a deadly silence (no shouts in CP) will be the more impressive to CP's readers—or to posterity—or conceivably to both. Is this all right? CP has an ear cocked, not for complaints, but for information as to how better to achieve this difficult goal of cybernetic justice.

Tolerances for Inaccuracy

᠅᠅᠅᠅᠅᠅᠅᠅᠅᠅᠅᠅᠅᠅᠅᠅᠅᠅᠅᠅᠅᠅᠅᠅᠅᠅᠅ 1961

IT is high time for someone to speak out about the social disadvantages of accuracy. For the scientists accuracy is the goal that is never forgotten. It is closely allied to honesty. When economic necessity forces the raw data out of the prime report, there is still the American Documentation Institute which, filing the data, provides absolution for the conscience of the scientist who did not quite tell all. Yet do we not all have acquaintances so "terribly frank" that we wish they could plan some reticences to reduce the jolts of communication?

Actually the ethics of communication can be structured in respect of levels of tolerance for inaccuracy, and surely the scientist should think more about them, in part because they affect what may and what may not be published. CP thinks that it can distinguish seven gross levels of this kind of tolerance. Here they are.

(1) *Privileged communication* comes first. What the client, the patient, the penitent, or the spouse has said need not be revealed to others by either party to the communication, nor may the court compel it. What one says to oneself is usually also privileged; thought can claim a privacy to which conduct has no right.

(2) *Generous inaccuracy* is properly found in the exercise of tact and diplomacy. There are many reticences that have survival value in intimate personal affairs as well as international relations. There are also the social amenities which include the "white lie." There is the gracious gesture of the insincere apology, which you utter but do not print. (The apologand may print it though, but he should not. He should have read these paragraphs.)

(3) *Casual conversation* halts under too much constraint. Some chattering is good, and discreet silence may also be golden even in the home. Because society recognizes the right of privacy, wire-tapping and "bugging" are de-

Reprinted with permission from *Contemporary Psychology*, 1961, **6**, 267.

plored and in some instances declared illegal. The condoning of inaccuracy is clear in the distinction between talking "off the record" and "for the record." The law requires the warning "beep" when telephone conversations are being recorded. For similar reasons it was not permissible, until recently, to quote the President of the United States directly. The human right to inaccuracy was so important for the President, whose slightest slip could have enormous effects, that indirect discourse was needed to weaken the guarantee of precision. Lying may be unethical but it is not illegal. Society accepts it and invented the oath to render it illegal on the proper occasions.

(4) *The writing of letters* produces a record. The fading and distortion of memory traces protect the privacy of conversation, but letters solidify the past. First-class mail is freed from inspection. He who has received a letter owns the paper and ink but not the ideas that they carry. He may not print them without permission, and *CP* thinks that the owner of the letter should not embarrass the author by asking for permission when the letter was written in friendly correspondence and not intended for publication. Suppose the letter contains a gracious but insincere apology. Must its author be forced to admit disingenuousness or to apologize somewhat insincerely in public? As letters retreat into the past the ethical constraints upon them diminish, for their responsibility—their bearing on changing events—weakens. More and more they become records of human personality or historical evidence for the understanding of the past. Posthumous letters are fairly free for publication unless they diminish the reputation of the author. Fifty years after the author's death, there is not often much reason for the living to hinder publication, and after a century letters pass into the public domain. It is also true that adults feel less fully identified with their childhood letters, less susceptible to injury from a past presumably outlived.

(5) *Lectures* are, however, another story. Through all his thirty-five years of teaching at Cornell, E. B. Titchener lectured in an Oxford Master's gown, because, he said, "It gives me the right to be dogmatic." And dogmatic he was, charmingly, excitingly, in beautiful English, with never a "hem" or an incomplete sentence. Such inaccuracies as his lovely generalizations contained were soon lost in the noisy channels of memory or in the rubble of students' notes, and he knew that. His writing was carefully protected with modifying clauses. He would never have consented to be taped had that machinery existed then, but is there anyone nowadays who wants his taped lecture published without revision? No, lectures should not be published unless written for publication and read, and it is not an easy task to make the same text attract the ear today and the eye tomorrow. The ear needs more redundancy.

(6) *Publication* asserts maximal accuracy, and there you accept minimal tolerance. Still even in publication statements of opinion enter. Who would take oath to the accuracy of his book review? In the dissents and counter-dissents that get into *CP*, values are tried out, and *CP* thinks that a con-

temporary equivalent of truth can sometimes be seen emerging. The experimental data must of course be specified as rigorously as possible, yet scientific "truth" is tentative and may change in a dozen or a hundred years. It is not something to take oath to.

(7) *The oath* remains largely outside the scientific domain, man's invention of a category for maximal accuracy. It forms in this series the anchorage point in respect of which all other communication is revealed as provisional.

Ortgeister

〰〰〰〰〰 1956

THERE are big cultural differences between nations and between centuries, and little differences between in-groups and between decades. The *Ortgeister* and the *Zeitgeister* are never fixed. They differ from place to place and from time to time. Even Tolstoy believed that, arguing, as he did, that Napoleon himself did nothing to change History, was himself but History's slave. In science these differences, these changes, occur in attitudes, values and importances, not merely in the facts and knowledge that make up the ever-expanding body of wisdom.

Take Germany and America as a paradigm. How different in the two countries in 1956 is the sense of what is important to psychology! How different it was in 1896! Here we have a two-parameter fourfold table. In Germany from introspection—*Selbstbeobachtung*, of course—to *Verstehen*. In America from function to behavior. In each longisection something stays the same and something changes, and also in each cross section something stays the same and something changes. In 1896 the leaders of American psychology, so many of them Leipzig-trained, thought they were importing the new German psychology into America, whereas actually they were, as they took the German product over, remodeling it to fit the practical climate of American thought and values. Thus can the 1890s be explained, but the present, the 1950s, are too close for such sure analysis by any mere editor of *CP*.

Still there is the difference needing to be understood. These distinguished German psychologists who come nowadays to America to see its psychological Goliath at close range, how bewildered they are at first! Line up the 15,000 members of the American Psychological Association along any handy seven-mile stretch that you wish, sending riders along the line to tell all phenomenologists to step two paces forward. How many phenomenologists will there be? Then ask the American-born phenomenologists to step two more paces forward. How many of them? *CP* will print the results of this census when they are available, along with the data for the German control,

Reprinted with permission from *Contemporary Psychology*, 1956, **1**, 145.

but *CP* says now that phenomenology fares better abroad than it does in the United States.

And so for other national differences. British psychology is noticeably different from American, though a common language, a long tradition, and a Darwinian heritage tend to bring them together. The atmosphere of French psychology was never like the German nor the British, nor is it now. The Soviet Union has emerged more recently on the scene and is unique in having a special accelerator for its *Zeitgeist*. At least Raymond Bauer says the Russian psychologists were environmentalists in the 1920s, and fiat-purposivists in the 1930s, with the kaleidoscopic Pavlov changing from hero to villain and back again to hero, all in a brief, twenty-year, largely posthumous career.

CP is, of course, American-born. Does that mean that it deals primarily with American psychology, this great, elephantine, very western movement that began as functional psychology, became behavioristic, and now threatens to become part or all of behavioral science? Hardly. *CP* may have a mandate to stick to the contemporaneous present but certainly not to the local scene. In this issue Henry David discusses the reviewing of foreign books in America and in Europe. He does not find it possible to make a strict comparison. Europe reviews more American books than America reviews European, partly because America has more books to review. You catch more fish in the pond with the more fish in it. David,[1] however, makes the point that American psychology, with its great size and the consequent tendency to try to dominate the world field, should not allow its sense of self-importance and self-sufficiency to induce the self-complaceny of what could become an enormous provincialism. *CP* is glad to publish this paper, to have David needle it into needling the American psychologists into looking abroad to examine what is going on outside of America. In-group complacency is not the means whereby psychology came to its present status, nor does it breed the dissatisfaction that will take psychology on to a future as unpredictable now as its 1956 present was in 1896.

How *CP* can work out better European coverage of books is not clear at the moment. *CP* needs all the information about outstanding European books it can get. Here some of its readers can help. Tell *CP* about important foreign books that it is likely to miss and say why they are important and who publishes them. Then *CP* also needs reviewers who are competent in special fields, who can read French, German, and some of the other European languages, and who know how to write interesting English. In America, where what has been called anti-intellectualism is not unknown, the scholar has no such prestige as will enable him to impose a dull version of truth upon a captive audience. In America the scholar must win his audience. So what *CP* wants are erudite linguists with winning ways who are nevertheless psychologists. Anyone finding such will please notify this office instantly.

[1] (*Editor's note*) A paper by H. P. David devoted to book reviewing in relation to the languages in which they had been written had appeared in the same issue of *CP*.

Isolationism in the Languages

🮰🮰🮰🮰🮰🮰🮰🮰🮰🮰🮰🮰🮰🮰🮰🮰🮰🮰🮰🮰🮰🮰🮰🮰🮰🮰🮰🮰🮰🮰🮰🮰🮰🮰🮰🮰🮰🮰   1956

WHAT is going to happen in America about knowledge of foreign languages? As the world gets smaller with improved communications, countless Americans as tourists and soldiers see foreign lands but they do not talk to the people in them—not much. They talk to one another in English. American isolationism protrudes thousands of miles from her shores. That is because of America's size, power, and self-sufficiency. The people of the United States are interested in Europe, Asia, and Africa, but not enough to learn even the more generally used languages. A greater isolationism exists in the Soviet Union where the will to power forbids an altruistic internationalism.

But what about the scholars and scientists? Do they not need the languages? Yes, sometimes; and, when they do, they get them up or use them ineptly or abandon a problem that runs into an impenetrable wall of Russian or Japanese—or, for that matter, of German or French, as the universities yield slowly to the unilingual self-sufficiency of America.

American psychology presents a special case, because it is so largely professional and because it has rapidly grown tremendous as compared with the European psychologies. While research may need foreign languages, professional work ordinarily does not, except when it undertakes its own research. Clinical and industrial psychologists seem to have little use for French and German, heretofore the regular concomitants of graduate education. Experimental psychology at present is dominated by research on learning, and Europe does not help out much with that topic. Sensory psychology, psychophysics, physiological psychology need German certainly, though he who can not read German may never know what he is missing. Everybody is busy, 100 per cent busy. If he takes time to learn German and French, what does he take it from? And, if he learns French and needs German, he is no better

Reprinted with permission from *Contemporary Psychology*, 1956, 1, 331–332.

off. Or, if he is persuaded to learn both French and German and needs Russian, did the educational system then play him false?

It is said: Why learn a language I would not use? And it is obvious that most of the teachers of graduate students in America, most of the possible father-images for the coming generation of psychologists, do not use French and German in their teaching and research. Can the disciple exceed the master? Yes, but he needs a compelling reason.

When is there a compelling need? The Ph.D. requirements are compelling, but to the student who expects not to use the languages again, whose teachers are not using them, these graduate-school requirements seem to represent an arbitrary authoritarianism based upon defunct values. He should have gotten his basic training in high school and college when young people more readily accept education without questioning its ultimate specific usefulness. The evidence is that not often does an older man get up a new language because his research demands it. Rather he changes his project. His need is not great enough, though it is great enough for an expatriate who comes to a new country to live. The newcomer has to have the vernacular and his age does not prevent him from learning it. Yet age can not be discounted. The older you get, the more proactive inhibitions you have.

Why French and German though? Why not Dutch and Spanish? Above all, why not Russian? That is a matter of the history of scholarship. A thousand years ago Byzantium was the center of the learned world and Greek was the scholarly language. Later the geography of scholarship followed the universities: first Italy, then Paris, then England, then Germany. Latin, having been the language of the Church, became the language of learning in Italy and then throughout the west, until a reaction against it occurred in the early nineteenth century. But Galileo in the seventeenth century wrote in Italian as well as Latin, and more and more during the next two hundred years important scientific works tended to be published in the vernacular. Italian faded out as the center of scientific activity moved northward; so, when Latin was discarded, French, English, and German were left. The scholars of the small nations, with their own special languages, were obliged more or less to accept this situation and to get their scientific contributions into one of the three accepted languages if they wanted a large audience. This was power linguistics and unfair, but it worked well enough to let learning get ahead marvelously well.

It is too bad that Latin went out. Had it stayed in, with high schools and colleges giving the necessary training in it, with most important learned publication in it, the problem of the internationalization of scholarship would have been solved.

Nowadays we are faced with another reaction away from French and German and toward English or toward Russian, depending on where you live and what your native tongue is. Will French and German retreat behind a partial language barrier as did Latin? Not soon probably, but we need to see the historical picture whole if we are to think wisely about this matter.

So where does wisdom lie right now? On this matter CP wishes to make two points.

A community of scholarship is good for civilization. The scholars and scientists should be able to communicate readily with one another. They lost Latin. They have had until the immediate present French, German, and English. The less populous or less productive nations accepted this inequality. Now the powerful Soviet Union will not and the demand for knowledge of Russian has to be considered. Let us, however, take no step, says CP, to diminish the present degree of community unless a substitute device for securing international comprehension is at hand. Above all let no one advocate a radical diminution of community when his thinking is based on the experience of any mere two or three decades. These cultural changes come slowly and impatience confuses prediction.

CP's other point is that basic training should be kept broad if science is to prosper maximally. It is nonsense to teach a graduate student German just because he is working in psychophysics. He will probably end up twenty years later working for the VA. It is nonsense to argue that a man who teaches rats to run mazes needs nothing but English for talk. He will probably turn up with Lorenz, the ethologist. Psychology is not yet split up into so many fields that the graduate student can make an irrevocable choice, and CP hopes that this process of fractionation will be retarded as much as possible. Psychologists accept basic research as good, spend their lives in investigations none of which may ever have practical value, for the ostensible reason that basic research yields practical dividends in the long run, and yields them the more surely because it has not aimed at being useful. So you do the research for its own sake, or for various social or economic motives. It would, indeed, be fortunate if the basic languages could be taken in the same way, as something that is good to know though the practical use for them is unforeseeable. Being educated is not always a waste of time.

References

Abbott, F. K., Marian Mack, & S. Wolf. The action of banthine on the stomach and duodenum of man with observations on the effects of placebos. *Gastroenterology*, 1952, **20**, 249–261.

Ach, N. *Ueber die Willenstätigkeit und das Denkens.* Göttingen: Vandenhoeck & Ruprecht, 1905.

Adrian, E. D. *The basis of sensation.* New York: Norton, 1928.

Allen, G. Hellas and civilization. *Gentlemen's magazine*, 1878, **243**, 156–170. (*a*) Reprinted in *Pop. Sci. Mon. Suppl.*, 1878, **17**, 398–406.

Allen, G. Nation making: a theory of national characters. *Gentlemen's magazine*, 1878, **243**, 590 f. (*b*) Reprinted in *Pop. Sci. Mon. Suppl.*, 1878, **20**, 121–127.

Allen, G. The genesis of genius. *Atlantic Mon.*, 1881, **47**, 371–381.

Allport, G. W. The psychology of participation. *Psychol. Rev.*, 1945, **53**, 117–132.

Ament, W. Ueber das Verhältnis der ebenmerklichen zu den übermerklichen Unterschieden bei Licht- und Schallintensitäten (Inaug. Diss.). *Philos. Stud.*, 1900, **16**, 135–196.

Andrews, T. G. (Ed.) *Methods of psychology.* New York: Wiley, 1948.

Angell, F. Untersuchungen über die Schätzung von Schallintensitäten nach der Methode der mittleren Abstufungen. *Phil. Stud.*, 1891, **7**, 414–468.

Angell, J. R. *Psychology: an introductory study of the structure and function of human consciousness.* New York: Holt, 1904. (and later editions)

Angell, J. R. The province of functional psychology. *Psychol. Rev.*, 1907, **14**, 61–91.

Avenarius, R. *Kritik der reinen Erfahrung.* Leipzig: Fues & Reisland, 1888–1890. 2 vols.

Bacon, F. Novum organum. In J. M. Robertson (Ed.), *Philosophical works.* London: Routledge, 1905. (1620)

Baernstein, H. D., & C. L. Hull. A mechanical model of the conditioned reflex. *J. gen. Psychol.*, 1931, **5**, 99–106.

Bain, A. *The senses and the intellect.* London: Parker, 1855.

Bain, A. *Mind and body: the theories of their relation.* London: Paul, Trench, Trubner, 1872.

Bakan, D. Learning and scientific enterprise. *Psychol. Rev.*, 1953, **60**, 45–49.

Baldwin, J. M. Types of reaction. *Psychol. Rev.*, 1895, **2**, 259–273.

Bell, C. *Idea of a new anatomy of the brain.* London: Strahan & Preston, 1811. Reprinted in *J. Anat. Physiol.*, 1869, **3**, 154–157.

(*Editor's note*) When a later edition for the early literature is used, the date of the original publication is carried in the text. In such cases that date in parentheses is carried at the end of the citation. Articles reprinted in this book are included in this bibliography only if cited in the other selections.

Bell, E. *Men of mathematics*. New York: Simon & Schuster, 1937.

Bennett, G. K., & L. B. Ward. A model of the synthesis of conditioned reflexes. *Amer. J. Psychol.*, 1933, **45**, 339–342.

Bentley, E. *The cult of the superman*. London: Hale, 1947.

Bentley, M. The psychological antecedents of phrenology. *Psychol. Monogr.*, 1916, **21**, No. 92.

Bergmann, G. Outline of an empiricist philosophy of physics. *Amer. J. Phys.*, 1943, **11**, 248–258, 335–342.

Bergmann, G. The logic of psychological concepts. *Phil. Sci.*, 1951, **18**, 93–110.

Bergmann, G. Theoretical psychology. *Annu. Rev. Psychol.*, 1953, **4**, 435–458.

Bergmann, G. *Philosophy of science*. Madison: Univ. Wisconsin Press, 1957.

Berkeley, G. *A treatise concerning the principles of human knowledge*. London: Tonson, 1734. (1710)

Berkeley, G. Essay towards a new theory of vision. In A. C. Fraser's (Ed.) *The works of George Berkeley*. Vol. 1. Oxford: Clarendon Press, 1901. (1732)

Bernal, J. D. *The social function of science*. New York: Macmillan, 1939.

Bernoulli, J. Described in I. Todhunter, *A history of the mathematical theory of probability*. New York: Chelsea, 1949, 56–77. (1713)

Bessel, F. W. *Astronomische Beobachtungen auf der Königlichen Universitäts-Sternwarte zu Königsberg*. Vol. 8. Königsberg: Leupold, 1823.

Bichat, M. F. X. *Anatomie générale, appliquée a la physiologie et a la médecine*. Paris: Bronow, Gabon, 1801.

Binet, A., & C. Féré. *Le magnétisme animal*. Paris: Alcan, 1887. (Eng. trans. 1888)

Binet, A., & V. Henri. La psychologie individuelle. *L'année psychol.*, 1896, **2**, 411–465.

Blumenfeld, W. Untersuchungen über die scheinbare Grösse in Sehraume. *Z. Psychol.*, 1913, **65**, 241–404.

Boas, F. Ueber die Grundaufgabe der Physiologie. *Arch. ges. Physiol.*, 1882, **28**, 566–576.

Bolton, F. E. Hydro-psychoses. *Amer. J. Psychol.*, 1899, **10**, 169–237.

Bolton, T. L. Review of J. M. Baldwin's Mental development in the child and race. *Amer. J. Psychol.*, 1895, **7**, 142–145.

Boole, G. *An investigation into the laws of thought*. London: Macmillan, 1854.

Boring, E. G. Cutaneous sensation after nerve-division. *Quart. J. Exp. Physiol.*, 1916, **10**, 1–95.

Boring, E. G. On the computation of the probable correctness of differences. *Amer. J. Psychol.*, 1917, **28**, 454–459.

Boring, E. G. The control of attitude in psychophysical experiments. *Psychol. Rev.*, 1920, **27**, 449–452. (*a*)

Boring, E. G. The logic of the normal law of error in mental measurement. *Amer. J. Psychol.*, 1920, **31**, 1–33. (*b*)

Boring, E. G. The stimulus-error. *Amer. J. Psychol.*, 1921, **32**, 449–471. Reprinted, pp. 255–273.

Boring, E. G. The problem of originality in science. *Amer. J. Psychol.*, 1927, **39**, 70–90. Reprinted, pp. 50–66.

Boring, E. G. *A history of experimental psychology*. New York: Century, 1929. (*a*)

Boring, E. G. The psychology of controversy. *Psychol. Rev.*, 1929, **36**, 97–121. (*b*) Reprinted, pp. 67–84.

Boring, E. G. The psychologist's circle. *Psychol. Rev.*, 1931, **38**, 177–182.

Boring, E. G. *The physical dimensions of consciousness*. New York: Century, 1933.

Boring, E. G. The relation of the attributes of sensation to the dimensions of the stimulus. *Phil. Sci.*, 1935, **2**, 236–245. Not reprinted in this book.

Boring, E. G. Psychophysiological systems and isomorphic relations. *Psychol. Rev.*, 1936, **43**, 565–587. Reprinted in Boring, 1961*a*.

Boring, E. G. A psychological function is the relation of successive differentiations of events in the organism. *Psychol. Rev.*, 1937, **44**, 445–461. Reprinted, pp. 304–317.

Boring, E. G. Statistical frequencies as dynamic equilibria. *Psychol. Rev.*, 1941, **48**, 279–300. Reprinted, pp. 226–244.

Boring, E. G. *Sensation and perception in the history of experimental psychology.* New York: Appleton-Century, 1942.

Boring, E. G. The use of operational definitions in science. *Psychol. Rev.*, 1945, **52**, 241–289. Reprinted, pp. 200–209.

Boring, E. G. I. Sechenov's selected works. *Psychol. Bull.*, 1949, **46**, 309–311.

Boring, E. G. A *history of experimental psychology.* (2nd ed.) New York: Appleton-Century-Crofts, 1950. (*a*)

Boring, E. G. Great men and scientific progress. *Proc. Amer. Phil. Soc.*, 1950, **94**, 339–351. (*b*) Reprinted, pp. 29–49.

Boring, E. G. The influence of evolutionary theory upon American psychological thought. In S. Persons' (Ed.) *Evolutionary thought in America.* New Haven: Yale Univ. Press, 1950, 268–298. (*c*) Reprinted, pp. 159–184.

Boring, E. G. Review of J. J. Gibson's The perception of the visual world. *Psychol. Bull.*, 1951, **48**, 360–363.

Boring, E. G. The validation of scientific belief: a conspectus of the symposium. *Proc. Amer. Phil. Soc.*, 1952, **96**, 535–539. Reprinted, pp. 245–252.

Boring, E. G. A history of introspection. *Psychol. Bull.*, 1953, **50**, 169–186. Reprinted in Boring, 1961*a*.

Boring, E. G. Psychological factors in the scientific process. *Amer. Scientist*, 1954, **42**, 639–645. Reprinted in Boring, 1961*a*.

Boring, E. G. Policies. *Contemp. Psychol.*, 1956, **1**, 13.

Boring, E. G. Rewarding success. *Contemp. Psychol.*, 1959, **4**, 171.

Boring, E. G. How many books are good? *Contemp. Psychol.*, 1960, **5**, 220–221.

Boring, E. G. *Psychologist at large: an autobiography and selected essays.* New York: Basic Books, 1961. (*a*)

Boring, E. G. Dissent. *Contemp. Psychol.*, 1961, **6**, 395. (*b*) Reprinted, pp. 85–86.

Boring, E. G. So many reviewers. *Contemp. Psychol.*, 1961, **6**, 238–239. (*c*)

Boring, E. G. The spirits against bosh: Review of G. Murphy's & R. O. Ballou's (Eds.) William James on psychical research. New York: Viking, 1960. *Contemp. Psychol.*, 1961, **6**, 149–151. (*d*)

Boring, E. G. et al. Symposium on operationism. *Psychol. Rev.*, 1945, **52**, 241–294.

Boring, E. G., & Margery Van de Water, et al. *Psychology for the fighting man.* Washington, D.C.: Infantry Journal, 1943.

Bouguer, P. *Traité d'optique sur la gradation de la lumière.* Paris: Guerin & Delatour, 1760.

Bouillaud, J. B. Rechercher clinique à démontrer que la parte de la parole correspond à la lésion des lobules antérieurs du cerveau et à confirmer l'opinion de M. Gall sur le siège de l'organe du langage articulé. *Arch. gén. de méd.*, 1825, **8**, 25–45.

Braid, J. *Neurypnology; or, the rationale of nervous sleep; considered in relation with animal magnetism.* London: Churchill, 1843. (Reprinted, 1899)

Bramell, J. M. *Hypnotism, its history, practice, and theory.* London: Richards; Philadelphia: Lippincott, 1903.

Bray, C. W. Transfer of learning. *J. exp. Psychol.*, 1928, **11**, 443–467.

Brentano, F. *Psychologie vom empirischen Standpunkte.* Vol. 1. Leipzig: Duncker & Humblot, 1874.

Brett, G. S. A *history of psychology.* Vol. III. New York: Macmillan, 1921.

Bridgman, P. W. *The logic of modern physics.* New York: Macmillan, 1927.

Bridgman, P. W. Some general principles of operational analysis. *Psychol. Rev.*, 1945, **52**, 246–249.

Broca, P. Remarques sur le siège de la faculté du langage articulé, suivi d'une observation d'aphémie (perte de la parole). *Bull. Soc. Anat.*, 1861, **36**, 330–357.

Bronfenbrenner, U. Soviet methods of character education. *Amer. Psychologist*, 1962, **17**, 550–564.

Brown W., & G. H. Thomson. *The essentials of mental measurement.* Cambridge, Eng.· Cambridge Univ. Press, 1921.

Brückner, A. Die Raumschwelle bei Simultanreizung. *Z. Psychol.*, 1901, **26**, 33–60.

Bush, R. R., & F. Mosteller. A mathematical model for simple learning. *Psychol. Rev.*, 1951, **58**, 313–323.

Butterfield, H. *History and human relations.* New York: Macmillan, 1952.

Buxton, C. E. Studying memory and transfer. In T. G. Andrews' (Ed.) *Methods of psychology.* New York: Wiley, 1948, 64–95.

Cabanis, P. J. G. *Rapports du physique et du moral de l'homme.* Paris: Caille & Ravier, 1802.

Calkins, Mary W. Converging lines in contemporary psychology. *Brit. J. Psychol.*, 1926, **16**, 171–179. (*a*)

Calkins, Mary W. Critical comments on the 'Gestalt-Theorie.' *Psychol. Rev.*, 1926, **33**, 135–138. (*b*)

Carlyle, T. *On heroes, hero worship and the heroic in history.* London: Chapman & Hall, 1840.

Carlyle, T. *History of Friedrich II of Prussia, called Frederick the Great.* Leipzig: Tauchnitz, 1865.

Carmichael, L. Heredity and environment: are they antithetical? *J. abnorm. soc. Psychol.*, 1925, **20**, 245–260.

Carmichael, L. The development of behavior in vertebrates experimentally removed from the influence of external stimulation. *Psychol. Rev.*, 1926, **33**, 51–58. (*a*)

Carmichael, L. Sir Charles Bell: a contribution to the history of physiological psychology *Psychol. Rev.*, 1926, **33**, 188–217. (*b*)

Carmichael, L. A further study of the development of behavior in vertebrates experimentally removed from the influence of external stimulation. *Psychol. Rev.*, 1927, **34**, 34–47. (*a*)

Carmichael, L. Robert Whytt: a contribution to the history of physiological psychology. *Psychol. Rev.*, 1927, **34**, 287–304. (*b*)

Cattell, J. McK. The psychological laboratory at Leipzig. *Mind*, 1888, **13**, 37–51.

Cattell, J. McK. Mental tests and measurements. *Mind*, 1890, **15**, 373–381.

Cattell, J. McK. Tests of the senses and faculties. *Educ. Rev.*, 1893, **5**, 285–293.

Cattell, J. McK., & L. Farrand. Physical and mental measurements of the students of Columbia University. *Psychol. Rev.*, 1896, **3**, 618–648.

Cattell, R. B. *Description and measurement of personality.* Yonkers, New York: World Book, 1946.

Coe, W. R. Divergent pathways in sexual development. *Science*, 1940, **91**, 175–182.

Cohen, I. B. *Science, servant of man.* Boston: Little, Brown, 1948.

Cohen, I. B. Orthodoxy and scientific progress. *Proc. Amer. Phil. Soc.*, 1952, **96**, 505–512.

Conant, J. B. *On understanding science.* New Haven: Yale Univ. Press, 1947.

Conant, J. B. *Science and common sense.* New Haven: Yale Univ. Press, 1951.

Cotzin, M., & K. M. Dallenbach. "Facial vision:" the role of pitch and loudness in the perception of obstacles by the blind. *Amer. J. Psychol.*, 1950, **63**, 485–515.

Curtis, J. N. Duration and the temporal judgment. *Amer. J. Psychol.*, 1916, **27**, 1–46.

Dallenbach, K. M. The history and derivation of the word "function" as a systematic term in psychology. *Amer. J. Psychol.*, 1915, **26**, 473–484.

Dallenbach, K. M. The place of theory in science. *Psychol. Rev.*, 1953, **60**, 33–39.

Darwin, C. *The origin of species by means of natural selection.* London: Murray, 1859.

Darwin, C. *The descent of man and selection in relation to sex.* New York: Appleton, 1871.

Darwin, C. *The expression of the emotions in man and animals.* London: Murray, 1872.

Darwin, C. *Insectivorous plants.* New York: Appleton, 1875.

Darwin, C., & F. Darwin. *Power of movement in plants.* New York: Appleton, 1881.

Davenport, C. B. *Heredity in relation to eugenics.* New York: Holt, 1911.

Davis, H. The physiological phenomena of audition. In C. Murchison's (Ed.) *A handbook of general experimental psychology.* Worcester, Mass.: Clark Univ. Press, 1934, 962–986.

Davis, R. C. Physical psychology. *Psychol. Rev.,* 1953, **60**, 7–14.

Day, L. M., & M. Bentley. A note on learning in paramecium. *J. animal Behav.,* 1911, **1**, 67–73.

Dearborn, W. F. The general effects of spaced practice on memory. *Psychol. Bull.,* 1909, **6**, 44.

Delabarre, E. B. Les laboratoire de psychologie en Amérique. *L'année psychol.,* 1894, **1**, 209–255.

Delboeuf, J. R. L. Etude psychophysique. *Mém. Acad. R. Belg.,* 1873, **23**, No. 5.

Delboeuf, J. R. L. (Ed.) *Eléments de psycho-physique générale et spéciale.* Paris: Baillière, 1883.

Descartes, R. Meditations on first philosophy. In *Philosophical works.* (Trans. by Elizabeth S. Haldane and G. R. T. Ross) Cambridge, Eng.: Cambridge Univ. Press, 1931. (1641)

Dewey, J. The reflex arc concept in psychology. *Psychol. Rev.,* 1896, **3**, 357–370.

Dewey, J. *Psychology and philosophic method.* Berkeley: Univ. Calif. Press, 1899.

Dewey, J. *The influence of Darwin on philosophy and other essays.* New York: Holt, 1910.

Dewey, J. The need for social psychology. *Psychol. Rev.,* 1917, **24**, 266–277.

Diserens, C. M. Psychological objectivism. *Psychol. Rev.,* 1925, **32**, 121–152.

Donders, F. C. Die Schnelligkeit psychischer Processe. *Arch. Anat. Physiol.,* 1868, 657–681. (1862)

Ebbinghaus, H. *Ueber das Gedächtnis.* Leipzig: Duncker & Humblot, 1885.

Ebbinghaus, H. Ueber negative Empfindungswerte. *Z. Psychol.,* 1890, **1**, 320–334, 463–485.

Ebbinghaus, H. *Grundzüge der Psychologie.* (2nd ed.) Vol. 1. Leipzig: Veit, 1905.

Ebert, E., & E. Meumann. Ueber einige Grundfragen der Psychologie der Uebungsphänomene im Bereiche des Gedächtnisses. *Arch. ges. Psychol.,* 1904, **4**, 1–232.

Eckhard, C. Beiträge zur Geschichte des experimentelle physiologie des Nervensystems: Geschichte der Entwickelung der Lehre von den Reflexerscheinungen. *Beiträge Anat. Physiol.,* 1881, **9**, 29–192.

Edgeworth, F. Y. Correlated averages. *Phil. Mag.,* 1892, **34**, 190–204.

Eiduson, Bernice T. *Scientists: their psychological world.* New York: Basic Books, 1962.

Eiseley, L. C. Charles Darwin, Edward Blyth, and the theory of natural selection. *Proc. Amer. Phil. Soc.,* 1959, **103**, 94–158.

Eisler, R. *Parallelimus, Wörterbuch der philosophischen Begriffe.* Berlin: Mittler, 1910.

Elliotson, J. *Numerous cases of surgical operations without pain in the mesmeric states; with remarks.* Philadelphia: Blanchard, 1843.

Elliotson, J. *The Harveian oration.* London: Baillière, 1846.

Ewert, P. H. Bilateral transfer in mirror-drawing. *J. genet. Psychol.,* 1926, **33**, 235–249.

Exner, S. Physiologie der Grosshirnrinde. In *Hermann's Handbuch der Physiologie.* Vol. 2. Leipzig: Vogel, 1879, 255–277.

Faraday, M. *Experimental researches in electricity.* Vol. 3. London: Taylor & Frances, 1855.

Fay, J. W. *American psychology before William James.* New Brunswick: Rutgers Univ. Press, 1939.

Fearing, F. *Reflex action.* Baltimore: Williams & Wilkins, 1930.

Fechner, G. T. *Elemente der Psychophysik.* Vol. I. Leipzig: Breitkopf & Härtel, 1860.

Fechner, G. T. *Revision der Hauptpunkte der Psychophysik.* Leipzig: Breitkopf & Härtel, 1882.

Feigl, H. Operationism and scientific method. *Psychol. Rev.,* 1945, 52, 250–259.

Feigl, H. Existential hypotheses: realistic versus phenomenalistic interpretations. *Phil. Sci.,* 1950, 17, 35–62.

Feigl, H. Some major issues and developments in the philosophy of science of logical empiricism. In H. Feigl, & M. Scriven's (Eds.) *The foundations of science and concepts of psychology and psychoanalysis.* Vol. I. Minnesota studies in the philosophy of science. Minneapolis: Univ. Minnesota Press, 1956, 3–37.

Feigl, H. The "mental" and the "physical." In H. Feigl, M. Scriven, & G. Maxwell's (Eds.) *Concepts, theories, and the mind-body problem.* Vol. II. Minnesota studies in the philosophy of science. Minneapolis: Univ. of Minnesota Press, 1958, 370–497.

Fisher, R. A. *The design of experiments.* London: Oliver & Boyd, 1935. (Later editions, 1937, 1942, 1947)

Fisher, S. C. The psychological and educational work of Granville Stanley Hall. *Amer. J. Psychol.,* 1925, 36, 1–52.

Fiske, J. Sociology and hero-worship. *Atlantic Mon.,* 1881, 47, 75–84.

Flourens, M. J. P. *Recherches expérimentales sur les propriétés et les fonctions du système nerveux dans les animaux vertébrés.* Paris: Crevot, 1824.

Flugel, J. C. *A hundred years of psychology.* New York: Macmillan, 1933.

Foucault, M. *L'illusion paradoxale et le seuil de Weber.* Montpellier: Coulet, 1910.

Frank, J. N. *Law and the modern mind.* New York: Brentano's, 1930.

Frank, P. The origin of the separation between science and philosophy. *Proc. Amer. Acad. Arts Sci.,* 1952, 80, 115–139.

Franz, S. I. New phrenology. *Science,* N.S., 1912, 35, 321–328.

Fraunhofer, J. v. Bestimmung des Brechungs- und Farbenzerstreuungs-Vermögens verschiedener Glassarten in Bezug auf die achromatische Fernröhre. *Denkschr. Acad. Wiss. München (math.-nat. Cl.),* 1815, 5, 193–226.

Fréchet, M. The diverse definitions of probability. *J. Unif. Sci.* (Erkenntnis), 1939, 8, 7–23.

Friedländer, H. Die Wahrnehmung der Schwere. *Z. Psychol.,* 1920, 83, 129–210.

Friedline, C. L. The discrimination of cutaneous patterns below the two-point limen. *Amer. J. Psychol.,* 1918, 29, 415–418.

Friedrich, M., E. Tischer, & M. Trautscholdt. [Early Leipzig experiments] *Philosophische Studien,* 1883, 1, various.

Fritsch, G., & E. Hitzig. Ueber die elektrische Erregbarkeit des Grosshirns. *Arch. Anat. Physiol.,* 1870, 300–332.

Fröbes, J. Ein Beitrag über die Vergleischungen übermerklicher Empfindungs-Unterschiede. *Z. Psychol.,* 1904, 36, 241–268.

Fullerton, G. S., & J. McK. Cattell. On the perception of small differences. *Penn. U. Phil. Ser.,* 1892, No. 2.

Galton, F. *Hereditary genius.* London: Macmillan, 1869.

Galton, F. *Inquiries into human faculty.* London: Macmillan, 1883.

Galton, F. *Natural inheritance.* London: Macmillan, 1889.

Gardner, M. The hermit scientist. *Antioch Rev.,* 1950, 10, 447–457.

Gardner, M. *In the name of science.* New York: Putnams, 1952.

Gates, E. J. The determination of the limens of single and dual impression by the method of constant stimuli. *Amer. J. Psychol.,* 1915, 26, 152–157.

George, F. H. Logical constructs and psychological theory. *Psychol. Rev.*, 1953, **60**, 1–6.

Getzels, J. W., & P. W. Jackson. *Creativity and intelligence.* New York: Wiley, 1962.

Gibson, J. J. *The perception of the visual world.* Boston: Houghton Mifflin, 1950.

Goddard, H. H. *The Kallikak family.* New York: Macmillan, 1912.

Goethe, J. W. v. *Zur Farbenlehre.* Tübingen: Cotta, 1810. 2 vols.

Goethe, J. W. v. Homer noch einmal. 1827. Reprinted in *Goethes sämtliche Werke*, **38**, 78. Berlin: Cotta, 1902.

Gosset, W. S. The probable error of a mean. *Biometrika*, 1908, **6**, 1–25.

Grassman, H. Zur Theorie der Farbenmischung. *Ann. Phys. Chem.*, 1853, **89**, 69–84 (English trans. in *Phil. Mag.*, 1854, **7**, 254–264.)

Griesbach, H. Ueber Beziehungen zwischen geistiger Ermüdung und Empfindungsvermögen der Haut. *Arch. Hygiene*, 1895, **24**, 124–212.

Grotenfelt, A. *Das Webersche Gesetz und die psychische Relativität.* Helsingfors: Frenckell, 1888.

Guilford, J. P. *Psychometric methods.* New York: McGraw-Hill, 1936.

Guilford, J. P. Factors that aid and hinder creativity. *Teachers Coll. Rec.*, 1962, **63**, 380–392.

Hackett, F. The novel and human personality. *New York Times Book Review*, 15 Aug., 1948, **1**, 15.

Hall, G. S. A sketch of the history of reflex action. *Amer. J. Psychol.*, 1890, **3**, 71–86.

Hall, G. S. A glance at the phyletic background of genetic psychology. *Amer. J. Psychol.*, 1908, **19**, 149–212.

Hall, G. S. *Founders of modern psychology.* New York: Appleton, 1912.

Hall, G. S. *Life and confessions of a psychologist.* New York: Appleton, 1923.

Hall, M. On the reflex function of the medulla oblongata and the medulla spinalis. *Phil. Trans.*, 1833, **123**, 635–665.

Haller, A. v. *Elementa physiologiae corporis humani.* Lausanne: Bousquet, 1757–1766. 8 vols.

Halstead, W. C. *Brain and intelligence.* Chicago: Univ. Chicago Press, 1947.

Hankin, E. H. A cure for tetanus and diphtheria. *Nature*, 1890, **43**, 121–123.

Hardy, J. D., H. C. Wolff, & H. Goodell. *Pain sensations and reactions.* Baltimore: Williams & Wilkins, 1952.

Harper, R. S. The laboratory of William James. *Harvard Alumni Bull.*, 1949, **52**, 169–173.

Harper, R. S. The first psychological laboratory. *Isis*, 1950, **41**, 149–151.

Hartley, D. Conjecturae quaedum de sensu, motu, & idearum generatione. In *De Lithontriptico a Joanna Stephens nuper invento dissertatio epistolaris.* (2nd ed.) Bath: Boddelt, 1746. Translated and reprinted as various conjectures on the perception, motion, and generation of ideas (1746) Los Angeles: William Andrews Clark Memorial Library, Univ. of California, 1959.

Hartley, D. *Observations on Man.* (5th ed.) London: Wilkie & Robinson, 1810. (1749)

Hastorf, A. H., & K. S. Way. Apparent size with and without distance cues. *J. gen. Psychol.*, 1952, **47**, 181–188.

Hayakawa, S. I. From science-fiction to fiction-science. *Etc. Rev. gen. Semant.*, 1951, **8**, 280–293.

Head, H. *Studies in neurology.* Vol. I. London: Oxford Univ. Press, 1920.

Head, H., & W. H. R. Rivers. A human experiment in nerve division. *Brain*, 1908, **31**, 323–450.

Head, H., W. H. R. Rivers, & J. Sherren. The afferent nervous system from a new aspect. *Brain*, 1905, **28**, 99–115.

Heidbreder, Edna. *Seven psychologies.* New York: Appleton-Century, 1933.

Helmholtz, H. L. F. v. Ueber die Erhaltung der Kraft. *Akad. d. Wiss. z. Berlin, Physikalische Abhandl.*, 1847.

Helmholtz, H. L. F. v. *Die Lehre von den Tonenpfindungen als physiologische Grundlage für die Theorie der Musik.* Braunschweig: Vieweg & Sohn, 1913. (1863)

Helmholtz, H. L. F. v. *Handbuch der physiologischen Optik.* Leipzig: Voss, 1867.

Helson, H., & R. M. Burgert. Prediction and control of judgments from tactual single-point stimulation. *Amer. J. Psychol.,* 1936, **48,** 609–616.

Henderson, L. J. *Pareto's general sociology.* Cambridge, Mass.: Harvard Univ. Press, 1935

Henri, V. Le calcul des probabilités en psychologie. *L'Année psychol.,* 1895, **2,** 466–500.

Henri, V. Quelques applications du calcul des probabilités à la psychologie. *L'Année psychol.,* 1898, **5,** 153–160. (*a*)

Henri, V. *Ueber die Raumwahrnehmungen des Tastsinnes.* Berlin: Reuther & Reichard, 1898. (*b*)

Henri, V., & G. A. Tawney. Ueber die Trugwahrnehmung zweier Dunkte bei der Berührung eines Punkte der Haut. *Phil. Stud.,* 1895, **11,** 394–405.

Hilgard, E. R., & D. G. Marquis. *Conditioning and learning.* New York: Appleton Century, 1940.

Hoagland, H. The Weber-Fechner law and the all-or-none theory. *J. gen. Psychol.,* 1930, **3,** 351–373.

Hocking, W. E. Mind and near-mind. *Proc. VIth Internat. Congr. Phil.,* 1926, 203–215.

Hodge, C. F. A sketch of the history of reflex action. *Amer. J. Psychol.,* 1890, **3,** 149–167, 343–363.

Hoisington, L. B. On the non-visual perception of the length of lifted rods. *Amer. J. Psychol.,* 1920, **31,** 114–146.

Holt, E. B. Materialism and the criterion of the psychic. *Psychol. Rev.,* 1937, **44,** 33–53.

Holt, R. R. Forcible indoctrination and personality change. In P. Worchel, & D. Byrne's (Eds.) *Personality Change.* New York: Wiley, 1936, in press.

Holton, G. Scientific research and scholarship. *Daedalus,* 1962, **91,** 362–399.

Holway, A. H. The moon illusion and the angle of regard. *Amer. J. Psychol.,* 1940, **53,** 109–116.

Hook, S. *The hero in history.* New York: Day, 1943.

Hull, C. L. *A behavior system.* New Haven: Yale Univ. Press, 1952.

Hume, D. *A treatise of human nature: being an attempt to introduce the experimental method of reasoning into moral subjects.* London: Noon, 1739–1740.

Humphrey, G. *The nature of learning.* New York: Harcourt, Brace, 1933.

Hunt, J. McV. *Intelligence and experience.* New York: Ronald, 1961.

Hunter, W. S. *Human behavior.* Chicago: Univ. Chicago Press, 1928.

Hunter, W. S. A consideration of Lashley's theory of equipotentiality of cerebral action. *J. gen. Psychol.,* 1930, **3,** 455–467.

Hunter, W. S. James Rowland Angell, 1869–1949. *Amer. J. Psychol.,* 1949, **62,** 439–450.

Hutten, E. H. On existence and complementarity in physics. *Amer. J. Physics,* 1943, **11,** 328–334.

Huxley, A. *The art of seeing.* New York: Harper, 1942.

Idhe, A. J. The inevitability of scientific discovery. *Scient. Mon.,* 1948, **67,** 427–429.

Israel, H. E. Two difficulties in operational thinking. *Psychol. Rev.,* 1945, **52,** 260–261.

Jacobson, E. On meaning and understanding. *Amer. J. Psychol.,* 1911, **22,** 553–577.

James, H. *The letters of William James.* Vol. I. Boston: Little, Brown, 1920.

James, W. Are we automata? *Mind,* 1879, **4,** 1–22.

James, W. Great men, great thoughts and the environment. *Atlantic Mon.,* 1880, **46,** 441–459. Reprinted in *The will to believe,* New York: Longmans, Green, 1897, 216–254.

James, W. *Principles of psychology.* New York: Henry Holt, 1890. (*a*)

James, W. The importance of individuals. *Open Court,* 1890, **4,** 2437–2440. (*b*) reprinted in *The will to believe,* 1899, 255–262.

James, W. A *pluralistic universe*. New York: Longmans, Green, 1909.

Jastrow, J. *Time-relations of mental phenomena*. New York: Hodges, 1890.

Jastrow, J. *Facts and fable in psychology*. Boston: Houghton Mifflin, 1901.

Jennings, H. S. *Contributions to the study of the behavior of the lower organisms*. New York: Columbia Univ. Press, 1904.

Jevons, W. S. *The principles of science: a treatise on logic and scientific method*. London: Macmillan, 1874. (or 2nd., 1883)

Jones, E. *The life and work of Sigmund Freud*, I, 1856–1900. New York: Basic Books, 1953.

Kattsoff, L. O. Facts, phenomena, and frames of reference in psychology. *Psychol. Rev.*, 1953, **60**, 40–44.

Katz, D. *Gestalt psychology: its nature and significance*. (Trans. by R. Tyson) London: Methuen, 1950.

Kennedy, J. L. An evaluation of extra-sensory perception. *Proc. Amer. Phil. Soc.*, 1952, **96**, 513–518.

Keynes, J. M. *A treatise on probability*. London: Macmillan, 1921.

Kincaid, Margaret. An analysis of the psychometric function for the two-point limen with respect to the paradoxical error. *Amer. J. Psychol.*, 1918, **29**, 227–232.

Klineberg, O. *Race differences*. New York: Harper, 1935.

Klineberg, O. *Social psychology*. New York: Holt, 1940.

Köhler, W. Ueber unbemerkte Empfindungen und Urteilstäuschungen. *Z. Psychol.*, 1913, **66**, 51–80.

Köhler, W. *Die physischen Gestalten in Ruhe und im stationären Zustand*. Braunschweig: Vieweg, 1920.

Köhler, W. Zur Theorie des Sukzessivvergleichs und der Zeitfehler. *Psychol. Forsch.*, 1923, **4**, 115–175.

Köhler, W. *Gestalt psychology*. New York: Liveright, 1929.

Köhler, W. *The place of value in a world of facts*. New York: Liveright, 1938.

Köhler, W. *Dynamics in psychology*. New York: Liveright, 1940.

Köhler, W. R. Held, & D. N. O'Connell. An investigation of cortical currents. *Proc. Amer. Phil. Soc.*, 1952, **96**, 290–330.

Koffka, K. Some problems of space perception. In C. Murchison's (Ed.), *Psychologies of 1930*. Worcester, Mass.: Clark Univ. Press, 1930, 161–187.

Koffka, K. *Principles of Gestalt psychology*. New York: Harcourt, Brace, 1935.

Kries, J. v. Ueber die Messung intensiver Grössen und über das sogenannte psychophysiche Gesetz. *Vtjschr. wiss. Phil.*, 1882, **6**, 257–294.

Kries, J. v. *Die Principien der Wahrscheinlichkeitsrechnung*. Freiburg: Mohr, 1886.

Kroeber, A. L. The superorganic. *Amer. Anthropologist*, 1917, **19**, 163–214.

Krohn, W. O. Facilities in experimental psychology in the colleges of the United States, *Report of U.S. Commissioner of Education*, 1891, 1139–1151.

Kuhn, T. S. Historical structure of scientific discovery. *Science*, 1962, **136**, 760–764. (*a*)

Kuhn, T. S. *The structure of scientific revolutions*. Chicago: Univ. of Chicago Press 1962. (*b*)

Külpe, O. *Grundriss der Psychologie*. Leipzig: Engelmann, 1893.

Külpe, O. *Outlines of psychology: based upon the results of experimental investigations*. (Trans. by E. B. Titchener) New York: Macmillan, 1895.

Külpe, O. Ueber die Objectivirung und Subjectivirung von Sinneseindrücken. *Phil. Stud.*, 1902, **19**, 508–556.

Külpe, O. *Vorlesungen über Psychologie*. Leipzig: Hirzel, 1920.

Kuntze, J. E. *Gustav Theodor Fechner*, Leipzig: Breitkopf & Härtel, 1892.

Lafleur, L. J. Cranks and scientists. *Scient. Mon.*, 1951, **73**, 284–290.

La Mettrie, J. O. *L'homme machine*. Leyden: Luzac, 1748.

Landis, C., & W. A. Hunt. *The startle pattern*. New York: Farrar, 1939.

Laplace, P. S. de. *Exposition du système du monde*. (3rd ed.) Paris: Courcier, 1808. (1796)

Lashley, K. S. Studies of cerebral function in learning. *Psychobiol.*, 1920, **2**, 55–135.

Lashley, K. S. Studies of cerebral function in learning. II. The effects of long-continued practice upon localization. *J. comp. Psychol.*, 1921, **1**, 453–468. (*a*)

Lashley, K. S. Studies of cerebral function in learning. III. The motor areas. *Brain*, 1921, **44**, 255–286. (*b*)

Lashley, K. S. Studies of cerebral function in learning. IV. Vicarious function after destruction of the visual areas. *Amer. J. Physiol.*, 1922, **59**, 44–71.

Lashley, K. S. The behavioristic interpretation of consciousness. *Psychol. Rev.*, 1923, **30**, 237–272, 329–353.

Lashley, K. S. Studies of cerebral function in learning. V. The retention of motor habits after destruction of the so-called motor areas in primates. *Arch. Neurol. Psychiat.*, *Chicago*, 1924, **12**, 249–276.

Lashley, K. S. *Brain mechanism and intelligence*. Chicago: Univ. Chicago Press, 1929.

Lashley, K. S. Mass action in cerebral function. *Science*, 1931, **73**, 245–254.

Laski, E. de. On perceptive forms below the level of the two-point limen. *Amer. J. Psychol.*, 1916, **27**, 569–571.

Lasswitz, K. *Gustav Theodor Fechner*. Stuttgart: Fromanns, 1896.

Lenard, P. *Grosse Naturforscher, eine Geschichte der Naturforschung in Lebensbeschreibung*. Munich: Lehmann, 1929. (6th ed., 1943, Eng. trans., 1933)

Levine, J. Studies in the interrelations of central structures in binocular vision. *J. genet. Psychol.*, 1945, **67**, 105–142.

Lichten, W., & S. Lurie. A new technique for the study of perceived size. *Amer. J. Psychol.*, 1950, **63**, 280–282.

Lindsay, R. B., & H. Margenau. *Foundations of physics*. New York: Wiley, 1936. (out of print)

Locke, J. *Essay concerning human understanding*. London: Basset, 1690.

Loeb, J. *Der Heliotropismus der Thiere und seiner Ueberstimmung mit dem Heliotropismus der Pflanzen*. Würzburg: Hertz, 1890.

Loeb, J. *Einleitung in die vergleichende Gehirnphysiologie und vergleichende Psychologie*. Leipzig: Barth, 1899. (Eng. trans., 1900)

London, I. D. The role of the model in explanation. *J. genet. Psychol.*, 1949, **74**, 165–176.

Lorenz, C. Untersuchungen über die Auffassung von Tondistanzen. *Phil. Stud.*, 1890, **6**, 26–103.

McClenahan, G., & K. M. Dallenbach. [Letters.] *Phoenix*, 1951, No. 241, 965.

MacCorquodale, K., & P. E. Meehl. Preliminary suggestions as to a formalization of expectancy theory. *Psychol. Rev.*, 1953, **60**, 55–63.

McDougall, W. Cutaneous sensation. In *Reports of the Cambridge Anthropological Expedition to Torres Straits*. Vol. II. Cambridge, Eng.: Cambridge Univ. Press, 1903, 141–223. (*a*)

McDougall, W. The nature of inhibitory processes within the nervous system. *Brain*, 1903, **26**, 153–191. (*b*)

McDougall, W. The state of the brain during hypnosis. *Brain*, 1908, **31**, 242–258.

MacGaughy, J. R. *Fiscal administration of city school systems*. New York: Macmillan, 1924.

McGill, V. J. Pragmatism. In D. D. Runes' (Ed.) *Dictionary of philosophy*. Chicago: Alliance Book, 1942, 245–247.

Mach, E. Ueber die Wirkung der räumlichen Vertheilung des Lichtreizes auf der Netzhaut. *Sitzungsber. Akad. Wiss. Wien*, 1865, **52**, 303–322.

Mach, E. *Beiträge zur Analyse der Empfindungen*. Jena: Fischer, 1886.

MacKinnon, D. W. The highly effective individual. *Teachers Coll. Rec.*, 1960, **61**, 367–378.

MacKinnon, D. W. What makes a person creative? *Sat. Rev.*, 10 Feb. 1962, **15–17**, 69.

McNemar, Q. Sampling in psychological research. *Psychol. Bull.*, 1940, **37**, 331–365.

Magendie, F. Expériences sur les functions des racines des nerfs rachidiens. *J. physiol. expér. Pathol.*, 1822, **2**, 276–279. (*a*)

Magendie, M. Expériences sur les fonctions des racines des nerfs qui naissent de la moelle épinière. *J. physiol. expér. Pathol.*, 1822, **2**, 366–371. (*b*)

Maloney, R. Inflexible logic. *The New Yorker*, Feb. 3, 1940.

Martius, G. Ueber die scheinbare Grösse der Gegenstände und ihre Beziehung zur Grösse der Netzhautbilder. *Phil. Stud.*, 1889, **5**, 601–617.

Marx, K. *Zur Kritik der politischen Oekonomie*. Berlin: Duncker, 1859.

Meinong, A. Ueber die Bedeutung des Weberschen Gesetzes. *Z. Psychol.*, 1896, **11**, 81–133.

Merkel, J. Die Abhängigkeit zwischen Reiz und Empfindung. *Phil. Stud.*, 1888, **4**, 545–547, 562–565; 1889, **5**, 245–291, 499–557; 1894, **10**, 203–248.

Merton, R. K. Priorities in scientific discovery: a chapter in the sociology of science. *Amer. sociol. Rev.*, 1957, **22**, 635–659.

Merton, R. K. Singletons and multiples in scientific discovery: a chapter in the sociology of science. *Proc. Amer. Phil. Soc.*, 1961, **105**, 470–486.

Mill, J. S. *A system of logic, ratiocinative and inductive, being a connected view of the principles of evidence and the method of scientific investigation.* London: Longmans Green, 1930. (1843)

Miller, J. G. *Unconsciousness.* New York: Wiley, 1942. (out of print)

Minami, H., & K. M. Dallenbach. The effect of activity upon learning and retention in the cockroach, *Periplaneta americana. Amer. J. Psychol.*, 1946, **59**, 1–58.

Mises, R. v. *Probability, statistics and truth.* New York: Macmillan, 1939.

Moll, A. *Der Hypnotismus.* Berlin: Fisher, 1889. (With 4 subsequent eds. with Eng. trans.)

Morgan, C. L. *Animal life and intelligence.* London: Arnold, 1890–1891.

Morgan, C. L. *Introduction to comparative psychology.* London: Scott; New York: Scribners, 1894.

Morgan, C. L. *Animal behaviour.* London: Arnold, 1900.

Morgan, C. T., & E. Stellar. *Physiological psychology.* (2nd ed.) New York: McGraw Hill, 1950.

Morgulis, S. Pavlov's theory of the function of the central nervous system and a digest of some of the more recent contributions to the subject from Pavlov's laboratory. *J. anim. Behav.*, 1914, **4**, 362–379.

Müller, F. A. *Das Axiom der Psychophysik und die psychologische Bedeutung der über'schen Versuche.* Marburg: Elwert, 1882.

Müller, G. E. *Zur Grundlegung der Psychophysik.* Berlin: Gruben, 1878.

Müller, G. E. Zur Psychophysik der Gesichtsempfindungen. *Z. Psychol.*, 1896, **10**, 1–82.

Müller, G. E. Die Gesichtspunkte und die Tatsachen der psychophysischen Methodik. (Vol. II) In L. Asher, & K. Spiro's (Eds.), *Ergebnisse der Physiologie.* Strassburg: Bergmann, 1903, 267–516.

Müller, G. E., & A. Pilzecker. Experimentelle Beiträge zur Lehre vom Gedächtniss. *Z. Psychol.*, Ergbd. 1, Leipzig: Barth, 1900.

Müller, J. *Zur vergleichenden Physiologie des Gesichtssinnes.* Leipzig: Cnobloch, 1826. (*a*)

Müller, J. *Ueber die phantastischen Gesichtserscheinungen.* Coblenz: Hölscher, 1826. (*b*)

Müller, J. *Handbuch der Physiologie des Menschen.* Coblenz: Hölscher, 1833–1840. 3 vols.

Münsterberg, H. *Beiträge zur experimentellen Psychologie.* (3rd ed.) Freiburg: Mohr, 1900.

Münsterberg, H. Emerson Hall. *Harvard psychol. Stud.*, 1906, **2**, 3–39.

Murphy, G. *Historical introduction to modern psychology.* New York: Harcourt, Brace, 1929.

Murphy, G. *Historical introduction to modern psychology*. (2nd ed.) New York: Harcourt, Brace, 1949.

Murphy, G., & Lois B. Murphy. *Experimental social psychology*. New York: Harper, 1931.

Murray, H. A. Psychology and the university. *Arch. Neurol. Psychiat.*, Chicago, 1935, **34**, 803–817.

Murray, H. A., et al. *Explorations in personality*. Oxford: Oxford Univ. Press, 1938.

Myrdal, G. *An American dilemma*. New York: Harper, 1944.

Nafe, J. P. The sense of feeling. In C. Murchison's (Ed.) *The foundations of experimental psychology*. Worcester, Mass.: Clark Univ. Press, 1929, 392–413.

Natanson, Analyse der Funktionen des Nervensystems. *Arch. physiol. Heilkunde*, 1844, **3**, 515–535.

Neiglick, H. Zur Psychophysik des Lichtsinns. *Phil. Stud.*, 1888, **4**, 28–111. *Phil. Stud.*, 1888, **4**, 41.

Newman, E. B. Max Wertheimer: 1880–1943. *Amer. J. Psychol.*, 1944, **57**, 428–435.

Newton, I., as transcribed from a communication of 1675. Vol. 3, page 262–269 in T. Birch's *History of the Royal Society of London*. London: Printed for A. Millar in the Strand, 1756–1757.

Newton, I. *Opticks*. London: Smith & Walford, 1704.

Ogburn, W. F., & Dorothy Thomas. Are inventions inevitable? *Polit. Sci. Quart.*, 1922, **37**, 83–93.

Okabe, T. An experimental study of belief. *Amer. J. Psychol.*, 1910, **21**, 563–596.

Ostwald, W. *Grosse Männer*. Leipzig: Akademische Verlagsgesellschaft, 1909. (French trans. 1912, no Eng. trans.)

Pascal, B. *The physical treatises of Pascal: the equilibrium of liquids and the weight of the mass of the air*. New York: Columbia Univ. Press, 1937.

Pavlov, I. P. *Conditioned reflexes: an investigation of the physiological activity of the cerebral cortex*. London: Oxford Univ. Press, 1927.

Pavlov, I. P. *Lectures on conditioned reflexes*. New York: International Publishers, 1928.

Payne-Gaposchkin, Cecilia. Worlds in Collision. *Proc. Amer. Phil. Soc.*, 1952, **96**, 519–525.

Peak, Helen, & E. G. Boring. The factor of speed in intelligence. *J. exp. Psychol.*, 1926, **9**, 71–94.

Pearson, K. Regression, heredity and panmixia. *Phil. Trans.*, 1896, 187A, 253–318.

Pearson, K. On the criterion that a given system of deviations from a probable case of a correlated system of variables is such that it can be reasonably supposed to have arisen from random sampling. *Phil. Mag.*, 1900, **50**, 157–175.

Pearson, K. On the probability that two independent distributions of frequency are really samples from the same population. *Phil. Mag.*, 1911, **8**, 250–254.

Perry, R. B. *Philosophy of the recent past*. New York: Scribners, 1926.

Perry, R. B. (Ed.) *The thought and character of William James*. Vol. II. Boston: Little, Brown, 1935.

Peterson, J. *Early conceptions and tests of intelligence*. Yonkers: World Book, 1925.

Pitts, W. A general theory of learning and conditioning. *Psychometrika*, 1943, **8**, 1–18, 131–140.

Plateau, J. A. F. Surla mesure des sensations physiques. *Bull. Acad. Belg. Cl. Sci.*, 1872, **33**, 376–388.

Pledge, H. T. *Science since 1500*. London: His Majesty's Stationary Office, 1939.

Podmore, F. *Modern spiritualism, history and criticism*. London: Methuen, 1902. 2 vols

Porterfield, W. *A treatise on the eye, the manner and phaenomena of vision*. Edinburgh: Miller, 1759.

Postman, Leo. (Ed.) *Psychology in the making: histories of selected research problems*. New York: Knopf, 1962.

Pratt, C. C. Faculty psychology. *Psychol. Rev.*, 1929, **36**, 142–171.

Pratt, C. C. Operationism in psychology. *Psychol. Rev.*, 1945, **52**, 262–269.

Pratt, C. C. *The logic of modern psychology.* New York: Macmillan, 1948.

Pratt, J. G., J. B. Rhine, B. M. Smith, C. E. Stuart, & J. A. Greenwood. *Extra-sensory perception after sixty years.* New York: Holt, 1940.

Price, D. J. de S. *Science since Babylon.* New Haven: Yale Univ. Press, 1961.

Priestley, J. *The history and present state of discoveries relating to vision, light and colours.* London: Johnson, 1772.

Purkinje, J. E. *Beobachtungen und Versuche zur Physiologie der Sinne.* Prague: Calve'sche Buchhandlung, 1819–1825. 2 vols.

Quantz, J. O. Dendro-psychosis. *Amer. J. Psychol.,* 1898, **9,** 449–506.

Quetelet, A. *Sur l'homme et le développement de ses facultés, ou essai de physique sociale.* Paris: Bachelier, 1835.

Rashevsky, N. Outline of a physico-mathematical theory of the brain. *J. gen. Psychol.,* 1935, **13,** 82–112.

Rashevsky, N. Mathematical biophysics and psychology. *Psychometrika,* 1936, **1,** 1–26.

Ratner, J. (Ed.) *The philosophy of John Dewey.* New York: Holt, 1928.

Ratner, J. (Ed.) *Intelligence in the modern world: John Dewey's philosophy.* New York: Modern Library, 1939.

Reichenbach, H. *Experience and prediction.* Chicago: Univ. Chicago Press, 1938.

Reif, F. The competitive world of the pure scientist. *Science,* 1961, **134,** 1957–1962.

Ribot, T. A. *German psychology of to-day.* (2nd ed.) New York: Scribners, 1886.

Richet, C. *Dictionnaire de physiologie.* Vol. 2. Paris: Alcan, 1897, 547–670.

Richter, C. P., L. E. Holt, & B. Barelare, Jr. Nutritional requirements for normal growth and reproduction in rats studied by the self-selection method. *Amer. J. Physiol.,* 1938, **122,** 734–744.

Riddick, T. M. Dowsing—an unorthodox method of locating underground water supplies or an interesting facet of the human mind. *Proc. Amer. Phil. Soc.,* 1952, **96,** 526–534.

Riecker, A. Versuche über den Raumsinn der Kopfhaut. *Z. Biol.,* 1874, **10,** 177–201.

Robertson, T. B. A biochemical conception of memory and sensation. *Monist,* 1909, **19,** 367–386.

Ruckmick, C. A. The history and status of psychology in the United States. *Amer. J. Psychol.,* 1912, **23,** 517–531.

Ruckmick, C. A. The use of the term function in English textbooks of psychology. *Amer. J. Psychol.,* 1913, **24,** 99–123.

Sachs, H. *Freud: master and friend.* Cambridge, Mass.: Harvard Univ. Press, 1946.

Sarton, G. *The history of science and the new humanism.* Cambridge, Mass.: Harvard Univ. Press, 1937.

Sarton, G. *A history of science: Ancient science through the golden age of Greece.* Cambridge, Mass.: Harvard Univ. Press, 1952.

Scheerer, M., K. Goldstein, & E. G. Boring. A demonstration of insight: the horse-and-rider puzzle. *Amer. J. Psychol.,* 1941, **54,** 437–438.

Schmidt, R. *Philosophie der Gegenwart in Selbstdarstellungen.* Leipzig: Meiner, 1924.

Scripture, E. W. *The new psychology.* New York: Scribners, 1897.

Sharp, Stella E. Individual psychology: a study in psychological method. *Amer. J Psychol.,* 1899, **10,** 329–391.

Sheldon, W. H., et al. *The varieties of human physique.* New York: Harper, 1940.

Sheldon, W. H., et al. *The varieties of temperament.* New York: Harper, 1942.

Skinner, B. F. The behavior of organisms. *J. gen. Psychol.,* 1931, **5,** 427–458.

Skinner, B. F. *The behavior of organisms: an experimental analysis.* New York: Appleton-Century, 1938.

Skinner, B. F. The operational use of psychological terms. *Psychol. Rev.,* 1945, **52,** 270–277.

Skinner, B. F. Are theories of learning necessary? *Psychol. Rev.,* 1950, **57,** 193–216.

Skinner, B. F. *Science and human behavior*. New York: Macmillan, 1953.

Skinner, B. F., & C. B. Ferster. *Schedules of reinforcement*. New York: Appleton-Century-Crofts, 1957.

Sleight, W. G. Memory and formal training. *Brit. J. Psychol.*, 1911, **4**, 386–451.

Smith, C. A. H. The discovery of anesthesia. *Scient. Mon.*, 1927, **24**, 64–70.

Solomon, R. L. An extension of control group design. *Psychol. Bull.*, 1949, **46**, 137–150.

Soury, J. *Le système nerveux central (structure et fonctions): Histoire critique des théories et des doctrines*. Paris: Carré & Naud, 1899.

Spencer, H. *Principles of psychology*. (2nd ed.) London: Williams & Norgate, 1870–1872. 2 vols. (1855)

Spencer, H. *The study of sociology*. London: Paul, 1873.

Spoerl, H. D. Faculties vs. traits: Gall's solution. *Charact. Pers.*, 1936, **4**, 216–231.

Stevens, S. S. The attributes of tones. *Proc. Nat. Acad. Sci.*, *Wash.*, 1934, **20**, 457–459. (*a*)

Stevens, S. S. Volume and intensity of tones. *Amer. J. Psychol.*, 1934, **46**, 397–408. (*b*)

Stevens, S. S. The operational basis of psychology. *Amer. J. Psychol.*, 1935, **47**, 323–330.

Stevens, S. S. A scale for the measurement of a psychological magnitude: loudness. *Psychol. Rev.*, 1936, **43**, 405–416. (*a*)

Stevens, S. S. Psychology: the propaedeutic science. *Phil. Sci.*, 1936, **3**, 90–103. (*b*)

Stevens, S. S. Psychology and the science of science. *Psychol. Bull.*, 1939, **36**, 221–263.

Stevens, S. S. On the theory of scales of measurement. *Science*, 1946, **103**, 677–680.

Stevens, S. S. Mathematics, measurement, and psychophysics. In S. S. Stevens' (Ed.) *Handbook of experimental psychology*. New York: Wiley, 1951, 7–49.

Stevens, S. S. On the psychophysical law. *Psychol. Rev.*, 1957, **64**, 153–181.

Stevens, S. S. Measurement and man. *Science*, 1958, **127**, 383–389.

Stevens, S. S., & H. Davis. *Hearing: its psychology and physiology*. New York: Wiley, 1938.

Stevens, S. S., & J. Volkmann. The relation of pitch to frequency: a revised scale. *Amer. J. Psychol.*, 1940, **53**, 329–353.

Stewart, B. *The conservation of energy*. New York: Appleton, 1900. (1874)

Stone, C. P. Learning: the factor of maturation. In C. Murchison's (Ed.), *Handbook of general experimental psychology*. Worcester: Clark Univ. Press, 1934, 352–381.

Stumpf, C. Vergleichungen der Tondistanzen. *Z. Psychol.*, 1890, **1**, 419–485.

Stumpf, C. Wundt's antikritik. *Z. Psychol.*, 1891, **2**, 266–293. (*a*)

Stumpf, C. Mein Schlusswort gegen Wundt. *Z. Psychol.*, 1891, **2**, 438–443. (*b*)

Supra, M., M. Cotzin, & K. M. Dallenbach. "Facial vision:" The perception of obstacles by the blind. *Amer. J. Psychol.*, 1944, **57**, 133–183.

Swift, E. J. Studies in the psychology and physiology of learning. *Amer. J. Psychol.*, 1903, **14**, 201–251.

Tannery, J. Correspondance à propos de la loi de Fechner. In J. R. L. Delboeuf's (Ed.) *Eléments de psychophysique, générale et spéciale: I. Psychophysique*. Paris: Baillière, 1883, 109–114, 132–139.

Tawney, G. A. The perception of two points not the space-threshold. *Psychol. Rev.*, 1895, **2**, 585–593.

Tawney, G. A. Ueber die Wahrnehmung zweier Punkte mittelst des Tastsinnes mit Rücksicht auf die Frage der Uebung und die Enstchung der Vexirfehler. *Phil. Stud.*, 1897, **13**, 163–221.

Taylor, C. W., & Frank Barron. *Scientific creativity: its recognition and development*. New York: Wiley, 1963.

Thorndike, E. L. Animal intelligence. *Psychol. Monogr.*, 1898, **2**, No. 8.

Thorndike, E. L. *Animal intelligence: experimental studies*. New York: Macmillan, 1911.

Thorndike, E. L., & R. S. Woodworth. The influence of improvement in one mental function upon the efficiency of other functions. *Psychol. Rev.*, 1901, **8**, 247–261; 384–395; 553–564.

Thurstone, L. L. A method of scaling psychological and educational tests. *J. educ. Psychol.*, 1925, **16**, 433–451.

Thurstone, L. L. The unit of measurement in educational scales. *J. educ. Psychol.*, 1927, **18**, 505–524.

Thurstone, L. L. Scale construction with weighted observations. *J. educ. Psychol.*, 1928, **19**, 441–453.

Thurstone, L. L. *Multiple-factor analysis: a development and expansion of the vectors of the mind.* Chicago: Univ. of Chicago Press, 1947.

Titchener, E. B. Simple reactions. *Mind*, 1895, N.S. **4**, 74–81.

Titchener, E. B. *Experimental psychology.* New York: Macmillan, 1901–1905. 2 vols., 4 pts.

Titchener, E. B. *A text-book of psychology.* New York: Macmillan, 1910.

Titchener, E. B. Description vs. statement of meaning. *Amer. J. Psychol.*, 1912, **23**, 165–182.

Titchener, E. B. *A beginner's psychology.* New York: Macmillan, 1915. (*a*)

Titchener, E. B. Sensation and system. *Amer. J. Psychol.*, 1915, **26**, 258–267. (*b*)

Titchener, E. B. On ethnological tests of sensation and perception, with special reference to tests of color vision and tactile discrimination in the reports of the Cambridge Anthropological Expedition to Torres Straits. *Proc. Amer. Phil. Soc.*, 1916, **55**, 204–236.

Titchner, E. B. Brentano and Wundt: Empirical and experimental psychology. *Amer. J. Psychol.*, 1921, **32**, 108–120.

Titchener, E. B. Wundt's address at Speyer, 1861. *Amer. J. Psychol.*, 1923, **34**, 311.

Titchner, E. B. The term "attensity." *Amer. J. Psychol.*, 1924, **35**, 156.

Titchener, E. B. *Systematic psychology: prolegomena.* New York: Macmillan, 1929.

Tolman, E. C. Operational behaviorism and current trends in psychology. *Proc. 25th Anniv. Celebr. Inaug. Grad. Stud. Univ. So. Calif.* Los Angeles: Univ. So. Calif. Press, 1936, 89–103.

Tolstoy, L. *War and peace.* New York: Simon & Schuster, 1942. (1869) Translated by Louise & Alymer Maude. See esp. bk. 9, sect. 1; bk. 10, sect. 1; bk. 11, sect. 1; bk. 13, sect. 11; 1st epilogue, sect. 1; 2nd epilogue; appendix entitled, Some words about *War and Peace.*

Toynbee, A. J. *A study of history.* (Abridged by D. C. Somervell) London: Oxford Univ. Press, 1946. 6 vols. (1933–1934)

Turner, F. J. The frontier in American history. New York: Holt, 1920.

Tyndall, J. *Heat considered as a mode of motion.* New York: Appleton, 1863.

Urban, F. M. *The application of statistical methods to the problems of psychophysics.* Philadelphia: Psychol. Clinic Press, 1908.

Urban, F. M. Professor Dodge's recent discussion of mental work. *Amer. J. Psychol.*, 1913, **24**, 270–274. (*a*)

Urban, F. M. Ueber einige Begriffe und Aufgaben der Psychophysik. *Arch. ges. Psychol.*, 1913, **30**, 113–152. (*b*)

Vierordt, K. v. Die Abhängigkeit der Ausbildung des Raumsinnes der Haut von Beweglichkeit der Körperteile. *Z. Biol.*, 1870, **6**, 53–72.

Visher, S. S. *Scientists starred in American Men of Science: 1903–1943.* Baltimore, Md.: Johns Hopkins Press, 1947.

Volkmann, A. W. Von der specifischen Reizbarkeit der Nerven. In R. Wagner's (Ed.), *Handwörterbuch der Physiologie.* Vol. 2. Braunschweig: Vieweg, 1844, 521–526.

Volkmann, A. W. Ueber den Einfluss der Uebung auf das Erkennen räumlicher Distanzen. *Ber. sächs. Akad. Wiss. Leipzig*, 1858, **10**, 38–69.

Walker, Helen M. *Studies in the history of statistical method.* Baltimore: Williams & Wilkins, 1929.

Walker, J. Everyone is a mindreader. *Fate,* 1950, **3,** 20–27.

Ward, J. An attempt to interpret Fechner's law. *Mind,* 1876, O.S. **1,** 452–466.

Warren, R. B. An attempt at perspective. *Proc. Amer. Phil. Soc.,* 1948, **92,** 271–281.

Washburn, Margaret F. *The animal mind.* New York: Macmillan, 1908. (Or any later date.)

Washburn, Margaret F. James Mark Baldwin 1861–1934. *Amer. J. Psychol.,* 1935, **47,** 168–169.

Watson, J. B. Image and affection in behavior. *J. Phil.,* 1913, **10,** 421–428. (*a*)

Watson, J. B. Psychology as the behaviorist views it. *Psychol. Rev.,* 1913, **20,** 158–177. (*b*)

Watson, J. B. *Psychology from the standpoint of a behaviorist.* Philadelphia: Lippincott, 1919.

Weber, E. H. *De pulsu, resorptione, auditu et tactu: annotationes anatomicae et physiologicae.* Leipzig: Koehler, 1834.

Weber, E. H. Der Tastsinn und das Gemeingefühl. In R. Wagner's (Ed.) *Handwörterbuch der Physiologie.* Vol. III. Braunschweig: Vieweg, 1846, 481–588.

Webster, R. N. The amazing Jimmy Walker and the imaginary Dr. McClenahan. *Fate,* 1951, **4,** 4–5.

Weld, H. P. Meaning and process as distinguished by the reaction method. In *Studies in psychology: Titchener Commemorative Volume.* Worcester: Wilson, 1917, 181–208.

Wertheimer, M. Experimentelle Studien über das Sehen von Bewegungen. *Z. Psychol.,* 1912, **61,** 161–265.

Wertheimer, M. Untersuchungen zur Lehre von der Gestalt. *Psychol. Forsch.,* 1921, **1,** 47–58.

Wever, E. G. The physiology of hearing: the nature of the response in the cochlea. *Physiol. Rev.,* 1933, **13,** 400–425

Wever, E. G., & C. W. Bray. Present possibilities for auditory theory. *Psychol. Rev.,* 1930, **37,** 365–380. (*a*)

Wever, E. G., & C. W. Bray. The nature of acoustic response: the relation between sound frequency and frequency of impulses in the auditory nerve. *J. exp. Psychol.,* 1930, **13,** 373–387. (*b*)

Wever, E. G., & C. W. Bray. The perception of low tones and the resonance-volley theory. *J. Psychol.,* 1937, **3,** 101–114.

Whyte, L. L. *The unconscious before Freud.* New York: Basic Books, 1960

Whytt, R. *An essay on the vital and other involuntary motions of animals.* Edinburgh: Hamilton, Balfour & Neill, 1751.

Wiener, N. *Cybernetics or control and communication in the animal and the machine.* Cambridge, Mass.: Technology Press, 1949.

Winch, W. H. The transfer of improvement of memory in school-children. *Brit. J. Psychol.,* 1908, **2,** 284–293.

Wolf, A. *A history of science, technology and philosophy in the 16th and 17th centuries.* London: Allen & Unwin, 1935.

Wolf, S. Effects of suggestion and conditioning on the action of chemical agents in human subjects—the pharmacology of placebos. *J. clin. Investigation,* 1950, **29,** 100–109.

Woodworth, R. S. *Experimental psychology.* New York: Holt, 1938.

Woodworth, R. S. Heredity and environment: a critical survey of recently published material on twins and foster children. *Soc. Sci. Res. Counc. Bull.,* 1941, No. 47.

Woodworth, R. S. *Contemporary schools of psychology.* (2nd ed.) New York: Ronald, 1948.

Woodworth, R. S., & H. Schlosberg. *Experimental psychology.* (Rev. ed.) New York: Holt, 1954.

Worchel, P., & K. M. Dallenbach. "Facial vision:" perception of obstacles by the deaf blind. *Amer. J. Psychol.,* 1947, **60,** 502–553.

Wundt, W. *Vorlesungen über die Menschen- und Thierseele.* Leipzig: Voss, 1863. 2 vols.

Wundt, W. *Grundzüge der physiologischen Psychologie.* (1st ed.) Leipzig: Engelmann, 1874.

Wundt, W. *Grundzüge der physiologischen Psychologie.* (2nd ed.) Leipzig: Engelmann, 1887.

Wundt, W. Vergleichungen von Tondistanzen. *Phil. Stud.,* 1891, **6,** 605–640. (*a*)

Wundt, W. Eine Replik C. Stumpf's. *Phil. Stud.,* 1891, **7,** 298–327. (*b*)

Wundt, W. Auch ein Schlusswort. *Phil. Stud.,* 1892, **7,** 633–636.

Wundt, W. *Gustav Theodor Fechner.* Leipzig: Engelmann, 1901.

Wundt, W. Des Institut für experimentellen Psychologie. *Festschrift zur Feier des 500-jährigen Bestehens der Universität Leipzig,* 1909, **4,** pt. 1, 118–133.

Wundt, W. *Einführung in die Psychologie.* Leipzig: Voitländer, 1911. (*a*) (English trans. 1912.)

Wundt, W. *Grundzüge der physiologischen Psychologie.* (6th ed.) Leipzig: Engelmann, 1911. (*b*)

Young, T. On the theory of light and colours (read in 1801), *Philos. Trans.,* 1802, **92,** 20 f.

Young, T. *A course of lectures on natural philosophy and the mechanical arts.* London: Johnson, 1807. 2 vols.

Index of Names

𐊀𐊀𐊀𐊀𐊀𐊀𐊀𐊀𐊀𐊀𐊀𐊀𐊀𐊀𐊀𐊀𐊀𐊀𐊀

The important items are keyed by subject and given first. Less important items and incidental mentions of a name are labeled "inc." (incidental) and given next. Citations of the literature in the text are labeled "ref." and given last; but for full citations see the References, pp. 337–353. No "inc." item is included when there is an important subject item or a "ref." item for the same page.

157; spiritualism, 127 f.; stimulus-error, 256, 259–61; inc., 116, 151, 272, 278, 301; ref., 181, 266
Feigl, H., operationism, 200, 205–7; ref., 253
Féré, C., ref., 69
Fermat, P. de, theorems, 38
Fernberger, S. W., Urban's student, 133
Ferree, C. E., Titchener's student, 133
Ferster, C. B., reinforcement, 153
Fichte, J. G., mind and brain, 53
Fisher, R. A., anticipated by Pearson, 157; statistics, 120 f., 155; inc., 123; ref., 182
Fiske, J., ref., 32
Flourens, M. J. P., brain localization, 37, 54, 58 f.; mind and brain, 57; progress in science, 91
Flugel, J. C., ref., 181
Foucault, M., ref., 267
Frank, J., scientific mind, 8 f., 322
Frank, P., ref., 225
Franklin, B., electricity, 33; inc., 10
Franz, S. I., brain localization, 58 f.; Cattell's student, 133
Fraunhofer, J. v., brightness, 143; inc., 297
Fréchet, M., ref., 227
Frederick of Prussia, Carlyle's hero, 6, 16
Freeman, F. N., as student, 135
Freud, S., as eponym, 6 f.; deterministic theory, 16; influence on Murphy, 135; in-group, 250; moment of insight, 22; unconscious thought, 13 f.
Friedländer, H., *Einstellung*, 266 f., 272 f.
Friedline, Cora L., fatigue and limen, 269 f.
Fritsch, G., motor centers, 58 f., inc., 277
Fröbes, J., ref., 266
Fullerton, G. S., stimulus-error, 262 f.; inc., 139, 257, 266; ref., 272

Gale, H., Wundt's student, 163
Galen, C., mind and brain, 57; nerves, 52; pupillary reflex, 60
Galileo, G., celestial bodies, 13; controversy with Kepler, 24; experimental method, 203; frequency of pitches, 142, 156; Jupiter's moons, 17, 35; pendulum, 45 f.; weight of air, 35; inc., 21, 335
Gall, F. J., brain localization, 58 f.; phrenology, 37, 53, 171
Galton, F., co-relation, 141, 154; creativity, 19; forerunner of Pearson, 157; hereditary genius, 30 f.; individual differ-

ences, 141 f., 167, 171 f.; influenced by Quetelet, 157; influence on Cattell, 163; measurement of genius, 40, 156; mental inheritance, 153 f., 158, 161, 176 f.; normal law of error, 155; statistical control, 120; inc., 10, 32, 264; ref., 183
Galvani, L., electricity, 35, 38
Gardiner, H. N., inc., 139
Gardner, M., unorthodoxies, 249; inc., 251; ref., 213
Garrett, H. E., as student, 135
Gates, A. I., as student, 135
Gates, E. J., ref., 267 f.
Gauss, C. F., errors of observation, 148; influence on Fechner, 156; least squares, 36; probability, 120, 141
George, F. H., ref., 225
Gesell, A., Hall's student, 133
Getzels, J. W., intelligence and creativity, 19
Gilbert, L. W., ref., 122
Goddard, H. H., Hall's student, 133; mental deficiency, 177; ref., 183
Goethe, J. W. v., color theory, 213; phenomenology, 102 f.; vision, 143, 160; *Zeitgeist*, 13, 89
Goldstein, K., ref., 41
Goodell, Helen, ref., 118
Goodenough, Florence, as student, 135
Gosset, W. S., anticipated by Pearson, 157; significant differences, 120 f., 155 f.
Graham, C. H., as student, 135
Grassmann, H., Newton's complementarities, 198
Gray, E., telephone, 36
Greenwood, J. A., statistics of ESP, 125, 243 f.
Griesbach, H., ref., 269
Gross, H., dowsing, 245, 248 f., 252
Grotenfelt, A., stimulus-error, 266; ref., 272
Guilford, J. P., creativity, 19; Dallenbach's student, 133; statistics, 155
Guthrie, E. R., Wolfe's student, 133

Hackett, F., Freud and novel, 16, 21
Haeckel, E. H., recapitulation, 170, 213
Haggerty, M. E., Stone's teacher, 133
Hall, G. S., as student, 136; as teacher, 133, 135; development of American psychology, 162–4, 179; evolution, 163, 168–70, 180; Johns Hopkins labora-

Index of Subjects